REPTILES OF THE WORLD

BY RAYMOND L. DITMARS

SNAKES OF THE WORLD

THRILLS OF A NATURALIST'S QUEST

THE FOREST OF ADVENTURE

THE GIANT MONITOR *Varanus komodænsis*

Largest known lizard, attaining a length of twelve feet and weight of two hundred and fifty pounds. It inhabits the island of Komodo and probably the westerly portion of Flores, in the Dutch East Indies.

REPTILES of the WORLD

THE CROCODILIANS. LIZARDS. SNAKES, TURTLES AND TORTOISES OF THE EASTERN AND WESTERN HEMISPHERES

By RAYMOND L. DITMARS, Litt.D.

CURATOR OF MAMMALS AND REPTILES AT THE NEW YORK ZOOLOGICAL PARK; FELLOW OF THE NEW YORK ACADEMY OF SCIENCES; FELLOW OF THE NEW YORK ZOOLOGICAL SOCIETY; CORRESPONDING MEMBER OF THE ZOOLOGICAL SOCIETY OF LONDON.

NEW REVISED EDITION

With a frontispiece and nearly 200 illustrations, from photographs taken by the author and from the files of the New York Zoological Society.

NEW YORK MCMXXXVI

THE MACMILLAN COMPANY

Reissued, February, 1922.
Reprinted, February, 1927, November, 1928, May, 1930.
Revised edition, October, 1933.
Reprinted, October, 1936.

PRINTED IN THE UNITED STATES OF AMERICA
BY THE POLYGRAPHIC COMPANY OF AMERICA, N.Y.

TO MY DAUGHTERS

PREFACE

In the present work the author has aimed to give in a popular manner a general survey of the reptiles of the world. While the manner aims to be popular, and while the purpose has been to make the book interesting reading, it is at the same time, the writer hopes, everywhere in accord with the latest results of the scientific study of the subject; and he believes the special student may find scattered through the volume new information drawn from the author's long and systematic observation of the various orders of reptiles, their habits, etc.—a course pursued both among the homes and haunts of these creatures in many parts of the world, and in the New York Zoological Park. The scope of the book prevents it from being, as a previous book by the same author was, primarily a volume intended to be used for identification purposes: it is here designed to consider the class of reptiles as a whole and in a general way. But for purposes of identification the profuse illustrations cannot fail to be serviceable in a high degree.

It is not unlikely that the quest of specimens and the methods employed in capturing them, of which much is said here and there in the text, will prove both entertaining to the layman and helpful to curators, to the collectors and students, amateur or professional. And the same may be said of what is written regarding the feeding and general care and treatment of reptiles in captivity.

Handling the entire class—the crocodilians, turtles and tortoises, lizards and snakes of both the New and the Old World—elaborate description is necessarily limited to *groups*. The method here has been to select representative types from these groups, treating them according to their importance as to anatomical characteristics and habits. The North American reptiles have, however, received considerable attention, as they naturally attract our special interest, while their habits and structure must be compared with their Old World allies, if a general idea of the Class *Reptilia* is to be acquired. But among the illustrations the South American and the Old World reptiles predominate, for here is a field quite neglected from a photographic standpoint, and demanding much space. Thus, to make room for the great array of foreign reptiles, the illustrations of the North American species have been limited to a condensed but representative series. To thoroughly round up the subject the author has prepared detailed charts showing the classification and approximate number of species among all the genera of reptiles found in all parts of the world. Such will impress upon the student the full scope of the subject, though references to numerous genera in the text must be omitted.

The author may be permitted to say, without being accused of immodesty, that, however the text of this volume may be received, its illustrations make it of high value, and indeed unique among books on the same subject. The plates from photographs taken from life will be useful to the student and interesting to the general reader. They are not merely pictures "snapped" at the most convenient moment, but life studies from poses displaying distinguishing characteristics, and involving work on many of the negatives requiring the use of restraining dyes to produce effects of coloration beyond the power of lens and color-sensitive plates. The results exceed in value the familiar pen drawings of reptiles ordinarily employed in popular works. Among the latter a snake is merely a scaled creature, and, unless exhibiting some striking development, produces no lasting impression in the mind of the student. It may tally with every word of an attending description, but would probably not be identified with an actual specimen seen soon after. Expert photography imparts, in a work like this, a strong individuality to each species, positively branding the various forms and capable of imitation only by such exceedingly painstaking draftsmen as are employed to illustrate the highly expensive monographs of the great museums—institutions having the means to pay for the labor of drawing a reptile scale by scale, each minute part of the integument receiving its share of work according to color value or shading and intricate structure. The cost of such labor would be enormous in a work like this, placing it beyond the reach of most popular readers. It is such illustrative work the author has tried, as far as possible, to approach in value in the pages following. The several hundred illustrations are the result of his personal endeavors. A number of the specimens photographed have been exhibited in the Reptile House of the New York Zoological Park.

In the pages that follow the author has drawn freely from observations made in the splendid Reptile House erected by the New York Zoölogical Society, whom he has the honor of serving.

R. L. D.

New York Zoological Park, 1933.

INTRODUCTION

Compared with the ages that are gone the reptile life upon our globe has decreased, in the dimensions and bulk of its representatives, to mere parasitic proportions. There was a time when a bird's-eye view of the earth's surface would have revealed varied, monstrous forms lumbering here and there, reveling in an atmosphere reeking with humidity; some browsing in giraffe-like fashion among high branches, others churning through the sea in pursuit of their prey; even in the murky atmosphere itself cold-blooded creatures flapped their way like gigantic bats in search of equally gigantic insects. At the present day a comprehensive view of the globe's surface would show no trace of reptile life. We might make clear by an illustration the size of reptiles of the past as compared with those of the present. The gaudy butterflies, the clumsy June "bugs," and "darning-needles" are forms apparent to the eyes of a man in a walking posture. Suppose they were all extinct; the tiny ants, the microscopic beetles, and the gnats forming the major part of our insect life would be insignificant and unseen; their presence would be apparent only to the interested observer crouching to look for them. And we can well compare the reptiles of the present with the legions of tiny insects, after we have examined the rock-imprisoned giants of the past. Moreover, a great number of the living reptiles are degenerating—adopting subterraneous habits with a consequent loss of eyes and ears. Others have become greatly specialized in the development of adhesive digits with which to climb, or wonderful instruments for the injection of a deadly venom. Then, in the zenith of their perfection, some of them have gradually swung into secretive habits producing an incongruous mixture of degenerating form attended by various highly specialized processes.

As our living reptiles stand, the classification may be outlined as follows:

Class Reptilia

Order *Rhynchocephalia.* Represented by a single species inhabiting New Zealand. Lizard-like in form but differing in skeleton and anatomy from all living reptiles. It is the sole remnant of an Order long extinct.

Order *Loricata.* The Crocodilians—Crocodiles and Alligators. About twenty-five species. Tropical and semitropical parts of the world. All are semi-aquatic. They attain the greatest size and bulk among living reptiles.

Order *Squamata.* The scaled reptiles—Lizards and Snakes. This order is divided into two suborders, as follows:

Suborder *Sauria.* The Lizards; about twenty-five hundred species. The distribution is general throughout tropical and semi-tropical parts of the world—quite sparing in the temperate regions. The habits may be terrestrial, subterraneous, arboreal, or semi-aquatic. The typical lizard, scaly-coated with four legs and tapering tail, is familiar, but many forms are limbless, moving about like snakes; as a rule, the serpentine forms may be distinguished from the snakes by the presence with the former, of functional eyelids.

Suborder *Ophidia.* The Snakes. About twenty-three hundred species are recognized. The distribution embraces tropical, semi-tropical and temperate parts of the globe; they are more abundant in the temperate regions than the lizards. Snakes have no functional eyelids—the eyes being always open. The greater number of species are terrestrial; many are arboreal, subterraneous, semi-aquatic, or marine.

The poisonous species are in the minority. It is wrong to imagine a poisonous snake may be told from the harmless species by a thick body and flattened, distinct head.

Order *Testudinata.* The Turtles (semi-aquatic and marine) and Tortoises (terrestrial). Over two hundred and twenty-five species are recognized. They are generally distributed throughout temperate and tropical parts of the world.

Thus we have a general idea of the Class *Reptilia.* In each of the four Parts of this work the classification of the respective Orders is treated in detail.

In compiling his descriptions the author has sought to employ the most simple phraseology possible, for his endeavor has been to create a book that may be readily comprehended by the beginner. Part IV, dealing with the snakes, is the most elaborate, both in description of structure and *habits,* as well as in illustrations. As in other works the serpents have received the least attention, the author has decided to give them here a generous share. Of serpents there are many important things to be told. Some of them are beneficial to man; others dangerous or fatal, and these latter it is well to recognize when encountered. The series of illustrations of the poisonous serpents is thoroughly complete; it will be noted that their variety of form—some of them gracefully slender—at once shatters many fallacious theories.

Before concluding his introduction the author would say a word regarding the Order *Rhynchocephalia,* only one species of which has survived to the present, the Tuatera of New Zealand; the technical name is *Sphenodon punctatus.* The author has removed this strange creature from the body of the work to follow, as it would appear incongruous to place a lizard-like form near the turtles and tortoises—where it appears to belong. It is literally a ghost of the past, the oldest surviving type of reptile. According to Boulenger, it is possible that the common ancestors of the turtles and tortoises, the *Plesiosauria* (now extinct) and the lizards would fall in the Order to which this reptile belongs—an Order of fossils, rock-bound for ages, that has in turn given rise and brought extinction to other Orders—yet permitted one remnant to survive, apparently immune to the dominant sway of evolution.

The Tuatera resembles in form stout-bodied modern lizards which we call iguanas; this resemblance is further intensified by a row of spines upon the back. It is dark olive, the sides sprinkled with pale dots. The eye has a cat-like pupil. Large specimens are two and a half feet long. While a superficial resemblance might tend to group this reptile with the lizards, its skeleton and anatomy show it to belong to a different part of technical classification. And now, as the author completes this work, it seems possible the Order *Rhynchocephalia* will soon have to be stricken from our lists of living reptiles. In comparatively recent years, the Tuatera was abundant on the larger islands of New Zealand, but the cultivation of land, the introduction of swine, and many other causes emanating from the all-powerful advance of civilization have annihilated the reptile from all but the smaller, uninhabited islands. Here they are diligently hunted for scientific institutions, and not many years will pass before the last Tuatera to remain in the flesh will repose within a museum jar.

CONTENTS

PART I

PART II

PART III

PART IV

ILLUSTRATIONS

CROCODILIANS

LIZARDS

SNAKES

TURTLES AND TORTOISES

PART I

THE CROCODILIANS

ORDER *LORICATA*

THE ORDER *LORICATA*—CROCODILES AND ALLIGATORS

Living in the warmer parts of the globe, in areas synonymous with tropical vegetation, swamps or sluggish water-ways and a humid atmosphere, are the giants among reptiles—the Crocodilians. Ponderous, lizard-like creatures, coated above with a rough armor of bony plates, they cause the great majority of reptile life around them to appear insignificant—almost parasitic in proportions. Some of the crocodilians attain a length of twenty feet—one species, thirty feet. Of direct, ancient lineage, they furnish us with a hint of the gigantic forms of reptile life once existing. Ages ago crocodiles and alligators were generally distributed throughout the world; the zone of decadence is now marked by rock-bound fossils in the temperate regions, giving way to the living representatives which have survived within that band of our globe embraced by the semi-tropical parallels—and though a few species stray out of this area, their distribution follows low coastal regions warmed by currents from the tropics.

Without exception, the crocodilians are amphibious and provided with a powerful tail that is flattened toward its terminal half. The feet are of practically no use in swimming, being folded against the side while lateral undulations of the tail send the animal rapidly through the water. As the crocodilian floats near the surface, with the top of the head alone above water, the webbed hind feet are employed in slow, treading fashion to maintain the animal in the desired position.

General Structure. As this is not a textbook, the writer does not propose to dive into a technical review of the anatomy. Certain parts of the structure, however, should be understood by the beginner. Let us first examine the massive, bony head, as about it are several interesting features. The eyes and nostrils are so elevated that the flat portion of the head may lay flush with the surface of the water—or slightly beneath it—while these organs are clear above it and performing their respective functions. Immediately behind each eye is a hinged, bony flap constituting an ear covering; this can be opened and closed rapidly; it is tightly shut as the creature goes beneath the surface. The tongue is very broad, thick and attached by its entire under surface to the lower jaw; it can be raised and lowered, forming a powerful valve to prevent water from rushing down the throat when the mouth is opened. An examination of the dentition shows a generous array of sharp, strong teeth of various sizes, but readily divided —on both jaws—into two series, consisting respectively of greatly enlarged teeth and smaller ones behind them. All of the teeth are frequently shed. At their base or root they contain a conical hollow and into this fits the tip of the new tooth, steadily pushing out the old member. It is a long-established custom for the keepers in the New York Zoological Park's reptile house to look for teeth when cleaning out the big 'gator pool. The pool is cleaned once a week, when the men sometimes find as many as a dozen teeth from the five large alligators on exhibition. Provided with such a formidable dentition, besides jaw muscles of enormous power, the dangerous nature of these huge, vicious brutes may be imagined. Peculiar to explain, the writer has seen a big alligator grab a good-sized dog, then with a single effort, crush the animal's bones with a sickening, dull, crunching sound, *yet that same crocodilian's jaws could be held shut by a moderately strong pair of hands,* for all the power appears to center in the *closing* of the jaws.

Often has the writer been asked the question—"What is the difference between an *alligator* and a *crocodile?*" In reality, the question is not a very important one, as of the twenty species of crocodilians there are but two "alligators,"[1] one inhabiting North America and the other the Yang-tse-Kiang River, in China. There is very little structural difference between the two, but from the frequency with which we hear the query it appears that many regard it as imperative, before commencing the study of natural history, to learn the points distinguishing an "alligator" from a "crocodile." And many have been the answers to the question, prepared in exhaustive fashion that causes the brain to whirl in an endeavor to assimilate the discussion. While we are discussing structure let us deal concisely with this alligator *versus* crocodile question, thus:

The American Alligator, *Alligator mississippiensis,* inhabiting the southeastern portion of the United States, is distinguished from the only other crocodilian found within its range—the American Crocodile—as follows—

Entire head broad; bluntly rounded at snout.
The ALLIGATOR, *Alligator mississippiensis.*
Head triangular; becoming very narrow toward snout.
The CROCODILE, *Crocodylus acutus.*

As to the Chinese Alligator—it is the only crocodilian found in the Yang-tse-Kiang River. The South American Caimans have been described as belonging to the "alligator group." All appeal to the two species of *alligator* in *internal* (osteological) characters; yet externally some look like the crocodiles, as they have a pointed snout; others have a typical blunt, "alligator-like" snout. This is a bird's-eye view of the whole controversy. The alleged "striking difference in structure of the teeth" will later be discussed in relation to the respective species

Let us return directly to the structure. On the chin of all crocodilians is a pair of glands capable of being literally

[1] Members of the genus *Alligator.*

turned wrong-side-out in expelling their contents. They contain a strong-smelling, musky secretion undoubtedly employed by the sexes in determining each other's whereabouts during the breeding season.

Except on the back, crocodilians are covered with tough, leathery plates or shields, oblong on the abdomen and rounded on the sides; it is this part of the hide that is commercially valuable. On the back and top of the neck is an armor of large, close-set bony plates, attached to a tough, leathery skin. Most of these plates are coarsely keeled; they are arranged in regular rows; from a technical point of view they compose the *dorsal sheet* and are useful in the determination of species, as their arrangement varies.

One important character of the internal structure should be noted. The development of the heart and vascular system is the most perfect among all reptiles.

General Habits. Crocodilians live in immediate proximity to fair-sized bodies of water. Crawling out on the banks to bask, they rush for the water when disturbed, diving to the bottom. A common habit is to float with the body parallel with the top of the water—a small portion of the head and of the rough back protruding above the surface. From a short distance, old individuals look precisely like floating logs. Both the young and old are carnivorous—the young feeding largely on fishes, the old ones stalking water fowl from beneath the surface, or, in a like fashion, watching for animals approaching the water to drink.

Man-Eating Crocodiles. Several species—among them the Salt-Water Crocodile, *Crocodylus porosus,* and the African Crocodile, *C. niloticus*—are notoriously dangerous to man. Old examples will rush from a stream, seize a human—adult or child—then drag the prey into the water to drown. However, these man-eating species are much in the minority. Most of the crocodilians will rush for cover at the sight of man. The American species seem to be particularly inoffensive, though some grow to huge proportions. It is probable, however, that certain particularly large individuals of any of the species might be tempted to attack a man if he audaciously goes bathing in their haunts. While there are no records of actual attacks upon man by the American Alligator—apparently the least vicious of all crocodilians—the writer has often noted the suspicious and treacherous actions on the part of very large captive alligators that have become too bold to be trusted. He believes a man would be quickly torn to pieces and devoured if he should fall into a tank containing such creatures.

Crocodilians produce their young from eggs, which are elongated, white, shining and with a thick, hard shell. The female either digs a hole in a sand bank where the eggs are deposited, then covers them with much care, or constructs a veritable nest, in the shape of quite a high mound; the eggs are laid near the bottom of this mound; the heaped-up sticks and decomposing vegetation covering them soon generates a considerable temperature, hastening their incubation.

Before entering upon details of structure distinguishing the various species, besides the habits, the student should be presented with a concise tabulation, showing the general standing of the crocodilians. Existing species show such perfect intergradation it is impossible to divide them into families. Hence they are all embraced in the family *Crocodylidæ*. A tabulated list follows:

	Habitat	Maximum size
A. *Snout extremely long and slender—extending from the head like the handle of a frying-pan.*		
Gavialis gangeticus, Indian Gavial.	Northern India.	30 feet.
Tomistoma schlegeli, Malayan Gavial.	Borneo and Sumatra.	15 feet.
B. *Snout very sharp and slender; of triangular outline.*		
Crocodylus cataphractus, Sharp-nosed Crocodile.	West Africa.	12 feet.
Crocodylus johnsoni, Australian Crocodile.	Australia.	6–8 feet.
Crocodylus intermedius, Orinoco Crocodile.	Venezuela.	12 feet.

	Habitat	Maximum size
C. *Snout moderately sharp; outline distinctly triangular.*		
Crocodylus acutus, American Crocodile.	Fla.; Mexico; Central and South America.	14 feet.
Crocodylus siamensis, Siamese Crocodile.	Siam; Java.	7 feet.
Crocodylus niloticus, Nile Crocodile.	Africa generally.	18 feet.
Crocodylus porosus, Salt-water Crocodile.	India and Malaysia	20 feet.
D. *Snout more oval—bluntly triangular.*		
Crocodylus robustus, Madagascar Crocodile.	Madagascar.	30 feet.
Crocodylus rhombifer, Cuban Crocodile.	Restricted to Cuba.	7 feet.
Crocodylus moreletti, Guatemala Crocodile.	Guatemala; Honduras.	7 feet.
E. *Snout short and broad; conformation barely suggesting a triangular outline.*		
Crocodylus palustris, Swamp Crocodile.	India and Malaysia.	16 feet
Osteolæmus tetraspis. Broad-nosed Crocodile.	West Africa.	6 feet.
D. *Outline of the head similar to that of Section D.*		
Caiman trigonotus, Rough-backed Caiman.	Upper Amazon.	6 feet.
Caiman sclerops, Spectacled Caiman.	Central and South America.	7–8 feet.
Caiman palpebrosus, Banded Caiman.	Trop. So. America.	7–8 feet.
F. *Snout very broad; bluntly rounded at tip.*		
Caiman latirostris,[1] Round-nosed Caiman.	Trop. So. America.	7–8 feet.
Caiman niger,[1] Black Caiman.	Trop. So. America.	20[2] feet.
Alligator mississippiensis, American Alligator.	Southeastern U. S.	16 feet.
Alligator sinensis, Chinese Alligator.	China.	6 feet.

From the table the student will see that the gradation, in the form of the head from the almost beak-like snout

[1] These species are exceptions in their genus. The snout is blunt like that of the genus *Alligator*.

[2] Alleged to grow to this size by competent observers.

of the gavial to the blunt, round snout of the alligator, is fairly complete. In consequence we can compile no startling definitions in the time-frayed "alligator and crocodile" query.

Judging from the great size of some species, theory, coupled with observations under inappropriate conditions, has led some writers to assert that crocodilians are remarkably slow in growing and live to an enormous age—never stated. One observer alleges it requires twenty years for an alligator to grow to a length of two feet. In a cold-water aquarium, provided with anything but the proper food, this would probably be the case. Placed in water matching the temperature of their native bayous, a brood of alligators born in the New York Zoological Park increased from a length of seven inches to the substantial size of over five feet *within five years' time*. This is one of numerous observations on the growth of young alligators made in that institution. In the description of the alligator the writer will explain, with more detail, the rapidity of growth.

Apparently the most gigantic of the crocodilians is the INDIAN GAVIAL, *Gavialis gangeticus,* confined to northern India, where it inhabits the Ganges and the Brahmapootra rivers and their tributaries, thence extending westward along the Indus and its water-ways. Wide portions of the rivers, where the speed of the current is much reduced, seem to be the favorite lurking places; on adjoining banks or island-bars, solitary monsters have their basking places. The very young and partially-grown individuals are more sociable, living in considerable numbers in shallow basins some distance from the river, though filled by the latter's erratic rising and falling under influence of the freshets.

Like many of the crocodilians, the Gavial is a timid animal, dashing into the silty, opaque water at the sight of man, to show, some time later, merely a pair of greenish, cat-like eyes and the extreme, lumpy tip of the snout. Again alarmed, there is no commotion. The creature sinks noiselessly, when a few viscid bubbles break on the brown current. Judging from the massive structure of a big specimen, one might be led to believe it would literally wallow for the water when frightened. Conditions are quite to the reverse. The great body is raised well from the ground when the creature *runs* for the sheltering, muddy current. From the agility displayed by even the most gigantic individuals, man must consider himself fortunate that this mammoth reptile is seldom or never hostile to him. Its prey consists largely of fish.

As is the case with a number of Indian reptiles, it is difficult to procure the Gavial for observation in a captive state. A maze of fascination surrounds the reptile life of delightfully mysterious India; the weird and varied forms, the flashing, or, to the extreme, sinister colors; the colossal proportions of wide-awake brutes more dangerous than the royal tiger, down to pigmy forms, totally blind, burrowing deep into the ground—looking at them collectively they appear to form a reptile world by themselves beyond the comprehension of a single human lifetime devoted to them.

Mr. Lorenze Hagenbeck informs the writer that a friend shot a Gavial *thirty feet long*. The gigantic carcass was fully three feet in diameter. As it bloated under the tropical sun it appeared like a stranded whale. Carl Hagenbeck has furnished most of the few Gavials exhibited in zoological institutions. Capture depends largely upon strategy. It is comparatively easy to catch an animal that has foolishly taken up its abode in a shallow, inland basin. After it is noosed it is dragged into a crate where it must subsist for some weeks without water other than an occasional dash thrown from a pail—and without food, as an infuriated reptile is in no mood to take nourishment; moreover, it generally fasts for some months after being placed in a commodious tank.

There is nothing striking about the general structure of the Gavial's body—it is the head which concentrates immediate attention. From in front of the eyes the snout extends forward in such slender fashion it might be compared to an enormously elongated, flattened, duck-like bill; at the extreme tip is a swollen and lumpy nob of flesh surmounted by the nostrils. Both upper and lower of the long jaws are so studded with stout though long and sharp-edged, close-set teeth, it would seem as if Nature had been over-generous in the development of the dentition—that food once mixed in the array of shining enamel, far in front of the throat, could not be worked or tossed back in a position to be swallowed. Moreover, it looks dangerous for the animal itself to quickly bring together such fang-studded mandibles. Nevertheless they close in a wonderful fashion, the upper and lower teeth alternating, forming a close-set, continuous row. A skull of a Gavial is strongly suggestive of a frying-pan—the snout forming the handle.

The MALAYAN GAVIAL, *Tomistoma schlegeli,* inhabiting Borneo and Sumatra, has a head very similar to the Indian species. Several osteological characters—mainly of the skull—place it in a separate genus. The species grows to a length of fifteen feet.

Leaving the Gavials we find before us the important genus *Crocodylus,* containing the majority of the big, plated reptiles composing the present family. Several of the species rival the Indian Gavial in size; two of them are alleged to grow larger. In the face of a storm of crocodile tales it is best to make some allowance for the excitement attending the spectacle of a fifteen or eighteen-foot specimen rushing for cover, usually resulting in a magnification of the functions of hearing and sight on the part of the observer; his consequent description is inevitably a warm one and may be entertaining enough as simple conversation, but what we want are the cold facts—a tape line down the monster's back. Alas, indeed, for romance and tales of adventure, if that could be frequently done!—how quickly would the bottom drop out of innumerable thrilling stories which so distort the study of natural history. In the tabulated list the writer believes he has quoted the maximum length of the crocodiles—has been generous at that and must explain that the enormous size applied to several of the species is quite exceptional; such giants are so few they would create as much interest if exhibited in their native country as in one of the zoological gardens in the midst of civilization. A fifteen-foot crocodile is a big fellow—in India, in Africa—and a giant in the New World. From the list it will be also seen that the typical crocodiles are by no means confined to the Old World. At the same time it should be noted that while some of the New World species grow to a large size, they are greatly outclassed by the huge crocodiles of India, Malaysia and Africa.

Now, once launched well upon our subject, we will again take up the crocodile *versus* alligator query and note, with more detail, the differences between them. We have already studied the varying outlines of heads and understand that part of the argument.

With the crocodiles, the fourth tooth—a large one—on each side of the lower jaw, projects slightly outward, fitting into a *notch* of the upper jaw when the mouth is closed; thus, these two teeth are visible like the others in front and behind them. With the genera *Alligator* and *Caiman,* the fourth tooth on each side of the lower jaw—an enlarged tooth—fits into a *pit* or cavity of conical shape on the upper jaw; thus these two large teeth are hidden, except on very old examples having very long teeth, when the two in question pierce each side of the upper jaw, protruding upward and in sight.

Crocodiles, as a rule, have larger teeth, considerably more exposed than the two species of alligators and the allies of the latter—the caimans. On several of the crocodiles the *first* two teeth of the lower jaw pierce the snout, near the extreme tip, when by constant wear they produce perfectly round orifices through which they protrude some distance, adding a strong point to the animal's surly physiognomy.

Taking the American Alligator and the Chinese species as *the* alligators and comparing these animals with the typical crocodiles, the writer would say the latter are by far the more active, agile in the water—having better developed tails for swimming—and more vicious. The caimans are quite crocodile-like in habits.

For the benefit of the beginner, the writer has divided the typical crocodiles into four groups, distinguished apart by the outline of the snout. The first group is composed of three members having a snout so slender as to be almost gavial-like—in fact, some writers have called them "false gavials." A glance at the head, however, will show the crocodile features—an inclination to adopt triangular lines, besides a cut-in, irregular outline toward the snout.

A good representative of group one—the narrow-headed crocodiles—is the ORINOCO CROCODILE, *Crocodylus intermedius,* growing to a length of twelve feet. Compared with the other New World crocodilians, the snout is extremely narrow—really beak-like. Reptiles of this species are abundant in the Orinoco as well as its tributaries. Older specimens seem to prefer living along the larger rivers, while many of the females and large numbers of young infest inland lagoons, where, protected by dense forest growth, the nests are constructed and the young partially concealed from their many enemies.

The AMERICAN CROCODILE, *C. acutus,* stands as a typical representative of the second group, where the head is fairly broad in front of the eyes, thence tapers sharply toward the snout, producing a triangular outline.

Quite partial to the neighborhood of salt or brackish water, we also find the present species to be the most extensively distributed of the New World crocodilians. In South America it is abundant in the coast regions of Ecuador, Colombia and Venezuela; it is generally distributed along the Central American and Mexican coasts as well as in the West. Indies. The presence of the American Crocodile in Florida was not discovered until 1875, when a pair of large size were collected at Arch Creek, at the head of Biscayne Bay, by Dr. William T. Hornaday. The male was fourteen feet, two inches long. Since that time many specimens have been taken in the southern portion of the peninsula. Lake Worth appears to be the northern limit. Undoubtedly the Florida colony was started from animals taking to sea, swimming across the Gulf of Mexico from the coast swamps of Yucatan, or northward from the West Indies. The reason for the species not extending its range farther north in the Florida peninsula is clearly explained when we appreciate that the crocodile is far more sensitive to cold than the alligator. In water of a temperature as cold as 45° Fahrenheit, a crocodile becomes absolutely helpless and will drown if permitted to remain in the same. An alligator withstands a like temperature with little inconvenience and though partially benumbed has sense enough to take care of itself and so regulates its breathing that it sinks, after once thoroughly aërating the lungs, then with nasal valves firmly closed, lies passive awaiting returning warmth.

To the observer who is familiar with fair-sized alligators, but has never been properly introduced to a crocodile, the writer would say a few words of caution. There is about as much difference in temper and activity between an alligator and a crocodile, as between a tortoise and a snapping turtle. An enraged alligator will throw its head from side to side, bang the jaws together sonorously and violently swish the tail, but a man with steady nerves may approach within a few feet of the animal, throw a noose over the head, tie the jaws together, push a pole toward the body—then, by successive nooses pulled backward over the head, and forward over the tail, splint the animal to the pole so it is entirely powerless. On one of a number of occasions, involving transferring alligators, operating upon them and the like, the writer, assisted by one man, in this way completely overpowered a vigorous, twelve-foot example. Throughout the process the big saurian hissed, grunted, snapped from side to side and made swings with his tail that would have knocked a man off his feet—but the animal remained in the same spot. Such proceedings would have been abruptly terminated with a crocodile. The writer well remembers his first acquaintance with a big fellow from Florida. Driven out of the crate the crocodile looked the picture of good nature. Standing away from what he thought to be the reach of his tail, the writer prodded the apparently sluggish brute with a stick to start it for the tank. Several things happened in quick order. With a crescentic twist of the body utterly beyond the power of an alligator, the brute dashed its tail at the writer, landing him such a powerful blow that he was lifted completely from the ground. As he left *terra-firma,* an almost involuntary inclination caused him to hurl his body away from a pair of widely-gaping, tooth-studded jaws swinging perilously near. Landing with a thud on one shoulder, though otherwise unhurt, the writer threw himself over and over, rolling from the dangerous brute that was actually pursuing him on the run, body raised high from the ground. For an instant it seemed as if the crocodile would win. As the writer suddenly sprang to his feet and glanced backward, he beheld the brute throw itself flat on its belly, open the jaws widely, then remain motionless as a statue. Such is the average crocodile—an active, vicious and, above all, treacherous brute. When the keepers of the reptile house in the New York Zoological Park clean out the big pool for crocodilians, they actually walk over the backs of some of the big 'gators, so tame are these. They never become unduly familiar with the crocodiles, finding it necessary to pen the latter behind heavy barred gates—and in the process the men are often chased from the enclosure.

The African Crocodile, *C. niloticus,* often called the Nile Crocodile, is generally abundant throughout Africa from the Nile to the Senegal, thence southward to the Cape of Good Hope. It also swarms in the inland rivers of Madagascar. None among the legions of wild brutes of the Dark Continent has caused greater loss of human life than the present terrible creature. And it is consequently no wonder this ponderous, vicious reptile has been notorious from ancient times down to the present. It was held sacred by the ancient Egyptians who preserved thousands of mummies of various-sized reptiles. Now the crocodile is nearly extinct in lower Egypt, though it swarms farther up the Nile.

Except from its *man-eating habits,* the African Crocodile differs little in its modes of life from others of the genus. It is hunted for various purposes—often for sport, and its plated back is by no means impervious to a modern rifled arm—even a revolver of fair caliber. Shooting is not, however, always productive of satisfactory results. If the game is in the water it sinks and is lost upon receiving a mortal wound. A huge baited hook attached to a rope is often employed in capturing crocodiles. A battle royal follows as the captors haul the monster from the sheltering waters. Once it is on the bank, braver members of the party endeavor to noose the limbs and tail, when a spear is plunged to the reptile's vitals—not always bringing a speedy termination of terrific struggles. Warriors of some of the African tribes use the plated hide as an armor. Against javelins and arrows the hide is undoubtedly invulnerable.

Another of the *man-eating saurians* is the great SALT-WATER CROCODILE, *C. porosus.* The range is extensive, embracing India, Ceylon and southern China, the Malay Archipelago, including the Solomon Islands, and North Australia. This extensive distribution, from the shores of Asia, through a maze of islands and across stretches of ocean to Australia, is easily explained: for this denizen of the coast swamps and brackish inlets unhesitatingly takes to sea, making vast excursions from one shore to another. Large and half-grown individuals are frequently seen from vessels when out of sight of land. Judging from such reptiles' nonchalant motions, they are in no danger of tiring, or ultimately drowning. The species is easily recognized by a prominent ridge in front of each eye. Old examples are dark olive-brown or black. Twenty-foot specimens have been recorded and through the larger islands of the

Malay Archipelago tales are many of the loss of human life owing to these bold brutes. It appears that the species does not occur far inland in any portion of its range, preferring the coastal swamps and inlets, or the larger rivers within tidal limits.

As an example of the Salt-Water Crocodile's vicious disposition, the writer remembers an experience with several specimens arriving in the port of New York from Singapore. They were on one of the big freighters that so often bring a miscellaneous collection of mammals, birds and big snakes from the East. Having word from the ship, the writer hurried to inspect the cargo. Arriving after dark, he was shown down into the hold by the light of several lanterns. The place looked like the interior of the Ark. Pairs of luminous eyes, moving this way and that, revealed the restless pacing of leopards and other cats. Snarls, growls, hisses and a stamping of hoofed feet denoted varied, restless forms, much crowded in their miserable quarters—many behind bars, others in slatted crates, a few of the weaker in weird bamboo cages, and yet more in closed boxes from which came no signs of life; the latter contained the snakes. As the inspection began, two black panthers became continually vociferous in spitting, snarling fashion. Yet above the voicing of their temper came a steady series of sharp hisses from an elongated crate. For a time the writer was too much occupied to pay much attention to the latter, unusual sound. It is a fascinating process to look over a newly-arrived contingent of animals from India. In the dingy hold of the ship some of the creatures with handsome pelts appear in startling contrast; and there are others with somber hues and ferocious mien that harmonize with their uninviting quarters. We find tiger cats, or clouded leopards with their beautifully marbled coats; the vividly marked leopard of the jungle often gentle enough to come rubbing against the iron bars, yet in an adjoining cage may be a black panther, its lips rolled back into a satanic snarl; last to be examined are those boxes containing the giant snakes of the Malay Peninsula [3]—and throughout one's investigations there is always the possibility of coming upon a modest crate, which, when opened, discloses some rare creature the investigator has never seen before, but has been mentally carrying his ideal of its actions and appearance in anticipation of finally making its acquaintance. In a search like this the writer neared the crate from which the chorus of hisses was arising, coming with such perfect rhythm as to catch the ear over the sounds from the entire yowling menagerie. The captain had thrown back a cover, disclosing a python colored like an Oriental rug, but the writer was all curious to see what the long crate contained. It was explained to him that the crate enclosed three young crocodiles—then the box was opened. The amount of ferocity crowded into those four-foot youngsters was amazing. They all but stood on their hind legs in an endeavor to bite. Nor for a moment, while under observation, did the fiendish little brutes relax their vigilance. In uncontrollable rage, one of them kept backing up and walking forward, and if a hand were moved over it, reared upward, snapping its jaws loudly.

The three crocodiles finally became the writer's property. They were positively the most vicious reptiles he has ever seen. For a time they would not feed. Strips of raw beef or fish thrown into the tank were instantly seized, when the animal threw its body into a rapid, rotary movement. Such exhibitions of rage were frequent. A stick poked at one of the reptiles was instantly seized and whirled out of the hand unless firmly held. All three of the specimens began feeding after a time, taking fish, mice and sparrows. With the increasing appetite came no signs of docility. The writer's mere approach started a vigorous hissing and three cottony-white mouths yawned widely for a chance to grasp some offending object, then dismember it by a quick twist.

Seemingly confined to the island of Cuba is a small species appropriately termed the CUBAN CROCODILE,

[3] *Python reticulatus.*

C. rhombifer. An adult is only seven or eight feet long. Meeting in front of the eyes is a pair of oblique ridges, which, together with the inner borders of the orbits, combine in forming a rhomb-like prominence. While the head is triangular and appeals to that of the two preceding species, it is broader, shorter and not so gradually tapering—hence the placing of this crocodile (and several others on the list) in another group, according to the outline of the head. The small size has no bearing on the temper. Two examples in the New York Zoological Park were extremely fierce, snapping at any one who came near their tank. As the food was brought they threw the forward portion of the body high out of the water by suddenly elevating the tail—the effect being a seesaw movement assisted by an upward leap. The seven-foot specimen could spring a yard from the water. The keeper was invariably careful of his hands when near the tank.

Rather alligator-like, from the short and broad snout, the MARSH CROCODILE, or "MUGGER," *C. palustris,* has almost as extensive a distribution as *Crocodylus porosus*—the Salt-Water Crocodile. Though another burly representative of the *Crocodylidæ,* it is a considerably smaller animal than the Salt-Water Crocodile, the maximum length being about sixteen feet. Unlike the other species mentioned, the present one ranges far inland, inhabiting marshes, rivers and lakes of India, Ceylon, Burma, the Malay Peninsula as well as many of the larger islands of the Malay Archipelago. During the droughts, the crocodiles become uneasy owing to the rapidly dropping water of their pools. They start on overland excursions for more favorable places and during such times may be found wandering through the jungle at what seem to be considerable distances from water.

The Marsh Crocodile is naturally a timid reptile, floundering for shelter at the sight of man. It should not, therefore, be included in the list of those crocodilians endangering human life. In some parts of India, colonies of these animals are partially confined and subjected to worship. The reptiles become amusingly tame, permitting audacious Hindoos to salaam within a yard of them. Incidentally, such exhibitions involve old specimens that have become so fat they are barely able to waddle from the water to the bank. The younger crocodiles in such places are vigorous enough, greeting the tourist with gaping jaws—though such actions are prompted by appetite alone and the reptiles are friendly to some extent, even taking food from the hand. The latter operation is risky, as without the least evil intentions, the crocodiles are liable to take more than the morsel offered.

For the AMERICAN ALLIGATOR, *Alligator mississippiensis,* little description is necessary. The snout is very broad—bluntly rounded at the tip. It lacks the notched, cut-in outline on each side (toward the tip) as seen with all of the crocodiles. The fourth tooth on each side of the lower jaw, enlarged and having the situation of a canine tooth, is hidden when the mouth is closed, as it fits into a pit in the bone of the upper jaw—except with some old specimens when these teeth entirely perforate the bone of the snout, the tips protruding. The latter curious character is to be noted with both young and old among the crocodiles, but relates always to the front (incisor) teeth. The canine teeth on the lower jaw of the crocodiles fit into a notch on the *outside* of the upper jaw when the mouth is closed.

The alligator is a more bulky, thick-set and considerably less active, less vicious animal than its near relatives, the crocodiles. Besides, its coloration is quite different. Young specimens are black with yellowish cross-bars. Mature examples are coal-black when the hide is wet—dark gray when perfectly dry; they lose the yellow markings altogether. There is a striking difference between the black of the alligator and the olive hue of the American crocodile; the difference may be noted from a distance of several hundred feet.

In its distribution the American alligator is confined to the southeastern portion of the United States, from the southern portion of North Carolina, southward throughout

Florida and westward to the lower part of the Rio Grande. It inhabits the low, coastal region. Unlike the crocodile, it is not partial to salt water. The maximum length appears to be sixteen feet. A specimen in the New York Zoological Park was twelve feet, five inches long and weighed eight hundred and twenty-five pounds. Twelve-foot alligators are now almost extinct. Over vast areas where these reptiles were once abundant in years past, the sight of even a small example, nowadays, is considered a novelty. Among the intricate swamps and lagoons of Florida and Georgia, the alligator yet exists in moderate numbers. In comparatively open situations, along rivers and lakes, the hunt for individuals of a size to yield commercially valuable hides has produced practical extermination.

With the present reptile we have one of the few crocodilians giving voice to a loud sound—a bellow or roar. A five-foot specimen emits a series of sounds not unlike the "mooing" of a cow, though shorter and more guttural. A ten or twelve-foot specimen lets out a rattling bellow that shakes the night air of the lagoons and may be heard for a mile. When so performing, the males emit vapory jets of musk from the glands on the chin. This saturates the surrounding, humid atmosphere, then, traveling on an indolent air current, attracts company to the solitary bellower.

Hunting for many miles along the Savannah River, the writer was not once rewarded in seeing an alligator. The search was primarily for water snakes, but our eyes were ever on the alert over those coffee-colored waters for the floating black line—so much like a log—showing the presence of a saurian. At length we struck inland, through the river low grounds. Lagoons bordered with heavy timber alternated with vast savannas. Through the timber, every tree was enormously broad at the base, this development giving way to a slender trunk—and all painted yellow for a height of at least a yard from the rise of the big stream during the freshets. In pools sheltered by these queer forests we found alligators—fairly secure from molestation.

One nest was investigated. It consisted of a mound of water-soaked twigs, dead masses of the hanging moss that had dropped from the trees and other débris. The mound was about 5 feet in diameter and 2 feet high. It contained 38 hard-shelled, white eggs 3¼ inches long and 1¾ inches in diameter. The eggs were collected during the middle of August and began hatching in the first week of October. They were deposited in two neat layers at the very bottom of the mound. As we dug down to them the rotting vegetable mass scooped together by the parent was found to be producing a considerable heat. Of the parent there was no sign during any part of the work of digging out the eggs and packing the material composing the mound into a number of bags to be shipped North.

Many have been the theories concerning the growth of the alligator. The general supposition points to a remarkably long period in attaining maturity. That such is by no means the case has been demonstrated by a large number of young alligators under the writer's charge. These outgrow one tank after another within a few years. It only takes four years for an alligator from the time of hatching to grow fully large enough to have a commercially valuable hide. The increase in size of a representative specimen hatching from one of the eggs described is given as an *average* example of an alligator's growth.

Oct. 1900—Hatched	Length 8 inches;	weight 1¾ oz.
Oct. 1901	Length 18 inches;	weight 9¼ oz.
Aug. 1902	Length 23 inches;	weight 3 lbs.
Mar. 1903	Length 45 inches;	weight 14 lbs.
Oct. 1905	Length 64 inches;	weight 50 lbs.
Oct. 1906	Length 72 inches;	weight 72 lbs.

An alligator 6 feet, 11 inches long received at the reptile house in 1899, in October, had increased to a length of 11 feet, 6 inches in October of 1905.

It is remarkable that the only other species of the genus *Alligator* occurs in China, along the Yang-tse-Kiang River. Externally it looks much like the New World species.

The color above is blackish olive, with obscure yellowish bands. This is a small species, growing to a length of about six feet.

The CAIMANS. Five species of the genus *Caiman* inhabit Central America and tropical South America east of the Andes. The snout of several species is much sharper than with the genus *Alligator,* to which these reptiles are most nearly related; on some of the species the outlines of the snout are strongly suggestive of the preceding genus. A distinguishing feature of the South American crocodiles is the fitting of the canine teeth of the lower jaw into a *pit* of the upper jaw, as with the alligator.

The SPECTACLED CAIMAN, *C. sclerops,* has the widest distribution of any of the species, occurring from southern Mexico through Central America and tropical South America into Argentina. A large example is eight feet long. The upper eyelids are swollen, wrinkled and on many specimens impart a suggestion of a pair of spectacles. On other specimens the eyelids are developed into blunt horns. Rather a vicious, treacherous disposition must be credited to the species if captive examples are to be taken as illustrations; they are much quicker than alligators and have longer, sharper teeth.

Caiman latirostris, another small species, is confined to tropical South America. The eyelids are frequently developed into horns.

The BLACK CAIMAN, *C. niger,* appears to be the largest of the New World crocodilians. It is alleged to grow to a length of *twenty feet.* This animal abounds in the upper systems of the Amazon. The eyelids are flat, but finely striated (wrinkled). The snout is bluntly rounded like that of the North American alligator. Young specimens have several radiating black bars (downward) from the eye. They are alligator-like in general configuration.

PART II

THE LIZARDS

ORDER *SQUAMATA*
SUBORDER *SAURIA*

SUBORDER *SAURIA*—THE LIZARDS

Looking down upon the vast Order now engaging the student's attention, even the most passive of observers cannot refrain from expressing amazement at the array of varied forms. In a subdivision, the *Sauria,* we shall consider creatures twelve feet long, with claws as long as those of the leopard—animals strong and active enough to leap at the throat of a young gazelle, tear, dismember and devour the prey; and passing such we stop to realize that tiny, limbless and worm-like, slow-moving things, burrowing their life away deep in the ground where they need no eyes—in fact, have none—are also true lizards. Among these hordes of scaly life we shall find lizards that rush over the ground with such speed they appear as but a streak to the human eye; others having adhesive digits and with equal speed can traverse the smooth face of a precipice or run head downward over a horizontal surface; and yet others that swim with the strength of crocodilians, while a few have parachute-like wings with which they sail from tree to tree. From one family we may abruptly arrive at another where the species are so slow in movements they rely upon a remarkable resemblance to the hues of their arboreal homes for protection, for with these the motions might appeal to us like the slow relaxation of the muscles of some dying creature. Again we come upon lizards without vestiges of limbs, gliding away like serpents, or species with limbs so small they fold these useless members against the side of the body in times of fright, when, with the aid of a sharpened snout, they plough their way, literally swim into the desert sands.

STRUCTURE OF LIZARDS

Lizards may be fairly well separated for popular study, according to the structure of their scales. Some have very coarse, overlapping scales, each terminating in a sharp point and having a strong keel; species thus coated are rough, lusterless and bristling with sharp points. Others have smooth, rounded scales as polished as glass. While a number of lizards have the scales arranged in oblique rows, many display a ringed arrangement on both the body and the tail. A good proportion of the larger (as well as the smaller) lizards have such a fine, granular scalation they appear to be covered merely with a bare, rough skin unless closely examined. Some of the degenerate, worm-like species have lost their scales, in place of which are hardened, polished and movable rings of skin encircling the body; these are used in precisely the same fashion as the segments of an earthworm—to assist in locomotion.

The general form, as has been previously mentioned, greatly varies. Yet the vast majority of lizards have four well-developed limbs. Among several of the families—and these by no means nearly allied—we find startling illustrations of degeneracy; and all along similar lines. In adopting subterraneous habits certain species have ultimately lost their limbs while their eyes have become small and nearly useless. Such degenerative tendencies are always marked with decided elongation of the body—into a snake-like or worm-like form. We find all stages of development. Most striking are those species with the limbs so aborted the creature folds them against the sides of the body and glides like a snake, or where *there is but one pair of microscopic limbs, these are of absolutely no use though going through all the motions of walking during the animal's gliding progress.* In the degenerate family *Amphisbænidæ,* not only the limbs[1] and scales have disappeared, but

[1] Except with three genera having only a pair of practically useless *front* limbs.

the pectoral and the pelvic arch have been reduced to mere vestiges.

The Tongue. The structure of the tongue varies greatly among lizards. With many of them it is long, black, deeply forked and snake-like; it is darted from the mouth to examine objects in the lizard's path. On others the tongue is flattened yet rather fleshy, and but bluntly nicked at the tip; in combination it is used as an organ of investigation and to pull the food into the animal's mouth. A number of lizards have a thick, viscid tongue, employed in the same fashion as that of the toad, namely:—to lap up small insect prey. The true chameleons have an enormously long tongue—club-shaped at the tip—that is darted at an insect which sticks fast when squarely hit.

The Teeth. With the arrangement of the teeth we find an important character bearing on classification. Two phases of development should be thoroughly understood. Some lizards have an *acrodont,* others a *pleurodont* dentition. *Acrodont* lizards have the teeth set along the *edges* of the jaws; there are no well-defined *alveoli* (sockets) or a longitudinal socket groove. *Pleurodont* lizards have the teeth set in a deeply-cleft, longitudinal, continuous socket. If it were not for these decisive arrangements we would be unable to separate the great family *Iguanidæ* (*pleurodont*) of the New World from the equally large family *Agamidæ* (*acrodont*) of the Old World, for the external characters would lead us to directly associate one family with another —even discuss the close relationship of different genera, as for most of the distinctly freak genera of the *Iguanidæ* we find forms of similar outlines in the *Agamidæ.*

The teeth of lizards may be comical or flat, straight or recurved, sharply pointed or terminating in queerly serrated fashion that makes each tooth look like a "bit" of some fancy drill. *Among the vast aggregation of lizards, only two are known to be poisonous;* these are the species of *Heloderma*—the Beaded Lizards, inhabiting the deserts of the southwestern portion of the United States, besides the arid regions of southern Mexico and northern Central America. The species are pleurodont; the teeth of the *lower* jaw are stout, slightly recurved and each is provided with a venom-conducting groove. In Borneo is a lizard technically known as *Lanthanotus borneensis;* its teeth have been alleged to be grooved, like *Heloderma.* Not much is known about this creature. Notwithstanding an apparent relationship to *Heloderma,* it would be unjust to describe the species as in any way venomous.

The Tail. For purposes of defense, the tail is an invaluable organ. With it, the larger lizards deal lashing, whip-like blows. Many lizards have a tail of extraordinary length—four or five times as long as the combined length of the head and body; a number possess a diminutive, stumpy appendage. With the majority of lacertilians the tail is readily discarded, and it is soon reproduced. Let us take one of the extremes of caudal development as an illustration, noting how the brittle appendage may save its owner's life in time of danger. Suppose a limbless lizard—a Glass "Snake"—is pursued by an active, reptile-eating serpent. The former's stiff, undulatory movements are hopelessly slow in comparison with the sinuous glide of the pursuer. In a moment the snake has seized its prey. There is a quick twist and instantly the snake is busily engaged in subduing what appears to be its frenzied victim. Actually, this is what has happened:—In that twisting movement the lizard has snapped off its tail. The muscles of the discarded member have been thrown into a state of great excitability—evidently a provision of Nature. Meanwhile, an abbreviated lizard has, under cover of the excitement occasioned by the antics of the tail, glided slyly for a safe retreat.

In catching some of the ground lizards among leaves—by slapping the hand down suddenly over a stalked specimen—the writer has many times been deceived and permitted lizards to escape, owing to a reptile's tail having become detached by the blow when it snapped and twisted among the leaves with such a commotion that the hand involuntarily made a fresh grab for it; then, a second commotion showed the consequent escape of the lizard itself, which had been primarily the prisoner. A number of the geckos run away from danger with the thick tail well elevated and the animal parts with the caudal member at barely a touch, when the tail jumps and wriggles in a manner sure to attract the attention of the enemy.

In this casting off of the tail the organ is not *"disjointed,"* as is often the popular idea. Owing to a curious structure of the caudal vertebræ the break occurs in the *middle* of a vertebral joint and the broken end of bone immediately begins a reconstructive process, resulting in a new tail. The new member is completed in a few months. It is seldom as long as the original one, nor covered with a normal scalation.

Changes of Color. Decided, though involuntary, changes of the body hues may be observed among several of the families. The process is influenced by light, temperature, excitement and the health of the individual. It is a mistake to imagine the color changes to be strictly in line of protection to the lizard in immediately conforming to the colors of surfaces on which the animal rests. A specimen capable of exhibiting all phases of coloration between a dull brown to an emerald green may for some time rest upon a dark tree trunk and be clad in a suit of conspicuous steel-gray; from this hue it may transform into a livid green; a few minutes later it may jump among the leaves and shrubbery, where it takes on an almost blackish hue. In fiction, theory is an excellent stand-by. Who can blame certain romantic authors for elaborating upon such an admirable point as the "power" displayed by a dull brown lizard to jump upon a leaf and transform into a leafy green, thence upon a tree trunk where it immediately turns brown again, and from there, possibly, upon a gorgeous flower where the reptile assumes a hue to match the richly-colored petals? The writer once observed an experiment made by a student who digested a great amount of theoretical natural history. The young man placed a number of American "chameleons" (*Anolis*) in a glass-topped box lined with large patches of green, gray, brown and black paper—then watched for results. The latter were decidedly, repeatedly and humorously negative. The most conspicuous examples of lizards that vary in hues and pattern are among the *Gekkonidæ, Iguanidæ, Agamidæ* and *Chamaeleontidæ;* others exhibit no trace of this characteristic; among the latter are the members of the *Lacertidæ, Teiidæ* and *Scincidæ.*

Reproduction. As a rule, lizards deposit a moderate number of oval, soft-shelled eggs, hatching in eight or ten weeks. In certain families, however, among which are the *Iguanidæ, Lacertidæ, Anguidæ* and *Scincidæ* are a number of species producing their young alive.

Distribution. Compared with snakes, a far greater proportion of the lizards are confined to the warmer portions of the globe; only a limited number of species occur in temperate latitudes. An examination of the classified list that follows will show the distribution generally, but concise mention of the more important families may not be amiss. The large family *Gekkonidæ* is distributed completely around the world, though restricted, as a rule, to semitropical and tropical latitudes; even in the tiny Polynesian Islands, this ring of distribution is continued. The extensive range may be accounted for by the secretive habits of many of the species, which are nocturnal. They are undoubtedly carried from one island to another in exchanges of produce. Another family inhabiting both the Old and the New World is the *Scincidæ*—and the species range well into the temperate regions of both hemispheres; one genus, *Lygosoma,* with over one hundred and sixty species, is represented in Malaysia, Australia, North America and Central America; nor is it an exception in this extensively distributed family. The large family *Iguanidæ* is restricted to the New World with the peculiar exceptions of a few representatives in Madagascar, the Fiji and the Friendly

Islands. The *Abamidæ, Lacertidæ* and *Varanidæ* are restricted to the Old World.

A tabulated outline, showing the classification and approximate number of species, is herewith given: *

SUBORDER *SAURIA*

	Number of Species	Distribution
Family *Gekkonidæ:*		
The GECKOS (Cosmopolitan)		
Genus *Nephrurus*	4	Australia.
Genus *Chondrodactylus*	1	South Africa.
Genus *Rhynchœdura*	1	Australia.
Genus *Teratoscincus*	1	Persia; Turkestan.
Genus *Ceramodactylus*	2	Persia; Arabia.
Genus *Ptenopus*	1	South Africa.
Genus *Stenodactylus*	6	North Africa; S. W. Asia.
Genus *Alsophylax*	2	Persia; Turkestan.
Genus *Homonota*	2	Southeastern South America.
Genus *Gymnodactylus*	38	So. Europe; Asia; East Indies; Polynesia and tropical America.
Genus *Agamura*	2	Persia; Baluchistan.
Genus *Pristurus*	6	Northern Africa; S. W. Asia.
Genus *Gonatodes*	18	Trop. So. Am.; West Indies; Southern India; East Indies.
Genus *Æluroscalabotes*	3	East Indies.
Genus *Heteronota*	3	Australia.
Genus *Phyllodactylus*	25	Trop. So. Amer.; Aust.; Africa and islands in the Mediterranean.
Genus *Ebenavia*	2	Madagascar.
Genus *Diplodactylus*	9	Australia.
Genus *Œdura*	7	Australia.
Genus *Calodactylus*	1	Southern India.
Genus *Ptyodactylus*	2	Northern Africa; S. W. Asia.
Genus *Thecadactylus*	2	Trop. So. Amer.; islands in Torres Straits.

* This summary is presented mainly to indicate the scope of this division of reptiles. It is practically revised, but to keep such a list "up to date" with regard to scientific nomenclature is almost an impossible task, without constant access to world sources of literature by technical workers engaged in investigations of priority, relationships affecting grouping of species, elimination of disproved forms, and addition of new species.

	Number of Species	Distribution
Genus *Hemidactylus*	33	Trop. So. Amer.; Southern Europe; So. Asia; Africa and Polynesia.
Genus *Teratolepis*	1	India.
Genus *Phyllopezus*	1	Brazil.
Genus *Aristelliger*	2	Central Amer.; West Indies.
Genus *Gehyra*	10	East Indies; Aust.; islands in the Southern Pacific; west coast of Mexico.
Genus *Perochirus*	5	Philippines; New Hebrides, Caroline Islands.
Genus *Spathoscalabotes*	1	East Indies.
Genus *Microscalabotes*	1	Madagascar.
Genus *Lygodactylus*	5	Africa; Madagascar.
Genus *Lepidodactylus*	10	East Indies; S. W. Australia and Polynesia.
Genus *Naultinus*	2	New Zealand.
Genus *Hoplodactylus*	5	So. India; islands in the So. Pac.
Genus *Rhacodactylus*	6	New Caledonia.
Genus *Luperosaurus*	1	Philippine Islands.
Genus *Gekko*	8	China; Japan.
Genus *Ptychozoon*	1	Malay Pn.; Java; Borneo and Sumatra.
Genus *Homopholis*	2	South Africa.
Genus *Gekkolepis*	2	Madagascar.
Genus *Eurydactylus*	1	New Caledonia.
Genus *Æluronyx*	2	Madagascar.
Genus *Tarentola*	6	Country bordering the Mediterranean; 1 species in West Indies.
Genus *Pachydactylus*	10	Africa.
Genus *Calopus*	1	South Africa.
Genus *Dactychilikion*	1	South Africa.
Genus *Phelsuna*	8	Madagascar; Seychelles; Mauritius; Rodriguez and Andaman Islands.
Genus *Rhotropus*	1	Southwestern Africa.
Genus *Sphærodactylus*	18	Central America; South America and the West Indies; So. Florida.
Genus *Psilodactylus*	1	West Africa.
Genus *Coleonyx*	4	S. W. United States; Mexico.
Family *Uroplatidæ:*		Central America.
Fringed *Geckos*	1	
Genus *Uroplates*	3	Madagascar.
Family *Pygopodidæ:* A family of snake-like lizards.		
Genus *Pygopus*	1	Australia.
Genus *Cryptodelma*	2	Australia.
Genus *Delma*	2	Australia.
Genus *Pletholax*	1	Australia.

	Number of Species	Distribution
Genus *Aprasia*	1	Australia.
Genus *Lialis*	1	Australia.
Family *Agamidæ:* Old World Lizards.		
Genus *Draco*	22	East Indies.
Genus *Sitana*	1	India; Ceylon.
Genus *Otocryptis*	2	Southern India; Ceylon.
Genus *Ptyctolæmus*	1	Northern India.
Genus *Aphaniotis*	1	Malaysia.
Genus *Lophocalotes*	1	East Indies.
Genus *Cophotis*	2	Sumatra; Ceylon.
Genus *Ceratophora*	3	Ceylon.
Genus *Harpesaurus*	1	Java.
Genus *Phoxophrys*	1	Sumatra.
Genus *Lyriocephalus*	1	Ceylon.
Genus *Gonyocephalus*	25	East Indies; Aust.; Polynesia.
Genus *Acanthosaura*	9	E. E. Asia.
Genus *Japalura*	6	Southern China.
Genus *Salea*	2	Southern India.
Genus *Calotes*	19	India and Malaysia.
Genus *Chelosania*	1	Australia.
Genus *Chorasia*	3	India.
Genus *Agama*	43	Southern Europe; So. Asia; Africa.
Genus *Phrynocephalus*	14	S. E. Europe; Central Asia.
Genus *Amphibolurus*	14	Australia.
Genus *Tympanocryptis*	2	Australia.
Genus *Diporophora*	3	Australia.
Genus *Physignathus*	7	Australia; Papuasia; Siam; Cochin China.
Genus *Chlamydosaurus*	1	Australia.
Genus *Lophura*	1	East Indies.
Genus *Liolepis*	1	S. E. Asia.
Genus *Uromastyx*	7	Southern Asia; Northern Africa.
Genus *Aporoscelis*	2	East Africa.
Genus *Moloch*	1	Australia.
Family *Iguanidæ:* New World Lizards, with the exception of three genera.		
Genus *Chamæleolis*	1	Cuba.
Genus *Xiphocercus*	2	Tropical South Amer.; West Indies.
Genus *Anolis*	107	Southern North Amer.; Mexico; Central Amer.; South Amer. and the West Indies.
Genus *Norops*	2	Cent. and So. Amer.; West Indies.
Genus *Tropidodactylus*	1	Trop. So. Amer.; West Indies.
Genus *Polychrus*	3	Trop. So. America.
Genus *Corythophanes*	3	Central America.

	Number of Species	Distribution
Genus *Læmanctus*	4	Central America.
Genus *Basiliscus*	4	Mex.; Cent. Amer. and No. South Amer.
Genus *Ophryœssa*	1	Tropical South America.
Genus *Enyalioides*	8	Tropical South America.
Genus *Enyalius*	6	Tropical South America.
Genus *Anisolepis*	1	Southern Brazil.
Genus *Urostrophus*	2	South America.
Genus *Liosaurus*	1	South America.
Genus *Diplolæmus*	1	Patagonia.
Genus *Pristidactylus*	1	Patagonia.
Genus *Scartiscus*	1	Paraguay.
Genus *Chalarodon*	1	Madagascar.
Genus *Hoplurus*	5	*Madagascar.*
Genus *Stenocercus*	7	Western South America.
Genus *Ctenoblepharis*	1	Peru.
Genus *Helocephalus*	3	N. W. South America.
Genus *Liolæmus*	22	So. Amer.—south of the equator.
Genus *Saccodeira*	3	South America.
Genus *Leiocephalus*	17	South America.
Genus *Tropidurus*	11	South America.
Genus *Uraniscodon*	2	South America.
Genus *Strobilurus*	1	Brazil.
Genus *Urocentron*	3	South America.
Genus *Phymaturus*	1	Chili.
Genus *Amblyrhynchus*	1	Galapagos Islands.
Genus *Conolophus*	1	Galapagos Islands.
Genus *Iguana*	2	Mex.; Cent. Amer.; tropical South America.
Genus *Brachylophus*	1	*Fiji and Friendly Islands.*
Genus *Metopoceros*	5	West Indies.
Genus *Ctenosaura*	4	S. W. United States; Mexico and Central America.
Genus *Cachryx*	1	Yucatan.
Genus *Hoplocercus*	2	South America.
Genus *Dipsosaurus*	1	Deserts of S. W. North Amer.
Genus *Sauromalus*	6	Deserts of S. W. North Amer.
Genus *Crotaphytus*	6	Southern U. S.; Northern Mexico.
Genus *Callisaurus*	4	Deserts of S. W. North Amer.
Genus *Uma*	3	Arizona; New Mexico.
Genus *Holbrookia*	5	Southern U. S.; Northern Mexico.
Genus *Uta*	20	Western U. S.; Mexico.
Genus *Sator*	2	Lower California.
Genus *Sceloporus*	41*	United States; Mexico.

* Listing of McCoy, Museum of Comparative Zoology, 1931.

	Number of Species	Distribution
Genus *Phrynosoma*	16	United States; Mexico.
Family *Xenosauridæ:*		
Genus *Xenosaurus*	1	So. Mexico and Cent. Amer.
Family *Zonuridæ:*		
Genus *Zonurus*	7	South Africa.
Genus *Pseudocordylus*	1	South Africa.
Genus *Platysaurus*	3	South Africa.
Genus *Chamæsaura*	3	South Africa.
Family *Anguidæ:* Old and New World lizards with a deep fold on each side. A number of the species are limbless.		
Genus *Gerrhonotus*	19	Western U. S.; Mexico and Central America.
Genus *Barissia*	1	Mexican boundary.
Genus *Ophisaurus*	5	S. E. Europe; Northern Africa; Asia; S. E. U. S. and Mexico.
Genus *Diploglossus*	16	Cent. Amer.; tropical and So. Amer.
Genus *Sauresia*	1	West Indies.
Genus *Panolopus*	1	West Indies.
Genus *Ophiodes*	2	South America.
Genus *Anguis*	1	Europe; Western Asia and Northern Africa.
Family *Anniellidæ:* Represented by a single, worm-like species.		
Genus *Anniella*	2	Extreme Western U. S.
Family *Helodermatidæ:* The Beaded Lizards. The only known poisonous lacertilians.		
Genus *Heloderma*	2	S. W. United States; Western Mexico.
Genus *Lanthanotus*	1	Borneo.
Family *Varanidæ:* The Monitors. The largest known species of lizards. All of the Old World.		
Genus *Varanus*	27	Southern Asia; Malaysia; Africa and Australia.
Family *Xantusiidæ:* Small, New World lizards.		
Genus *Lepidophyma*	1	Central America.
Genus *Xantusia*	5	California; Arizona.
Genus *Cricosaura*	1	Cuba.
Family *Teiidæ:* New World lizards.		
Genus *Tupinambis*	3	South America; West Indies.
Genus *Dracæna*	1	South America.

	Number of Species	Distribution
Genus *Centropyx*	5	South America.
Genus *Monoplocus*	1	Western Ecuador.
Genus *Ameiva*	27	Central Amer.; So. Amer. and West Indies.
Genus *Verticaria*	7	Lower California.
Genus *Dicrodon*	5	Western So. Amer.
Genus *Cnemidophorus*	13	U. S.; Mexico; Cent. and So. Amer.
Genus *Callopistes*	2	Peru.
Genus *Dicrodon*	2	Peru; Chili.
Genus *Teius*	1	S. E. South America.
Genus *Crocodilurus*	1	Tropical South America.
Genus *Neusticurus*	2	Tropical South America.
Genus *Alopoglossus*	3	Ecuador; Peru.
Genus *Leposoma*	2	Brazil; Colombia.
Genus *Loxopholis*	1	Colombia.
Genus *Pantodactylus*	1	S. E. South America.
Genus *Arthrosaura*	1	Ecuador.
Genus *Mionyx*	1	Upper Amazon.
Genus *Prionodactylus*	5	Brazil.
Genus *Cercosaura*	1	Brazil.
Genus *Placosoma*	1	Brazil.
Genus *Anadia*	4	Cent. Amer.; Northern So. America.
Genus *Ecpleopus*	2	South America.
Genus *Pholidobolus*	1	Ecuador.
Genus *Euspondylus*	4	Venezuela to Peru.
Genus *Argalia*	1	Venezuela to Colombia.
Genus *Oreosaurus*	4	Northern South America.
Genus *Proctoporus*	4	Ecuador and Peru.
Genus *Scolecosaurus*	2	Northern South America.
Genus *Cophias*	5	Northern South America.
Genus *Ophiognomon*	3	Western South America.
Genus *Heterodactylus*	2	Brazil.
Genus *Colobosaura*	1	Brazil.
Genus *Iphisa*	1	Brazil; Guianas.
Genus *Tretioscincus*	2	Cent. Amer.; So. Amer.
Genus *Micrablepharus*	1	Brazil; Paraguay.
Genus *Gymnopthalmus*	4	Tropical So. Amer.; West Indies.
Family *Amphisbænidæ:* The Worm Lizards. Old and New World.		
Genus *Blanus*	3	Shores of the Mediterranean.
Genus *Amphisbæna*	27	Trop. So. Amer.; trop. Africa.
Genus *Anops*	2	S. E. So. Amer.; Western Africa.
Genus *Geoclamus*	1	East Africa.
Genus *Monopeltis*	11	East Africa.
Genus *Trogonophis*	1	Southwestern Africa.
Genus *Pachycalamus*	1	Socotra.

	Number of Species	Distribution
Genus *Agamodon*	1	East Africa.
Family *Bipedidæ:*		
Genus *Euchirotes*	1	Lower California.
Genus *Bipes*	1	Mexico.
Genus *Hemichirotes*	1	Mexico.
Family *Lepósternidæ:*		
Genus *Rhineura*	1	Florida.
Genus *Leposternon*	16	South America.
Family *Lacertidæ:* Typical lizards of the Old World.		
Genus *Tachydromus*	4	Eastern Asia; Japan; Malaysia.
Genus *Poromera*	1	West Africa.
Genus *Gastropholis*	1	East Africa.
Genus *Lacerta*	21	Europe, Asia, and Africa north of the Equator.
Genus *Algiroides*	3	Southern Europe.
Genus *Psammodromus*	4	S. W. Europe; opposite shores of Africa.
Genus *Tropidosaura*	1	South Africa.
Genus *Nucras*	2	Central and Southern Africa.
Genus *Latastia*	4	East Africa, north of the Equator; Arabia.
Genus *Acanthodactylus*	10	Southern Spain; Africa north of the Equator; Southwestern Asia.
Genus *Cabrita*	3	India.
Genus *Ophiops*	6	S. E. Europe and So. Asia; Northern Africa.
Genus *Ichnotropis*	2	Africa south of the Equator.
Genus *Eremias*	24	Asia and Africa.
Genus *Scapteira*	9	Central Asia; So. Africa.
Genus *Aporosaura*	1	Western Africa.
Genus *Holaspis*	1	Western Africa.
Family *Gerrhosauridæ:*		
Genus *Gerrhosaurus*	5	Central and Southern Africa.
Genus *Tetradactylus*	3	Southern Africa.
Genus *Cordylosaurus*	2	S. W. Africa.
Genus *Zonosaurus*	3	Madagascar.
Genus *Tracheloptychus*	2	Madagascar.
Family *Scincidæ:* Smooth-scaled lizards, most of them polished and glassy; some with diminutive limbs—others limbless. Old and New World.		
Genus *Egernia*	9	Australia.
Genus *Carucia*	1	Solomon Islands.
Genus *Trachysaurus*	1	Australia.

	Number of Species	Distribution
Genus *Tiliqua*	5	Malaysia; Australia.
Genus *Hemisph riodon*	1	Queensland; Australia.
Genus *Macroscincus*	1	Cape Verde Islands.
Genus *Mabuia*	66	Africa and Madagascar; So. Asia; Central Amer.; So. Amer.; West Indies.
Genus *Leiolopisma*	160+	S. E. Asia; Malaysia and Australasia; Central and South Africa; Southern No. Amer.; Mexico and Cent. Amer.
Genus *Ablepharus*	16	S. E. Europe; S. W. Asia; Australia; Central and Southern Africa.
Genus *Ristella*	4	India.
Genus *Tropidophorus*	8	S. E. Asia; Borneo and the Philippine Islands.
Genus *Tribolonotus*	1	New Guinea.
Genus *Eumeces*	31	North America; Mexico and Cent. Amer.; Asia and No. Africa.
Genus *Neoseps*	1	Florida.
Genus *Brachymeles*	4	Philippine Islands.
Genus *Scincus*	8	No. Africa; Arabia; Persia.
Genus *Ophiomorus*	6	S. E. Europe; S. W. Asia, as far east as N. W. India.
Genus *Chalcides*	11	So. Europe; Africa, north of the equator; S. W. Asia.
Genus *Scelotes*	13	Central and South Africa; Madagascar.
Genus *Herpetoseps*	1	South Africa; Madagascar.
Genus *Sepsina*	10	South Africa; Madagascar.
Genus *Malanoseps*	1	East Africa.
Genus *Sepophis*	1	Southern India.
Genus *Chalcidoseps*	1	Ceylon.
Genus *Acontias*	9	Ceylon; So. Africa; Madagascar.
Genus *Typhlacontias*	1	Southwestern Africa.
Genus *Pygomeles* *	1	Madagascar.
Family *Anelytropsidæ:* A small, worm-like lizard; limbless; eyes hidden under skin; *no ear opening.*		
Genus *Anelytropsis*	1	Mexico.
Family *Feyliniidæ:* Small, worm-like lizards; eyes hidden.		
Genus *Feylinia*	1	West Africa.
Genus *Typhlosaurus*	4	South Africa.

* Relationship doubtful.

	Number of Species	Distribution
Family *Dibamidæ:* Represented by blind, limbless, burrowing species.		
Genus *Dibamus*	2	New Guinea; Moluccas; Celebes.
Genus *Ophiopsiseps* *	1	Australia.
Family *Chamæleontidæ:* True Chameleons.		
Genus *Chamæleon*	44	Principally Africa and Madagascar; Southern Spain; Arabia; Southern India and Ceylon.
Genus *Brookesia*	3	Madagascar.
Genus *Rhampholeon*	2	Tropical Africa.

The GECKOS. Two families come under this head, the extensive, cosmopolitan *Gekkonidæ,* and the *Uroplatidæ*—the latter composed of a single genus and three species. The group is well worthy of the life study of a technical worker. Few of the geckos attain a large size—a length of fifteen inches. The majority of the species are small, stout-bodied, with a thick, stumpy tail.

Family *Gekkonidæ.* There should be no difficulty in recognizing the average gecko. Its thick-set body, broad, flattened head, stumpy tail and the *round disk or "sucker" on each toe* are good characters; but add to these the soft, smooth appearance of the skin—coated with minute, granular scales—and we have a creature looking quite unlike the popular idea of a lizard, as most geckos have a really toad-like skin—often coated with numerous warts or tubercles. Debarring a few exceptions, *the species of the present family are devoid of eyelids;* the eyes are protected and move readily under a cap like a diminutive watch crystal. Most of the geckos have an elliptical (cat-like) pupil, indicating, as is indeed the case, the prevalence of nocturnal habits. Yet there are geckos having round pupils; but such species live in open sandy places and are diurnal.

The tongue of a gecko is thick, fleshy and viscid. It is capable of considerable protrusion though little em-

* Relationship doubtful. A worm-like species.

ployed as an organ of investigation. In catching the insect prey the tongue is decidedly useful as the animal stalks its quarry, then rushes, and if the latter be small it is snapped up by the sticky organ in a manner peculiar to all the thick-tongued lizards.

Not all of the geckos are thick-bodied, stumpy-tailed and have adhesive digits. Among them are certain species that have wearied of a wall-climbing life and taken to the ground. With such, Evolution has been busy in adapting them to widely different conditions than experienced by the ancestral forms. The average gecko lives on the trunks of trees, the faces of cliffs or walls, traversing smooth, vertical surfaces with remarkable facility owing to its expanded digits—even running at remarkable speed on the under side of flat, horizontal surfaces—like a ceiling. Such is the representative gecko, a nocturnal animal that seldom runs over the ground. The exceptional species have actually taken to the fine sands of the open deserts, where their wall-climbing relations would be as awkward as a tortoise in the water. Note the consequent development along lines of adaptation for a life on the sands! The body is lighter and more slender than that of the climbing forms, and the tail is more elongated. The adhesive digits have disappeared and in the place of "suckers" which would be quite useless, in fact, a hindrance to a sand-running creature, *we find the toes to be slender and furnished on each side with a projecting fringe of scales; the fringes acting as admirable supports in keeping the foot from sinking into the sand.* A development like this is to be noted with *Teratoscincus scincus,* a species attaining a length of six to seven inches and inhabiting the arid or actual desert regions of Turkestan and Persia, and as well with the genera *Ceramodactylus, Ptenopus* and *Stenodactylus,* in all about eight species.[2] The single species of *Ceramodactylus* inhabits the deserts of

[2] Exactly the same form of development for a desert life is to be seen with the species of *Uma*—American lizards of the family *Iguanidæ,* inhabiting the deserts of the southwestern United States. See illustration.

Persia and Arabia. *Ptenopus* is represented by a very small species inhabiting South Africa—Damara Land. The five species of *Stenodactylus* are small and inhabit the sterile sands of northern Africa and southwestern Asia.

For the uninitiated tourist in a tropical country there is usually an unpleasant surprise—furnished by venturesome geckos. One generally anticipates an awakening of insect life with the coming of darkness, and he is not disappointed. Swarms of winged forms are attracted to his lamp. Great, hard-shelled beetles enter the window with a sonorous hum like from a distressed buzz-saw, dash against the lamp chimney, then flounder on the floor; moths of various sizes dart hither and thither or whirl in dizzy gyrations about the light; a colony of tiny, ghost-like things dance up and down or are instantly consumed in the flame; there is a continuous buzz varying in its cadence and taxing to the nerves of any but a naturalist, when, without warning, a silent gray form darts obliquely across the wall, jumps from the vertical surface to the ceiling over which it flees, and like a streak of light continues down the opposite wall; perhaps for a moment it may stop, exhibiting a body as big as that of a small rat, glittering, cat-like eyes and a pulsating throat. To the nervous traveler, already annoyed by varied hordes of insect forms, the apparition of these heavy but stealthy forms darting across the ceiling over his head is weird and startling. An attempt at capture intensifies the impression, for the strange thing darts over the walls with the ease of a gigantic fly. Suddenly it may scurry for the window and away, but if the light continues to burn, others of its kind soon appear. Thus is life in the tropics associated with visits of the geckos that enter the houses in search of insect prey.

Among lizards the present creatures are about the only forms that produce sounds beyond sharp, angry hissing. A number of the geckos gives voice to a distinct clicking sound which might roughly appeal to such words as *yecko* or *gecko*—sounds produced by clicking the tongue against the roof of the mouth—hence the origin of the popular name. In places where the geckos are very numerous these sounds may be as continuous as the calls of nocturnal insects. The voice of a gecko appears to be produced by a convulsive movement of the tongue. A few species are alleged to produce sharp sounds by rubbing certain plated portions of the body—in the same fashion as all insects produce their calls.

Geckos are oviparous, depositing white, bluntly oval or round, hard-shelled eggs. The males are generally larger and proportionately stouter than the other sex. Decided changes of color are to be observed among the majority of the species.

Curiously enough, these absolutely innocuous animals are often regarded as extremely venomous; they are not only thought to be capable of dealing an envenomed bite, but actually poison every object over which they run. And most peculiar is the fact that this belief is persistent in various parts of the world. Thus, in southern Europe the geckos are regarded with considerable hatred; again, in the United States, the single, diminutive species found in Texas, New Mexico and southern Arizona is often called "poison lizard," while many larger lizards of really forbidding aspect are acknowledged to be perfectly harmless.

Gymondactylus, containing nearly forty species, is represented in both the Eastern and Western Hemispheres. The species are mostly small and not well adapted to running up vertical surfaces unless on rough tree trunks, as the digits are not dilated in the form of suckers, though fully clawed. *Gonatodes* is similar in development and has a like distribution; several of its small species are common in the West Indies. *G. occellatus*—the type from Tobago—has a vivid, eye-like spot on each shoulder.

Phyllodactylus is a genus extensively distributed throughout the warmer parts of the world. The species occur in tropical America, the West Indies, and in the Galapagos Islands; thence in the Old World in Africa and Madagascar, the islands of the Mediterranean and in Australia. The digits are expanded into the shape of strong suckers on the under surface, but are not round and disk-like at the tip—the entire toe of some species looks flattened from above though it is the tip that is adhesive. If the under side of the toe is examined closely it will be seen to be furnished with a pair of pads; between these the claw is retractile, like that of a cat.

The writer has kept several of the Central American species, some of which grow to a length of five inches. The general coloration of all is a yellowish brown with obscure markings. The specimens were kept in a large cage occupied by some big constricting snakes. It was thought that in these quarters they would eat the roaches. This they did at night, even darting over the backs of the slow-gliding snakes with little traces of fear. The approach of the writer, however, was followed by a scurrying up the walls to dark corners. If a lantern was moved slowly in front of the cage, the middle of which was provided with an upright post that caused a consequent moving shadow, the lizards stubbornly ran into the shadow, steadily following it as if to dodge from the light. The several specimens had their favorite hiding places during the day. One was always to be seen, head downward, on an upright water pipe; another clung to the framework of the ventilating apparatus on the ceiling, and a third always rested on a perforated copper heat-blast—which metal protected the hot-water pipes; when the latter specimen was forced to leave its sleeping place by the intruding folds of the big snakes, it retired but a short distance up the wall and as soon as a serpent shifted its coil, leaving the coveted spot vacant, the lizard was back again.

Some of the largest species of the present family belong to the genus *Gekko. G. stentor* of the Malayan Peninsula and the larger islands grows to a length of 14 to 15 inches and is stout in proportion. The animal utters a fairly loud, sharp cry of two syllables. It feeds largely on insects and lizards, but does not hesitate to devour young birds and rodents if such are discovered during nocturnal rambles.

Some of the species of the genus *Gekko* have traces of webs between the toes. This characteristic is extraordinarily developed with the single species of the genus *Ptychozoon* —*P. homalocephalum*, though not for purposes of swimming. There is a wide, membranous flap of skin on each side of the body, while the tail has a veritable feathered edge of thin skin, like an arrow. The thin attachments of skin serve the animal in parachute-like fashion, enabling it to make long, scaling leaps from tree to tree.

Tarentola is made up of five typical geckos, four inhabiting northern Africa and the borders of the Mediterranean; the remaining species is found in the West Indies. Each digit is strongly dilated at the tip, the under side of which forms an adhesive disk. If this disk is closely examined the suctorial appendage will be found undivided —thus we find a difference from such genera as *Phyllodactylus,* where there is *a pair* of adhesive pads on each toe. By such characters the various genera of the geckos are separated and arranged in technical classification. In an accompanying illustration will be seen the under side of a gecko—*Tarentola annularis*—on a pane of glass. The illustration not only shows the clinging power of the "suckers," but their structure as well. The disks are strikingly like the magnified pads on the foot of a fly; and their method of adhesion is the same—not aided by a sticky secretion, but through actual suction produced by close-set, concave areas. When a gecko moves over very rough surfaces the claws are called into play like those of an ordinary lizard. If a tame gecko runs over one's hand and an attempt is made to shake it off, an indescribable, clammy sensation is produced by the animal's feet that show a surprising amount of adhesive power. A similar development among lizards will be found among the species of *Anolis,* of the family *Iguanidæ.*

Tarentola annularis is a fine, stout gecko inhabiting Abyssinia, Egypt and Arabia. It grows to a length of six inches. The usual hue is a pale clay color, sometimes pinkish, with dark bands crossing the back. On the forward portion of the back—over the shoulders—are four vivid white spots. The back is studded with small tubercles, as is the anterior portion of the sides of the tail, where the tubercles are long, pointed and directed backwards.

During an attempt to photograph some examples of this species on a sheet of glass, the writer experienced all kinds of difficulty. After focusing a specimen, the movement of fitting the plate-holder in the camera—no matter how cautiously made—sent the reptile scurrying out of the field or jumping to the floor; the shock of the latter performance invariably resulted in the loss of the lizard's tail, making that particular specimen an unfit object for the camera. In a desperate attempt to effect some tractability among his subjects, the writer placed the remaining perfect individuals in a gauze cage, thence in a refrigerator, at a temperature of about 35° F. There they were kept for fifteen minutes. Again placed on the glass, and the same put in a vertical position, a new difficulty was encountered. While the lizards were too sluggish to run away, their adhesive digits so imperfectly performed their functions the reptiles slid rapidly down the glass as soon as they were placed upon it. The consequent difficulty in obtaining desirable photographs may be imagined.

The specimens mentioned have lived for a long time in a large cage occupied by several big snakes. During the day the lizards sleep at the very top of the cage on that part of the wall immediately adjacent to the angle of the ceiling, their bodies parallel with the latter. At night they dart about in search of roaches. But they are by no means strictly insectivorous. A number of American "chameleons" —*Anolis*—placed in the cage disappeared at a suspiciously rapid rate. The movements of the geckos are wonderfully quick. Observed at night, they dart over the walls and ceiling at a gliding gait equaling the speed of a frightened mouse on the floor.

Among the most tiny of the geckos are the species of *Sphærodactylus*. They are to be found in the West Indies, Central America and Colombia. Some of them have a round pupil. There is a single, adhesive pad on each digit. *S. notatus* is so diminutive it might be mistaken for an insect. Most specimens are under two and a half inches long. The color is rusty brown with obscure dark markings arranged in longitudinal streaks. This species is found on some of the most southern of the Florida keys, in Cuba and the Bahama Islands. It may often be discovered hiding under the eaves of houses during mid-day. During the late afternoon the active little creatures emerge in search of parasitic insect prey. Some of the species of *Sphærodactylus* are prettily blotched, speckled or banded.

There are members of scattered genera represented in Africa, India, North America and Central America, which depart from the usual run of the present family by differences in the structure of the vertebræ and the skull, besides *having functional eyelids.*

The two North American species, genus *Coleonyx,* occur in the southwestern portion of the United States, from southwestern Texas to California. They grow to a length of three or four inches and are pretty creatures, quite gecko-like in form, with a brown ground color crossed by bright bands of lemon-yellow—though some individuals are speckled wih a paler hue. They live in fissured, rocky places, retreating into crevices during the daytime, and come forth late in the afternoon and at night, feeding on insect prey. The species are not very agile and if handled emit a faint, squeaking sound.

The Family *Uroplatidæ,* composed of a single genus and three species, is removed from the *Gekkonidæ* owing to certain differences in the skull. Externally, the members look like typical geckos.

Leaving the group of geckos, the arrangement of scientific classification halts at a family of some doubt as to its exact position in the system. Certain it is that the members of this are as unlike the geckos as could possibly be imagined, for they are all serpentine of body, entirely devoid of the front limbs, while the hind limbs are merely represented by scaly flaps. The present creatures form the family *Pygopodidæ*. Though their bodies are scaled and their heads plated like the serpents—which characters would seem to place them yet more distantly from the group we have just passed, certain parts of the structure may point to a remote relationship and warrant their present place in classification. Among these characters are a similarity in the skull (the most important), the absence of eyelids, and the elliptical pupil.

The *Pygopodidæ* is distributed throughout Australia, Tasmania and New Guinea. A species of wide distribution in Australia and Tasmania is technically known as *Pygopus lepidopus*. It grows to a length of twenty-four inches, of which the tail, which is very brittle, occupies two-thirds. The serpentine aspect is intensified by the symmetrical shields on the head. The body scales are keeled. This creature progresses by a series of lateral undulations, the flap-like vestiges of hind limbs appearing to be quite useless. *Delma fraseri* is another species of the family, and has smooth scales. The tail is three or four times as long as the combined head and body, while the flap-like, rudimentary hind limbs are much smaller than with the preceding species. The *habitat* is Australia.

Leaving the *Pygopodidæ,* which is practically unknown aside from the study of alcoholic examples, we arrive at a large and important family from which may be selected many striking forms for discussion—and these fortunately obtainable alive, to be photographed and thus figure among our illustrations.

The Family *Agamidæ*. The members of this strictly Old World family may be at once distinguished from their allies by the *acrodont* dentition—*the teeth set on the edges of the jaw bones* (not in grooved sockets or surrounded by *alveolæ*). As a rule, the teeth of the *Agamidæ* may be divided into incisors, canines and molars. Lizards of this family have a short, fleshy tongue. Their limbs are strong and well developed. The eyes have a round pupil, are decidedly small, though withal acute of vision and provided with functional lids. Thus the reader will at once appreciate that the members of this important family, about two hundred in number, are alert, diurnal, active lizards, devoid of those marked degenerative processes which have reduced certain members in various other families into sluggish, burrowing forms. The species exhibit great diversity of form and scalation. Those leading a terrestrial life are decidedly flattened, while the strictly arboreal members are as markedly compressed vertically. Some have a fine, almost granular scalation. A number bristle with spines. Many have a crest of high, dorsal spines like the New World *iguanas*. Here it is not inappropriate to mention a peculiar parallelism of markedly characteristic genera in the *Agamidæ* and the New World *Iguanidæ*. This in no way relates to adaptation. It points directly to unique, really grotesque development along such similar lines that if it were not for the adamantine obstruction—the difference between *acrodont* and *pleurodont* dentition dividing the two families—scientific workers might justly fuse a number of these twin genera. As examples we might mention the familiar horned "toads" of the *Iguanidæ,* and in the *Moloch horridus* of the *Agamidæ* we have a parallel form; the crested iguanas of the *Iguanidæ* are matched by the species of *Physignathus* of the *Agamidæ;* again, the genus *Phymaturus* of the former family, with rings of coarse spines about the tail and granular scales on the body, brings vividly to mind the twin genus *Uromastix*—the Spiny-Tailed Lizards of the *Agamidæ.*

The *habitat* of the *Agamidæ* embraces Africa, Asia, Malaysia, Australia and Polynesia. The richest distribution covers India, Malaysia and Australia. While the family is poorly represented in Africa, it is curious to explain that no species occurs in Madagascar.

The FLYING "DRAGONS," genus *Draco,* serve as good introductory subjects to the *Agamidæ.* Over twenty, in number of species, and natives of the Malay Peninsula and Archipelago, these nimble, prettily-marked lizards are the most remarkable representatives of their family. A number of the ribs are greatly prolonged, movable (laterally) and attached to a pair of membranous sheets of skin. When these processes are at rest they are folded in wing-like fashion against the sides of the body. Thus the reptile carries the appendages when running or jumping over horizontal boughs in search of insect prey. Suddenly it may wish to change its hunting to another bough—possibly to another tree—and it leaps forward. The flying membranes are widely dilated and flash with colors that rival the wings of a beautiful butterfly—indeed, as the creature leaps, the idea of a brightly-colored insect is at once suggested. It gracefully scales at a downward angle, then reaching the desired spot instantly closes its aeroplanes and scampers or hops away, the motions being much like those of the New World *Anoles.* At no time does the lizard actually *fly*, the wings merely serving it like a parachute.

The "wings" of the Flying Dragons are spread in the same fashion as the "hood" of the cobra-de-capello and other serpents that flatten the anterior part of the body. Among the geckos we have already noted the use of membranous skin at the sides of the body to serve in the fashion of a parachute, though with those lizards the apparatus was not so perfected—not involving a special development of the ribs.

Before the army of lizards, many grotesque of form, others singularly beautiful in coloration, has passed in array before the student, the latter must be confused by the aggregation of scaly wonders; yet of the strangest forms, the Flying "Dragons" attract instant attention. Museum specimens look more suitable to be placed on slender insect pins than in preserving jars. With the membranes spread, the lizards appear mostly wings—the slender limbs and delicately tapering tail seeming quite supplementary.

Draco volans grows nearly a foot long, but the body and tail are so slender the animal seems much smaller. There are three pointed, flaplike processes on the throat, the center one very long and slender. The length and shape of these throat "fans" greatly vary with the different species; *D. everetti* has the central appendage short and blunt, while *D. quinquefasciatus* has an extremely slender, veritable hanging comb, which is really a third as long as the body. *D. volans* seems to be the commonest species. The body is lustrous gray or greenish with dark wavy cross-bands and spots. The wing membranes are brilliant orange, on which, in striking contrast, are blotches or bands of black. With the male, the throat appendage is orange; that of the female is blue.

Calotes, with nineteen species, is an interesting genus, not from any marked structural development, but from the habit of its members of rapidly changing their colors. The species have coarse, rough scales and an extremely long, slender tail. Many have a crest of very sharp spines on the forward part of the body or on the head. Several of the species reach a length of two feet. Their *habitat* covers India, southern China and Malaysia; throughout these regions they are among the most abundant of lacertilians. They are typical tree lizards and mostly insectivorous.

The "BLOODSUCKER," *Calotes versicolor*, one of the commonest lizards of continental India, derives its name from an altogether harmless trait. When the lizard is excited or angered, the brownish body turns yellow, while the sides of the head, the throat and the neck become brilliant red. This, however, is merely one of the numerous color variations. Broad, dark bands are often visible on the back, these broken by a central stripe of straw-color; this coloration may give way to a rich, uniform cinnamon, thence to a funereal black. The most startling changes of color occur among the males during the breeding season, when the members of this sex engage in frequent fights.

The present species is also very abundant in Ceylon, where it seems to grow larger than on the continent, reaching a length of sixteen inches; of this measurement the tail takes up about eleven inches. The "Bloodsucker" lives principally in trees or on fallen trunks. The female lays about a dozen oval, soft-shelled eggs, burying them in the soft débris of a rotten log or in mould. Fully two months elapse before the young lizards emerge; at the time of deposit the eggs are about half an inch long.

To the popular student it would be monotonous and wearing on interest to describe group after group of the *Agamidæ;* still it is hard to pass many of them by, as the writer recalls weird forms and strange habits among the many examples he has had under observation. However, in this work the idea has been to present a general *resumé* of the reptile world, so we must confine ourselves to *representative* species of large families. Looked at from a bird's-eye point of view, the genera of the *Agamidæ,* with the exception of *Draco* and *Moloch*—both highly specialized—form fairly unbroken chains toward the various extremes in development, so we are unable to divide this family into groups. The genus *Calotes*, just passed, stands as representative of a large number of arboreal, insectivorous species belonging to a number of genera. Nearly all of these species have an extremely long, slender tail, yet the elongate appendage is not brittle as is the case with the *Iguanidæ, Teiidæ, Lacertidæ, Scincidæ, Anguidæ* and other families.

Further progress brings us to the genus *Agama*, with over forty species, found in southeastern Europe, southern Asia and in Africa. None grows to a length of much over a foot. The species have a decidedly stout, rather flattened body, a blunt head and a moderately long tail. There is a fleshy fold across the throat.

Agama stellio is called HARDIM by the Arabs. It is the

most abundant species of its genus in Egypt, Asia Minor and southwestern Europe and characterized by the fleshy folds on the sides of the neck, these thickly studded with spiny scales. There are also close-set rows of spiny scales across the back. An adult specimen is about fourteen inches long and its colors are not attractive, being olive, brown or grayish above, clouded with black. The colors vary according to light and temperature. This is an exceedingly active lizard, haunting ancient ruins or rocky places and scampering here and there at a speed causing it to look like a mere streak to the human eye. Owing to a habit seen among lizards of many families the reptile has incurred the hatred of the more pious Mohammedans; for often when a lizard is disturbed, it runs for a short distance, stops suddenly, then nods its head downward a number of times as if going through a mock prayer. The Mohammedans consider this to be a travesty on their methods of devotion, killing every lizard they can catch. Thanks to the reptile's agility, they are in no danger of immediate extermination.

Captive examples must be kept very dry, warm and accessible to the sunlight for several hours daily. They are particularly fond of meal worms, learning to take these from one's fingers.

Leaving the stout little Agamas, our search for striking types brings us to a species of really sensational development and dramatic actions. The FRILLED LIZARD, *Chlamydosaurus kingi,* found in Queensland, in fact generally over northern Australia. There is no mistaking the Frilled Lizard. While in a passive mood a large cape is folded back over each shoulder. A flash of anger brings about a startling transformation. The capes spring forward, expanding into an enormous collar with sharply serrated edges, which remarkable appendage is continuous under the chin, though divided directly over the head. From the umbrella-like concavity protrudes the creature's head, jaws gaping showing formidable teeth, of which the canine are much enlarged. The frill is operated by veritable cartilaginous ribs, springing from the sides of the head and extending through the capes like the ribs of an umbrella.

The Frilled Lizard grows to a length of three feet. Several examples have been studied by the writer, who must confess, however, that the species is not so striking in appearance as usually portrayed in drawings which might lead the student to believe the reptile to be as big as an alligator and a regular "man-eater." The writer's largest specimen had a body eight inches long and a long, whip-like tail. When the reptile was in a passive mood the capes were not very noticeable. They were, however, thrown forward upon a slight provocation, though at most times for a few seconds only. With the big frilled collar standing out stiffly the lizard opens the jaws widely, disclosing the most curious of mouth parts—of a saffron-yellow hue. At a sudden movement of the observer, the reptile turns to follow the object of annoyance, hisses sharply, opens the jaws wider and may even rear upon the hind limbs in an attempt to bite. The writer's specimens were persistently arboreal, scampering over the boughs of an old cedar tree placed in their cage. They were seldom seen on the gravel of the floor. They finally became very tame, feeding upon grasshoppers, crickets and meal worms; they learned to take food from the hand and at length could not be induced to spread their capes. If placed on the floor, then suddenly startled, they would, like many species of several families, rear upon the hind limbs and run swiftly in that position. Their color was a dull, slaty gray, often varying according to their mood or changes in the temperature.

The SPINY-TAILED LIZARDS, *Uromastyx*. The six species are sometimes called MASTIGURES. All have a much flattened body covered with granular scales, a small blunt head, tiny bead-like eyes and a thick, curious tail like a spiked war-club. These lizards inhabit the desert regions of southwestern Asia and northern Africa. *Uromastyx spinipes* is the largest species, living in portions of the

Sahara Desert. The spines on the tail are arranged in regular rings and so sharp are the protuberances the organ serves as a formidable weapon. The hue of the body is uniform dull brown or yellowish, to match the sterile soil on which the creature lives. So tiny are the eyes they might seem to us to furnish inadequate powers of vision; but appearances are deceiving. The Mastigure has keen sight and makes off at a lumbering gait at the approach of an intruder. If it reaches its burrow, or crevice among rocks, instant advantage is taken of the shelter; however, the reptile's progress is rather clumsy and a man can easily overtake it. Then it vigorously prepares to defend itself, slashing the formidable tail from side to side or rearing upward in an effort to bite. As the jaw bones are practically bare—within the mouth—and come to a sharp edge, besides provided with thickly-set, curiously-flattened teeth, an adult example can bite deeply, then aid the effort by a quick rotary twist of the body, producing anything but a superficial laceration. It seems probable, too, that the bristling tail of the Mastigure serves as an effective means of closing the animal's burrow to intruders; for rash indeed would be the antagonist trying to force its way past that spike-studded weapon.

By some writers who have observed the Mastigure in a captive state the lizard has been described as being "stupid" in a refusal to feed and become accustomed to its quarters. Such declarations are altogether unjust. Nature permits no *stupid* creature to live. What appears to be stupidity on the part of a wild animal is bewilderment among conditions wholly unsuited to it, mingled with a vague longing for liberty. If a human were to be suddenly transferred from the comfortable center of his dwelling and diversions to the desert wastes of animals he has characterized as stupid, what frenzied wanderings and flight from wild beasts would be his lot! Consider a lizard created for the dunes and sun-baked rocks of the desert transported thousands of miles to the low temperature and humidity of a temperate climate, then placed in a small, glass-fronted cage. The prevailing temperature is lower than that the reptile has sought to avoid each night in its desert home by retreating into a burrow in the heated sand. Can the captive be blamed if it mopes, or dashes against such queer substance as glass, or steadily refuses food? One fault of many observers has been the neglect of furnishing enough heat for captive reptiles. Such observers have described all tortoises as slow; yet the writer has seen species, kept in a temperature almost unendurable to a man, get over the sand at almost a run. To make a Mastigure display its normal vivacity it should be kept in a temperature of from 85 to 95 degrees Fahrenheit.

In a big sanded cage open at the top to receive the diffused glare of a glass conservatory the writer has witnessed the Mastigures dashing about with a great show of animation *when a Fahrenheit thermometer recorded 110 degrees.* In a temperature of seventy degrees these specimens were markedly sluggish, flattening their bodies, then slanting them directly toward the sun to receive its full benefit. Late in the afternoon they retreated to their burrows.

It has been stated that the captive Mastigures live but a short time despite occasional nibbling at lettuce leaves and the like. Such specimens do not usually die for want of food —they die from a lack of water. It was quite by accident the writer discovered how such specimens may be saved, for they will seldom drink from a pan, or lap the drops from vegetation. The specimens described were kept in a very hot, dry place and to relieve the monotony of this a few cacti were planted in the sand. The lizards stubbornly refused water, became flabby and emaciated and were, in fact, slowly dying. Every inducement was put into operation. Drinking pans were sunk flush with the top of the sand—and passed by the lizards, unnoticed. Leaves of celery, lettuce and cabbage were plentifully sprinkled with water and placed directly in front of the lizards, with the hope they would lap up the hanging drops, and this was unsuccessful. Finally the various specimens were teased until they opened their mouths and the water squirted into the latter from the tip of a small syringe. But immediately after such a process, before it had received enough to nourish a specimen of one-tenth its size, the jaws of a lizard would snap firmly shut and no amount of coaxing would make it possible to administer more. One day when the cacti were being watered the solution of the trouble was discovered. A few drops of water were accidentally scattered over the lizards' backs, where they were instantly absorbed, while the resulting dark spots spread as if on a piece of gray blotting-paper. Taking this as a valuable hint, the writer had all the lizards thoroughly sprayed with a "mist" nozzle. A change was soon noted. The Mastigures became more vivacious. This spraying was repeated day after day. Meanwhile the reptiles took on plumper outlines, feeding with more energy. It seemed curious to see lizards absorbing water through the skin like a shriveled toad or frog. If a specimen were held in a shallow tray of water a dark, spreading line of moisture soon ascended the sides and finally over the back. Still these eccentric creatures could not be induced to lie in the pans of their own accord. It is possible that in their desert homes the quick changes of temperature, influenced by day and night, may produce a certain condensation of moisture, like a dew, thus enabling the thirsty skin of the animal to absorb the needed fluid. Since this discovery the writer has carried on similar observations among many lizards having a granular scalation—and representing other families. He is convinced that a large number of species drink through the skin, at least receive a part of their liquid nourishment in this manner. As a rule, these are species of dry, arid places. If kept in a continually damp cage they soon die, showing that too much of even a very necessary element may prove as detrimental as an utter lack of it.

Judging from experiences with Mastigures, it would

seem they are omnivorous, though preferring tender leaves, small flowers and berries. Their habits, as well as their make-up—except the spiny tail—are very similar to an American desert lizard of the family *Iguanidæ,* and known as the Chuckawalla, *Sauromalus ater.* The feeding habits of captive Mastigures are rather eccentric and hard to understand. While a variety of food may be presented, something greatly craved appears lacking and difficult to imitate. If fresh lettuce leaves are thrown into the pen there is an immediate show of interest. The lizards run up to these, nibble a few mouthfuls, then wander away with a clearly disappointed air. A saucer of meal worms produces the same effect. The lizards feed sparingly—yet they act hungry and ever on the watch for something. Some of the writer's specimens have eaten very young birds.

Family *Iguanidæ.* In the way of introduction to this family we can say little, or repeat what has been already said about the *Agamidæ,* as the general structure follows closely the extreme variation of the latter. This strange parallelism has already been explained under the head of the *Agamidæ.* The members of the *Iguanidæ* differ chiefly in their *pleurodont* dentition. The tongue is pink, thick and viscid. With the exception of the species of *Holbrookia* and a few of the horned "toads"—*Phrynosoma*—all representatives of the *Iguanidæ* have an exposed and well-developed ear-drum—tympanum.

Habits are as varied as structure. Some species are entirely arboreal; others live in the deserts, while a few are semi-aquatic. We have, in fact, a complete repetition of the habits noted with the *Agamidæ,* except members with parachute-like wings like the Dragons. Yet the *Iguanidæ* has species with expanded and adhesive digits—the Anoles—differing from any of the forms of the *Agamidæ.*

The *Iguanidæ* is a New World family with the remarkable exception of two genera occurring in Madagascar and another in the Fiji and Friendly Islands.

The ANOLES, genus *Anolis.* At the start we encounter

the largest genus of the family, embracing over a hundred species. The Anoles are sometimes called chameleons, though the title properly belongs to an Old World family, the members of which are remarkable in continually varying from one hue to another. Yet the members of the present genus are well worthy of the title. Their color changes are quite as pronounced and rapid as with the clownish members of the *Chamæleontidæ*.

None among the Anoles grows to a large size. The development of the feet is striking and unique among lizards. With most of the species each toe is expanded in the form of an adhesive pad. The effect is not like that of the gecko's foot—a disk-like "sucker" at the end of each toe. The adhesive pad occupies the central portion of the toe and is of an elongated form. Thus provided, the Anoles can run up smooth, vertical surfaces, or run, body downward, on a horizontal plane. The body is covered with minute, granular scales. Quite large in proportion to the animal's size, the head is rather alligator-like in its outlines —hence the species are sometimes called "alligator" lizards. The tail is rather long and slender; it may be much compressed, or round.

The Anoles are extremely lively and pretty creatures, either running with great speed or jumping from branch to branch; and the latter movements are the more characteristic owing to the great development of the hind limbs. The colors vary from brown to yellow and vivid shades of green. Male specimens are provided with a movable throat appendage, which is distended in fan-like fashion when the animal is excited, flashing a dazzling hue of red or yellow, according to the species.

The distribution of this genus is from southern North America throughout Mexico, Central America, tropical South America and the West Indies. *A. equestris,* of Cuba and Jamaica, grows to a length of 16 inches and appears to be the largest species. Like many others, the tail is compressed and has a serrated upper edge. When the males are engaged in their frequent fights a decided ridge appears on the back; as the animal becomes quiescent, the body assumes a rounded appearance. *A. sagræ* is an abundant species of the Bahamas, Cuba, Jamaica and the eastern portion of Central America. It has a much flattened tail, with strong indications of a serrated crest above. This lizard reaches a length of 6–7 inches and is one of the species of its genus that displays considerable color variation, yet seldom or never takes on shades of green. The commoner pattern is a rich golden brown over which are scattered dark brown dots and blotches. There are often pale, longitudinal bands on the back—sometimes dark rhombs on each side of the back.

The AMERICAN "CHAMELEON," *Anolis carolinensis,* abounds in the southeastern portion of the United States and in Cuba. This species has a round tail and assumes brilliant shades of green. It may be seen running along fences, on the walls of buildings, or among vegetation, where it hops from leaf to leaf with seldom a fall, clinging to smooth surfaces like a big fly.

A five or six-inch "Chameleon" is full grown and makes a pretty pet—though it will not thrive upon a diet of sugar and water, as is the prevailing idea. Captive specimens should be kept in a warm, sunny place. They will eat meal worms and flies, soon becoming tame enough to take food from one's fingers. It is amusing to see one of these lizards catch a fly. The entire performance recalls the movements of a cat stalking a bird. The lizard slinks cautiously toward the unsuspecting prey until three or four inches away it stops, opens the mouth slightly and protrudes the tongue; the limbs quiver for an instant—then the creature darts forward. Few flies escape these manœuvres.

A captive "Chameleon" may die of thirst while a pan of water remains in its cage. The cage should be *sprinkled,* when the specimens lap up the drops, as is their custom in drinking the dew from the leaves when in a wild state.

Changes of color are produced by light, temperature and

mental conditions. During the brightest hours of sunshine the lizards are usually somber brown, but two males spying one another undergo a rapid change. They nod their heads violently, and each distends the throat "fan," which shines a bright pink in the sunlight. Approaching nearer in dancing fashion, the head-nodding is repeated. Again the dewlap of each pugnacious little creature flashes brilliantly. Meanwhile, the lizards have taken on a shade of ashy gray. Then there comes the rush and combat to determine the supremacy of that particular fence rail. Like miniature squirrels the reptiles dart from one side of the run-way to the other, when a scampering, tailless individual, faded to a dull yellow, indicates the defeated one. A few seconds later the victor struts into view clad in vivid green. But a few moments' basking transforms the beautiful creature into a dull brown lizard, alert for flies and gnats.

Basiliscus embraces four striking species that are often termed the BASILISKS. The feet are lacking adhesive pads and the body is covered with moderately fine scales. These lizards are numerous in tropical Mexico, Central America and extreme northern South America. The males are peculiar in having a high crest on the back and tail, or a unique, comb-like protuberance on the back of the head. *B. americanus* is the largest species, reaching the length of about a yard, though much of this is taken up by the greatly elongated tail. The crest on the back is supported by bony rays and is often as high as the body; it is covered with large, very thin scales. The caudal crest is equally decorative, appearing almost like some paper adornment. On the head is a hood-shaped crest. *B. plumifrons* has high crests like the former, but is distinguished by the divided head crest, the forward portion of which is low, while the posterior portion is greatly developed. *B. americanus* ranges from southern Mexico well through Central America. The allied species seems to be restricted to Costa Rica. Both live in trees, often along river banks. They are wonderful climbers and jumpers, and frequently, when alarmed, dive from an overhead bough into the water.

The BANDED BASILISK, *B. vittatus,* found from tropical Mexico to Ecuador, reaches a length of two feet. It is olive brown with a wide, vivid yellow band on each side of the body. With this species the crest on the back is reduced to a mere bony ridge, though the head is adorned with a greatly developed crest like the comb of a fine rooster.

The writer has kept a number of specimens. Their tails were enormously long and whip-like, while the hind legs looked quite out of proportion in their powerful development, actually causing the specimens to squat, at times, like frogs. Verily, the Basilisk is an animal of mixed gaits! It can make its way through thick vegetation with a series of hops and leaps, much like the Anoles. And these appear to be its normal actions, as in a natural state it is decidedly arboreal. Placed on the ground, however, it runs at such speed as to look like a mere streak—then it stops so suddenly the human eye is bewildered, and the reptile seems to mysteriously disappear. It often adopts different tactics, rushing away on its hind legs, not hopping, but running with amazing swiftness and with the body at an angle as if about to take a hurdle.

Though the various species of Basilisks have often been described as "strictly herbivorous," the writer has found all his specimens—representing two species—to be quite insectivorous. They are fond of meal worms and caterpillars. An occasional individual could be induced to eat small berries and flowers, though not when the insect larvæ were in sight.

Among the females of the four species the crests on the head are reduced to mere rudiments. This is also the case with young male examples.

Liocephalus is made up of over seventeen species abundantly represented in tropical South America and the West Indies. All are of moderate size. The body is covered with coarse, rather bristling scales and there is usually a low, crest-like row of enlarged scales on the back. The species are both terrestrial or arboreal; they are very active. Most of them are strictly insectivorous. *L. carinatus* is common in Cuba. It reaches the length of a foot. With this species the crest is reduced to a mere serration.

Uraniscodon is another South American genus, containing but two species. The scales are very minute. There is a row of enlarged scales on the back. The species have quite a stout body and a very long, slender tail. They attain a length of sixteen inches. *U. plica* inhabits northern South America, Trinidad and the island of Granada. It is a curious lizard, having very long hind legs, while all of the toes are much elongated. It is olive gray above, spotted or marbled with rusty brown; there is also a dark collar. This reptile haunts old ruins and the rough trunks of great trees. It attentively watches the ground, descends with a run to catch a passing insect, then retreats to its post of observation. It is invariably seen head downward.

The IGUANAS. Several genera of large, powerful lizards form a fairly distinct group. These are the largest members of the *Iguanidæ,* some of them growing to a length of six feet.

As a rule, Iguanas have quite a high, compressed body surmounted by a high crest of lance-like spines—a characteristic rather rudimentary with the females. The tail is long, powerful and usually flattened. The teeth are flat and terminate in curious three-pointed fashion—*trilobate.*

From one writer on zoology to another has been handed down the assertion that Iguanas are "strictly herbivorous," a purely fallacious idea. They do feed largely upon tender leaves and fruits, but are veritable terrors to small birds and mammals, while they eat insects as well. They not only rob birds' nests of the eggs, but chase small mammals over the ground with a speed and ferocity approaching the warm-blooded beasts of prey. Species like the Rhinoceros Iguana can easily overpower an animal as large as a half-grown hare. The victim is quickly torn to pieces by vigorous shaking. Large fragments are gulped down entire.

Iguanas occur from the extreme southwestern portion of the United States southward throughout tropical South America and in the islands of the West Indies. Two species inhabit the Galapagos Islands, while one inhabits the Fiji and the Friendly Islands. A number of the Iguanas are esteemed as food. Their flesh is alleged to be white and tender, like that of a chicken.

The genera embracing the typical Iguanas are *Amblyrhynchus,* 1 species—Galapagos Islands; *Conolophus,* 1 species—Galapagos Islands; *Iguana,* 2 species—Mexico, Central America, tropical South America and the West Indies; *Brachylophus,* 1 species—Fiji and Friendly Islands; *Cyclura,* 5 species—West Indies; and *Ctenosaura,* 3 species —Mexico and Central America. *Cachryx, Hoplocercus* and *Dipsosaurus* are closely related genera.

The MARINE IGUANA, *Amblyrhynchus cristatus,* shares with one other species the characteristic of frequenting the seacoast and entering salt water. It is a big, stocky brute with a sullen, bulldog mien. The colors are dull black or brown. This is a gregarious animal, assembling in flocks of several hundred individuals, a unique habit among lizards. Mr. R. J. Beck, who visited Narborough Islands, in the Galapagos group, in 1902, explains that on the comparatively smooth lava of the shore he found an astounding colony of these creatures. *Over an area of at least three acres the lava was literally hidden by a great army of iguanas.* The reptiles were quite tame and could be approached with little caution.

The tail of the present species is decidedly flattened. On the neck, back and tail is a continuous crest of recurved spines. The head is short and stout; it is provided on the top with blunt, close-set tubercles. A large specimen is four and a half feet long. Owing to the flat tail the species is an agile swimmer and seems to dive to a considerable depth to obtain the seaweed forming its food, most of which grows below tide line. The several living examples in the writer's care survived but a short time—a few weeks—refusing all food. They tolerate handling without an attempt to bite, which is a very different attitude from that of the Galapagos land iguana.

The COMMON IGUANA, *Iguana iguana,* is well known throughout tropical America, as it is a favorite article of food. The tail is long and compressed. Most remarkable about the animal is the crest of large, lanceolate spines extending from the neck to the basal portion of the tail. These spines are quite soft and leathery, nor are they rigidly attached, sometimes laying over on one side or the other. With female specimens the length of the spines is much reduced. This iguana is also peculiar in having a large circular shield beneath each ear-drum; the only other species of the genus, *I. delicatissima,* differs in an absence of this round shield. Both species have a much-developed, comb-like throat pouch.

A phase of the Common Iguana found in Mexico and Central America has several erect spines upon the snout; it is technically known as *Iguana iguana rhinolopha.*

The Common Iguana is essentially an arboreal animal, delighting to bask on horizontal boughs, even balancing its stout body on quite slender branches while the hind legs sprawl downward in a fashion indicating utter laziness and nonchalance. Here we find one of the two distinctly outlined phases of habits among the iguanas—a desire to live in the trees or lead a strictly terrestrial life; the species of the genus *Cyclura,* large and active as they are, are examples of the ground forms.

Inhabiting southern Mexico, Central America, tropical South America and the West Indies, the Common Iguana is generally abundant and grows to a length of six feet. It is pale, greenish gray, marked on the sides with bold black bars; on the tail are broad black rings. The spines of the males are pinkish. Female examples are darker, usually brownish, while the young of both sexes show a considerable amount of bright green.

A friend tells the writer he once observed a peculiar sight in which iguanas participated. It was along the line of a South American railroad. Running parallel with the track was the proverbial line of telegraph poles. These had a rough surface, having evidently been cut from the adjacent forest, which was typical of the tropics in the density of growth. Each telegraph pole was crowned with a cluster of iguanas, piled on one another's backs on the cross-arm and clinging around the pole for a short distance beneath this. The train passed through several miles of this curious scenery. As the locomotive passed each pole the mass of iguanas would be seen making vigorous efforts to get higher, with the result of many losing their hold and falling to the ground, when they scurried for the undergrowth. Those remaining excitedly and repeatedly nodded their heads, their antics being easily noted from a train pulled by a tardy, wood-burning engine.

This species is largely herbivorous, though by no means strictly so. As a captive it is fond of lettuce, celery, clover, bananas and berries. Most specimens will eat meal worms voraciously; few are averse to young birds and such small rodents as mice and young rats. Very young individuals chase about actively for insect larvæ, being lively enough to make successful jumps for an occasional fly.

Throughout tropical America a very cruel method is employed in exhibiting iguanas at the markets, where they are described as having flesh very much like that of a young fowl. The tip of the longest toe on each hind foot is caught in a small instrument like pliers and the tendon stretched from the toe itself; by means of these tendons the hind feet are tied together—often the front feet as well—a process rendering the lizard entirely helpless. The specimens are classified into different sizes, thrown into crates and offered for sale. In this condition iguanas are often brought to New York. Though they have endured torture for possibly many weeks, they may be liberated by clipping the ends of the tendons, when they run about as if nothing had happened. Thus we see an illustration of the tenacious hold upon life possessed by these and many other reptiles.

The WEST INDIAN GROUND IGUANAS, *Metopoceros* and *Cyclura*. Five powerful, stockily formed species, with a compressed body, form this genus. In proportion to their size the tail is rather short. This organ is different from that of the other species in having rings of enlarged scales at short intervals apart; with one species—*C. carinata*—these scales assume a spiny development approaching a structure to be seen with the species *Ctenosaura*—Mexican and Central American iguanas. The species of *Cyclura* are almost entirely terrestrial, living in sandy places or on rocks. They dig burrows in which to retire at night or during stormy weather. They attack small birds and mammals with great ferocity, though they are also herbivorous.

The RHINOCEROS IGUANA, *Metopoceros cornutus*, receives its name from the three blunt, conical horns on the snout, the larger of which is often three-eighths of an inch high. There is a well-developed crest of lanceolate spines on the back. Old specimens are dark brown, which somber hue, together with their grotesque make-up, recall the imaginative pictures of strange reptiles of the past. The head is very massive, with big, rounded protuberances on the top and much swollen at the junction of the jaws; there is a hanging throat pouch; on the neck and shoulders the skin rises in coarse, vein-like folds. The species has a habit of squatting flat upon the hind quarters with the forward portion of the body reared high upon the strong front legs. In this position a lizard will remain for some time as motionless as if carved from stone.

The Rhinoceros Iguana is rather difficult to obtain. It is a far more showy creature than the Common Iguana. A good pair is worth about $50.00 if purchased from a dealer in the United States, while fine examples of the Common

Iguana, *I. iguana,* may be bought for three or four dollars each. The present species is hunted with dogs especially trained for the purpose. All newly-arrived specimens examined by the writer were extremely vicious, lashing the tail from side to side and rearing upon the hind legs in an effort to bite. If grasped quickly and properly by a strong hand, they are comparatively helpless; if handled incautiously they can lacerate a hand and arm as badly as a wild cat. In transferring specimens from one crate to another, the writer makes a grab for the back of the animal's neck, holding the brute firmly to the ground; with the other hand he quickly presses back the hind legs, then holding the lizard in this position is able to lift and carry it with little trouble. The animal cannot turn and bite, nor can it use its claws. After a time these lizards become very tame. They will rush to meet the person who feeds them, unhesitatingly taking food from the fingers. Very fond of young chickens, they rush upon a fowl, killing it by several vigorous shakes. If the prey is too large to be swallowed entire, it is further shaken until torn in several pieces, the lizard quickly swallowing the portion retained, then rushing for the section that has been cast a distance away. Rats are devoured in the same fashion. Some specimens will eat pieces of beef. There is a marked preference, however, for small animals in full feathers or fur. Aside from this diet of flesh, the favorite food is bananas. Berries are also eaten, besides lettuce, the tender tips of celery, clover and various flowers, The Rhinoceros Iguana is found only in Hayti and Porto Rico.

The BAHAMAN IGUANA, *C. bæalopha,* looks much like the preceding species in its burly structure. Its habits are similar as well. In place of the horns the snout is covered with close-set, tubercular shields, these usually in three pairs. The species is generally distributed in the more southern of the Bahaman Islands, in Cuba and Jamaica. It is strictly terrestrial. Adult lizards are vicious fighters, dealing hard blows with the tail besides employing both teeth and claws if restrained. The males look especially hostile, as the *cornea* of the eyes is bright red.

Cyclura carinata, inhabiting the Turk's Islands, is a smaller, greenish-gray species, immediately told by the small, regular scales on the snout. Like the two preceding species it makes deep burrows in the sand in which it hides during the night. It is persistently hunted by the negroes, who esteem it a delicate article of food.

The SPINE-TAILED IGUANAS, genus *Ctenosaura,* differ from other iguanas in having a body that is little compressed and a perfectly round tail, which organ is provided with rings of very sharp, spiny shields, making it a formidable organ. There is a crest of lanceolate spines on the back. The three species range from the extreme southwestern portion of the United States through Mexico and Central America.

The BLACK IGUANA, *C. acanthura,* ranges abundantly through Mexico and Central America. The old lizards are generally uniform jet black; some are black with marblings of olive or even exhibiting reddish blotches. They are surly brutes, immediately showing fight when cornered, not only endeavoring to bite, but dealing ugly blows with the generously-spiked tail. From painful experience the writer can testify that a blow from the spiny tail is capable of producing a severe laceration. If an avenue of escape is open, most specimens prefer flight to combat. If discovered while sunning in their favorite position, on the top of a rock in a forest opening, the creature hurls itself into the shrubbery, making as much noise as a frightened cow as it goes thrashing away to a considerable distance. The species is not much in the habit of ascending trees; it can, however, climb fairly well. On the ground it is very fleet, running with the body high, the tail slightly elevated. A strong lizard can easily outrun a man as to speed, invariably escaping by darting into a thicket. Very young specimens are uniform bright emerald green. They are persistently terrestrial, running on their hind legs in kangaroo-like fashion when frightened.

Observations made in large yards with a number of species of lizards, however, have demonstrated to the writer that the habit is prevalent among many of the long-bodied lacertilians of both the *Agamidæ* and the *Iguanidæ*. He has thus far noted the habit among the species of ten genera. It seems probable we have here a hereditary character, handed down from the gigantic reptiles of the past, for several of those creatures, now known only by the ponderous fossils imbedded under mountains of rock, were constructed to stalk about on their powerful hind legs.

Leaving the iguanas we come to a number of miscellaneous genera. While each is distinctly different from another, they naturally fall into a step-like arrangement, carrying us forward in the classification. If unceremoniously mixed up they would appear as a most incongruous assortment. First in order is *Sauromalus,* a genus restricted to the southwestern portion of the United States and containing two species. One is well known in the deserts of Arizona, New Mexico and Utah, where it is called the CHUCKAWALLA or CHUCK-WALLA, the name being of Indian origin; technically it is recognized as *Sauromalus ater*. It is a fat-bodied lizard with a thick, stumpy tail, strongly suggestive of the Mastigures of the *Agamidæ;* the tail, however, is quite devoid of spines. A big specimen is about a foot and a half long. The color is uniform dull rusty brown. Young specimens are banded or marbled.

At its best gait the Chuckawalla gets over the ground at hardly more than a rapid waddle; the young specimens are speedy enough. The food consists largely of flowers and very tender leaves. Captive specimens are indifferent to food unless kept in what is to a human an almost unendurable temperature. If the heat of their native deserts is not thus imitated they become sluggish, lying with eyes half closed, slowly starving to death.

Genus *Crotaphytus*. Several pretty and active species are found in the western portions of the United States, living in open, sterile places. The COLLARED LIZARD, *C. collaris,* exhibits a striking coloration, particularly during the breeding season. Then the male is rich green, profusely dotted with pale yellow spots; on the neck is a double sooty black collar; as completing touches to the gay coloration, the throat is of a deep orange hue, while there are numerous rusty red spots scattered over the hind legs. Not to be outdone, the female as well takes on especially gay colors during the early summer. She is normally a slaty gray, with a much narrower collar than the male. Before the eggs are laid, however, her sides assume the brightest of brick-red hues, dots of the same color appearing on the limbs and sides of the tail. Notwithstanding its stoutness of body, the Collared Lizard runs at great speed—generally upon the hind legs. These lizards are also able to hop and jump like a frog, owing to the long hind legs; such tactics are adopted in traversing rocky places.

The range of this species is from Kansas to Arizona. *C. wislizenii*—the LEOPARD LIZARD, is closely allied. It lacks the black collar and the head is proportionately narrower. The coloration is brownish gray with bold brown spots and blotches; across the back are brick-red streaks; the limbs are reticulated with the latter hue.

Uma, Callisaurus and *Holbrookia* are closely allied genera of western North America. The species are small, yellowish gray, with two or more rows of dark blotches on the back. *Callisaurus draconoides* is called the Zebra-tailed Lizard, as in running it carries the tail curled over the back, showing the under side of that appendage, which is chalky white with bold black bars. There are five species of *Holbrookia.* All are easily distinguished from *Callisaurus* by the absence of an ear opening.

The SWIFTS. Lizards of the important genera *Uta* and *Sceloporus* abound in western North America, Mexico and Central America; in the former country they are generally called Swifts. The term is appropriate, as they display great agility, rendering capture anything but easy. Some live on rocky ground; others on fallen trees. Although examples of many of the species will dart up a tree to evade capture, the general inclination is to live close to the ground. The majority of Swifts are from six to eight inches long; a few grow to a length of ten inches; two species of *Uta* reach a length of twenty inches, but a great part of this is composed of the very long and slender tail. Between the two genera there is a great difference in the scalation; in the general form, however, is a marked similarity. There is also a similarity in the not particularly attractive coloration of the upper surfaces, as well as the markings on the throat and abdomen of the males, where there are brilliant patches of blue or green.

The genus *Uta,* SMALL-SCALED SWIFTS. The twenty recognized species inhabit the southwestern portion of the United States—mostly the deserts. The body is moderately stout and flattened, with a rather small head; the tail may be of moderate length or extremely long and slender. Over the greater part of the body the scalation is very fine; some of the species have four to six rows of much enlarged scales on the central portion of the back.

The Small-scaled Swifts are particularly common in the desert regions of Nevada and Arizona; the largest species are found in Lower California. They live in rocky places, running with great speed and darting into crevices or under shelving stones when seeking concealment. Dull gray or brown, in keeping with the rocks on which they live, are the prevailing colors on which are darker transverse markings. Two members of the genus are exceptions to this rule of somber coloration. They are closely related, inhabiting the peninsula of Lower California. One of them is known as the THREE-BARRED SWIFT, *U. thalassina.* It is not only the handsomest but the largest of its genus, occasional specimens being two feet long; of this measurement the slender tail consumes about sixteen inches. Above, the color is rich, dark green, crossed by three sooty black bars on the *forward* portion of the body. All of the scales are small and of uniform size.

A pigmy in comparison with the preceding is STANSBURY'S SWIFT, *U. stansburiana,* which little lizard is found throughout the southwestern United States, literally swarming in many parts of the Colorado Desert, where it scampers over blistering hot rocks in search of insect prey. The scalation is uniform and granular, and the usual coloration is dark gray or greenish with small dark, rounded blotches surrounded by bluish dots. A mature specimen is about five inches long, of which the tail occupies about two and a half inches; a specimen like this would have a body five-eighths of an inch wide and a head showing a width of half an inch.

As an example of those Small-scaled Swifts characterized by several rows of greatly enlarged scales on the central portion of the back, we may take the WHITE-BELLIED SWIFT, *U. ornata.* Most specimens have an orange-yellow throat; the glaring blue patches so persistently present on the throat and abdomen of the males of other species are usually absent. The illustration shows the arrangement of the enlarged scales; they are distinctly keeled. Common in the desert regions of Arizona and eastern California, this lizard is six inches long when fully grown. Its ashy hue, with narrow, wavy cross-bands, renders it an inconspicuous object as it basks on the rocks.

Receiving a small box from Arizona, the writer slid back the lid and was startled by a furious scramble of small gray lizards. In an instant the box was empty. From beneath it, on the floor, darted a series of radiating streaks as the reptiles scurried in all directions; some continued their progress up the curtains, where they hid among the folds at the top; afterward, the writer discovered that half a dozen had jumped from the box to his sleeve, thence to his back, where they dodged away from his grasp like squirrels on a tree trunk. Placed in a gauze cage with fine sand and rocks, in a sunny window, the lizards flourished. Unless the sun blazed upon them they stubbornly refused the meal worms placed in their cage. On dull, cloudy days all were stupid and inactive. A considerable variation of color was noted; on dull days the color was dark brown; in the sunshine this gave way to ashen hues on which the dark transverse bands were intensified.

Genus *Sceloporus,* SPINY SWIFTS. For the twenty-two species comprising this genus, the present popular name is appropriate. The scales of the upper surface are large, overlapping, usually coarsely keeled and terminating in a sharp point; on some of the species the tips of the scales are really needle-like, curling slightly outward and producing a generally bristling aspect. Mexico and Central America are the headquarters of these lively creatures, which scamper over the ground or on logs with a speed that defies capture unless trickery is employed; and the United States is well represented in species of the genus, particularly in the Western States, where several of the larger species extend northward from Mexico; there are a few species characteristic of the country lying north of the boundary; in the United States there is but one species extending eastward as far as the Atlantic Coast. Few of these swifts have any but dull brown or gray hues on the upper surfaces; the pattern consists of darker cross-bands—sometimes of pale longitudinal bands on the sides. The student will note such colors to be in harmony with the rocks and tree trunks on which these creatures live. The chin and abdomen of the males are decorated with glaring patches of blue or green, exhibiting varying degrees of intensity according to the activity of the individual.

Common in the deserts and sub-arid regions of the Southwest is a large species known as CLARK'S SWIFT, *Sceloporus clarkii,* often displaying a length of ten inches. At times it is uniform, dull gray. Again, when sporting in the sunshine, a curious transition of color takes place. In the center of each scale a bright green spot appears. Still this intensification of color does not render the lizard conspicuous. Lying motionless on a twisted stratification of rock it looks green from a short distance away and might readily be mistaken for a thick stem or a root projecting from some crevice.

Let the observer approach within, say fifteen feet, of the reptile, and he will find he is intensely watched. With head twisted slightly so that one of the sharp little eyes may study every movement of the intruder, the lizard rears the body slightly in preparation for a dash. One step more on the invader's part and he is treated to a show of agility almost too quick for the human eye to follow. A gray streak whisks out of sight in an instant. Almost simultaneously, a scaly head is seen peeping around a projection of the rock. It belongs to the same lizard, now ready to engage in tactics that resemble hide-and-seek if its capture is attempted.

The largest and finest species of this genus is the COLLARED SWIFT, *S. torquatus,* that so bristles with coarsely-overlapping, spine-tipped scales it has also been called the porcupine lizard. Greenish gray above, it is decorated with a broad, black, yellow-bordered collar. Mexico is the home of this stout species. A variety of it known as *poinsettii* extends into the United States, where it lives in rocky areas of Arizona, New Mexico and southwestern Texas.

Of easterly distribution in the series of spiny swifts found in the United States is the COMMON SWIFT, called in the Eastern States the FENCE SWIFT, *S. undulatus.* This typical form is abundant from New Jersey to Florida. The range was quite recently noted to extend northward into New York state, a few specimens having been captured in Westchester County. Its color is grayish, crossed with wavy black bands, these often broken into two series of irregular V's. This is a small species; a mature example is about five inches long.

Old fences are much frequented by this species. The lizards scamper along the stiles, or, if approached, dodge over on the side opposite to the observer. In the dry pinelands of the southeastern portion of the United States, there is a swift or two for every fallen tree trunk. To catch a specimen one must exercise considerable ingenuity, as a rush at the creature would cause it to scurry under the tree trunk, there to wriggle its way into the débris, or jump from the log, run to the nearest tree and ascend to a perfectly safe distance to peer saucily downward. As the collector approaches a log on which a swift is basking, the lizard generally dodges over the side, away from view. The spot whence the specimen has disappeared should be noted; for it will usually be found that the lizard has simply danced round the horizontal trunk. Bringing the hand slowly over the log, but keeping the body out of sight as much as possible, the collector should take an instant's glance to locate his specimen, then slap the hand down over the reptile. In two instances out of three the rough little body squirms under the hand. Not so unless the motion of securing the prize is lightning quick. How many times has the writer gazed ruefully upon a lizard's spasmodically wriggling tail, realizing that as the hand descended the reptile started, yet not quick enough to get away with all its possessions. Swifts may be hunted around sawmills, especially if a number of *old* logs are lying about, for on these the reptiles find such food as the fat-bodied grubs of the wood-boring beetles.

In most families of lizards there is some particular genus, or a small group of genera embracing species of such eccentric form that a superficial examination would lead one to suppose they had no near relations. The *Iguanidæ* furnishes marked examples in the shape of the HORNED "TOADS," composing the genus *Phrynosoma*—and here let us change a misleading title, now we have for duty's sake employed it.. We will call these creatures the HORNED LIZARDS. They inhabit the United States and Mexico; principally the former. The fifteen species are characteristic in having wide, flat, toad-like bodies on which there is a marginal fringe of spines and erect, scattered spines of various sizes on the back; over the general surface of the back the scalation is exceedingly fine and granular. Most interesting is the head; on most of the species it is armed with spines that are huge in proportion to the size of the possessor; and these spines are generously provided. There are two or three large ones on each temple; behind these—on the back of the head—is usually the largest and stoutest pair of spines. On the chin, and parallel with the line of the mouth (on each side) is a row of keen-edged and projecting plates.

If the species of Horned Lizards are collectively examined they impart a weird impression. The student is reminded, as he examines the varied structure of their heads, of certain Indians who wear all manner of freakish masks in their dances and ceremonies. When one species after another has been examined, it will be seen there is considerable difference in the arrangements of the scales on the chin; this character, together with the head spines, helps greatly in identification. While the title, Horned Lizards, is a very good one for the group, the writer must acknowledge that not all of the species have well-developed horns; a few have no traces of horns.

Over all portions of the southwestern United States, the Horned Lizards abound. They are especially partial to dry, sterile areas, and quite at home throughout the vast wastes of the Colorado Desert. Here these little gnomes of the sand dart about on their short legs at a bewildering speed, in search of insect prey. During the hours of burning sunlight, when the whole atmosphere is a-quiver with radiating heat waves, they are at their best; as the sun begins to cast long shadows they squirm their way into the sand and are completely buried before night brings the peculiar chill that settles over desert areas.

Following is a *résumé* of the Horned Lizards:

COMPARATIVELY HORNLESS SPECIES *

Douglass' Horned Lizard,	*Phrynosoma douglassii.*	Pacific Region, U. S.
Ditmars' Horned Lizard,	*Phrynosoma ditmarsi.*	Northern Mexico.

* In compiling this simple list the arrangement of technical classification is not rigidly followed.

SPECIES AND VARIETIES WITH SHORT TO MODERATE HORNS

Hernandez's Horned Lizard,	*P. douglassii hernandezi.*	Great Plains; Rocky Mountain District.
Red Horned Lizard,	*P. orbiculare.*	Mexico.
Little Horned Lizard,	*P. modestum.*	S. W. U. S.; Mexico.
Smooth Horned Lizard,	*P. platyrhinos.*	Southwestern U. S.
Nelson's Horned Lizard,	*P. nelsoni.*	Lower California.
Schmidt's Horned Lizard,	*P. schmidti.*	Lower California.
James' Horned Lizard,	*P. jamesi.*	Lower California.
Boulenger's Horned Lizard,	*P. brevicorne.*	Texas.
Girard's Horned Lizard,	*P. brevirostre.*	Great Plains.

SPECIES WITH LONG HORNS

MacCall's Horned Lizard,	*P. m'callii.*	Colorado Desert.
California Horned Lizard,	*P. blainvillii.*	So. Calif.; Lower Cal.
Cerros Island H. Lizard.	*P. cerroense.*	Cerros Island.
Texas Horned Lizard,	*P. cornutum.*	Great Plains.
Crowned Horned Lizard,	*P. coronatum.*	Lower California.
Regal Horned Lizard,	*P. regale.*	S. W. U. S.; Mexico.
Bracconier's H. Lizard,	*P. bracconieri.*	Mexico.
Mexican Horned Lizard,	*P. taurus.*	Mexico.
Long-spined H. Lizard,	*P. asio.*	Mexico.

DOUGLASS'S HORNED LIZARD, *P. douglassii,* really belies its name, as the "horns" are represented by mere tubercles. It is one of the smallest species and has very short limbs. Moreover, it is found farther northward than any other member of the genus, occurring in the northern Pacific region of the United States including the slopes of the Sierra Nevada Mountains. A curious variety known scientifically as *P. douglassii ornatissimum* inhabits the dry plateaus and deserts east of the typical form from southern Canada to Mexico. It displays remarkable phases of "mimicry." Examples found on pinkish rocks exactly match the pale hue; others, from the yellow, desert sands, are of the same color as the soil and it is difficult to see them unless they are moving. Another variety of the species is HERNANDEZ'S HORNED LIZARD, *P. douglassii hernandezi,* growing to a considerably larger size than the typical form; it has pronounced, though very stubby, horns. This lizard is abundant throughout the Great Plains and Rocky Mountain District. A near ally is the RED HORNED LIZARD, *P. orbiculare,* of Mexico. Above, the color is dark, brick red with little or no traces of markings.

Without doubt the most showy species of *Phrynosoma* is the REGAL HORNED LIZARD, *P. regale.* With this extraordinary lizard the rear part of the head is decorated with a crown or crescent of large flat spines. It is the only horned lizard that has *four* central head spines; so perfect is the alignment of these with the temporal spines that the crown-like effect is striking. Besides being thus decorated the species reaches the substantial length—for one of its kind—of seven inches. Its markings are obscure, a condition usually to be noted among the desert animals. In various portions of the Colorado and the Gila Desert it is fairly abundant. It is particularly common in the immediate vicinity of Phoenix, Arizona.

A well-known species in the southern Pacific region, thence extending into the peninsula of Lower California, is the PACIFIC HORNED LIZARD, *P. blainvillii.* At a glance it will be seen to have different outlines from the other horned lizards. The body is narrower, the tail thicker and more elongate. On the back, the entire surface is profusely scattered with spiny scales giving the animal a very bristling aspect. Most specimens are grayish above, with a large reddish brown patch on each shoulder and three transverse bands of similar color on the back. Two in number, the central head horns, as well as those on the temples, are markedly flattened.

While measuring a lizard of this kind the writer noted a characteristic attributed to the horned lizards alone and about which he had always been sceptical. This is the alleged habit of squirting a stream of blood from the corner of the eye in time of anger. After examining the specimen in question the writer decided to measure the horns. A pair of calipers figured in the process. The shining metal seemed to greatly excite the lizard, which puffed up to such an extent that the eyes bulged. Then, without warning, a jet of blood as fine as a hair shot from what appeared to be the corner of one of its eyes, striking a wall fully five feet away, where it was distributed in a shower of tiny drops. After this amazing exhibition the lizard was turned loose. Running about as if nothing unusual had happened, it was feeding within a few hours. Subsequently, the writer noted the performance with specimens of the Mexican Horned Lizard, *P. orbiculare*.

Most familiar of the species is the TEXAS HORNED LIZARD, *P. cornutum*. It is the proverbial horned "toad" brought East by the tourist, while it is the most widely distributed and abundant of any of its genus, ranging as far eastward and northward as Missouri, abounding throughout the greater part of Texas and extending all the way westward to eastern California. The head spines are large; there are two *rounded* central spines directed rather sharply upward; besides these there are three spines on each temple. The body is very flat and round, with a short, thin tail. The outlines are in strong contrast to the preceding, elongated species. From behind the head and nearly to the end of the tail is a bright yellow band; on each side of this are three large, round blotches that are dark and bordered at their rear edges with a yellow crescent. Each shoulder is marked with a large and similar blotch.

The greater number of captive horned lizards die because they are not kept warm enough or given sufficient sun. They should be placed in a fair-sized box on the bottom of which are several inches of fine, dry sand. The box should be placed in the sunlight for several hours each day; while it is there the lizards should be fed. They seldom take food unless warmed and cheered by the sun. Meal worms are a favorite article of diet, but should be varied with *soft-bodied* insect larvæ, as the former block the intestines with an accumulation of their chitinous bodies. Ants are a favorite food and the *black* species should be selected, as the reddish kinds reek with formic acid. In a temperature below 70° Fahrenheit, horned lizards become sluggish and refuse all food.

The Family *Xenosauridæ,* made up of a single genus (*Xenosaurus*) and one species, *X. grandis* (inhabiting southern Mexico), seems to be a connecting link between the *Iguanidæ* and a succeeding family—the *Anguidæ.* Boulenger explains:—"Its affinity to the former is shown by the T-shaped clavicle, the absence of symmetrical bony shields on the head and of osteodermal plates on the body"; its affinity to the *Anguidæ* is evident by the structure of the tongue, which has a flat, narrow and feebly incised anterior portion that is retractile, and the structure of the teeth, as well as the separated palatine bones. The single representative grows to a length of about ten inches. The body is depressed, with well-devéloped limbs and a fairly long tail; it is covered with fine, irregular granules mixed with conical protuberances. On each side of the body is a distinct fold in the skin, strongly suggestive of the *Anguidæ.*

The Family *Zonuridæ.* This also seems to connect the *Iguanidæ* with the *Anguidæ.* The dentition is pleurodont. The four genera inhabit tropical and South Africa and Madagascar. *Zonurus* is the largest genus, with seven species. They are distinguished by the large bony plates on the back and tail; on the latter they are pointed and bristling, looking much like the structure of the Mastigures' tail, though proportionately coarser. The species live in sterile, rocky places. *Zonurus giganteus* is about fifteen inches long when adult. It is a uniform, yellowish brown. The *habitat* is South Africa.

Pseudocordylus and *Platysaurus* have small scales on the back in place of the bony plates. The former has a spiny tail; with the latter species the tail is covered with rings of smooth plates. *Chamæsaura* contains serpentine members of the *Zonuridæ.* The body is slender and cylindrical, covered with lanceolate scales; the tail is extremely long. Three species are found in South Africa, one reaching a length of twenty inches; externally, it looks much like some members of the *Anguidæ,* as the limbs are quite rudimentary.

The Family *Anguidæ.* Among the members of the present family the influence of evolution has been markedly felt. We find a curious mix-up in the phases of structure from creatures which run speedily on strong limbs, to utterly limbless forms gliding like serpents and employing a black tongue to investigate their way in truly snake-like fashion. The species are terrestrial (or burrowing). The greater number occur in Mexico and Central America. A few, however, inhabit the United States; some the West Indies and tropical South America. A small number inhabit Europe and the borders of the Mediterranean. One occurs in India.

The members of the *Anguidæ* are pleurodont lizards, yet the teeth vary considerably in formation; these are always solid; instead of growing into the hollow bases of the old teeth, thus forcing them out, the new ones grow in *between* the former. Among some of the species the teeth are recurved and fang-like; with one, the teeth show the faintest trace of a groove, a condition possibly indicating the development, with time, of veritable fangs and attendant glands for the injection of some virus to stupefy the prey, like the apparatus of *Heloderma.*

Among all members of the *Anguidæ,* the body is coated with bony plates underlying the scales, which are arranged in overlapping, imbricate fashion—*in rings.* The tongue is composed of two distinct parts; the posterior portion is thick and fleshy; anteriorly the organ is thin and nicked at the tip; the anterior portion is retractile into the rear, fleshy part. Two genera are characterized by a deep fold in the skin on each side of the body. Throughout the family, the tail is very brittle. In this family we find viviparous species. The members are carnivorous and insectivorous.

The PLATED LIZARDS, genus *Gerrhonotus.* Nearly two dozen lizards, looking very much alike, come under this head. Several species inhabit the western portion of the United States. Mexico and Central America, however, are their headquarters. The back and tail are covered with large, square shields or scales, giving one the idea of shingles. On each side of the body is a deep fold, the skin adjacent to which is covered with granular scales. The abdomen is plated with square, smooth shields. Many of the species have a very long tail. With all, the limbs are well developed.

Technical students find the lizards of this genus particularly difficult to identify. Much depends upon the arrangement of the plates on the head, the number of rows of scales on the body and the *smooth* or *keeled* surface of these scales or plates. On some of the species most of the plates are comparatively smooth; on others they are marked with dull keels; several of the species have a certain number of the plates on the back keeled while those on the sides are smooth; one species has every row of plates above the folds sharply keeled. Such are the points employed by the scientist to separate the different species.

The KEELED OR PLATED LIZARD, *G. multicarinatus,* common in the United States from Texas to California and northward to Vancouver, stands as a typical species. All of the plates above the fold on the sides are sharply keeled. Among different individuals the length of the tail greatly varies. Some have an exceedingly long tail, nearly twice as long as the combined head and body. A big specimen is sixteen inches long.

Plated Lizards are most frequently found on fallen trees in sparse belts of timber. They are very shy, dodging around the log so as to get on the side opposite the observer. Few lizards are found actually ascending the living trees; their only reason for haunting the fallen trunks is apparently to search for wood-boring insects. If stalked carefully they may be caught without much trouble. They are not nearly so active as many lizards of their size. But care should be taken not to grasp the reptile by the tail. In that event a single, slight twist on the animal's part discards an organ that immediately begins to cut up a series of astonishing capers; writhing and twisting in one's fingers it may suddenly begin a quivering motion, when without warning comes a sudden twist, freeing it from the fingers to jump about on the ground like a live thing. For the instant, the observer is involuntarily attracted to the strange object. In the meantime, the much shortened owner has made good its escape—to grow another tail within a few months; the second appendage to be not nearly so elaborate as the original one.

In its coloration the Plated Lizard is sober and unattractive, being dull brown with darker cross-bands; some of the scales are tipped with white.

Gerrhonotus kingii, of Arizona, New Mexico and Mexico, is one of the prettiest of the genus. Pale greenish brown is the predominating hue, crossed by dark, yellow-bordered bands. On the back, the scales are bluntly keeled; the scales of the sides are quite smooth.

The Genus *Ophisaurus.* Five snake-like species of the Old and the New World form the genus. With the exception of a pair of minute spikes at the vent of two of the species, they are entirely devoid of external limbs.

As these lizards have an extremely brittle tail and an aspect that is anything but lizard-like, they are generally known as THE GLASS "SNAKES." Necessarily, they move like serpents, by lateral undulations. They exhibit a close relationship to *Gerrhonotus* in the presence of a deep fold on each side of the body. As the novice might easily mistake one of them for a snake it is well to understand that *they have movable eyelids and an ear opening,* characters not existing among the serpents.

The SHELTOPUSIC OR GLASS "SNAKE," *O. apodus,* ranges generally over southeastern Europe, southwestern Asia and northern Africa. This is the largest member of the genus. A big specimen is four feet long and an inch and a half in diameter at the thickest part of the body. The body and tail are covered with thin, square plates, set in ring-like fashion like shingles. To the touch the entire animal is extraordinarily hard, feeling actually bony; it looks as if it were freshly varnished. Despite the serpentine form there is something about the creature's looks and ways entirely foreign to a snake. The proportionately large and distinct head, with its blinking eyes and well-formed ear openings, seems incongruous when compared with the limbless body. In its locomotion the animal is stiff and ungraceful, utterly unlike the sinuous movements of a snake. When a Glass "Snake" is handled it really appears to creak in the tight-fitting, bony armor; if grasped by the tail it disengages that organ with a single twist, no blood attending the shedding of an organ that thrashes in livelier fashion than when attached to the original possessor. It is almost needless to say that the story of the Glass "Snake" hunting up the discarded tail, or *vice versa,* with a view of patching up matters, is purely fallacious.

Captive Glass "Snakes" are intelligent reptiles, becoming keen observers of one's movements. They will advance from a far corner of their cage and take food from the hand, evincing a studied care not to bite the fingers holding the morsel. The bright yellow eyes not only seem sharp and cunning; they are actually keen of vision. The writer feeds his specimens small pieces of raw beef stirred in well-beaten egg. This, varied with a diet of meal worms, keeps them flourishing for years. They will break the eggs of small birds—even those as large as a pigeon, then lap up the contents with their flat, nicked tongues. Their jaws are powerful and they do not hesitate to attack small mammals like mice and young rats, giving the prey a few vigorous shakes, biting hard at the same time. The prey is swallowed practically entire, in an awkward, gulping fashion.

The American Glass "Snake," *O. ventralis,* while a considerably smaller animal than its European ally, is a much prettier species. It more properly deserves the title of glass snake. Not only is the tail more brittle; the scales of the body and tail have a highly polished surface, like glass. The coloration is variable. Some specimens are blackish with a bright green spot in each scale; others are olive, each scale containing a cluster of yellow dots; on many the dots fuse in the form of longitudinal stripes.

During several collecting trips in the South, the writer noted a condition pointing to the nocturnal habits of the Glass "Snake." There was a scarcity of specimens abroad during the day. In the early morning, however, we would find them in the wells, where they had evidently tumbled during a nightly search for insects. Because of their stiff, really clumsy motions, they were unable to ascend the rough sides of the shaft, a feat of comparative ease for a serpent. Yet they were able to keep from drowning by thoroughly inflating the lungs.

The American Glass "Snake" is almost wholly insectivorous. In the eastern part of the United States it does not extend farther north than North Carolina; in the Mississippi Valley it ranges northward to southern Illinois, thence southward into Mexico as far as Jalapa.

In the second group of the *Anguidæ* are species lacking the deep fold on the sides. Several genera embrace species with well-developed limbs; others with much aborted members; one includes a snake-like form. *Diploglossus,* of tropical America, contains fifteen species. They look much like big skinks (members of a succeeding family—the *Scincidæ*), but may be recognized by the ring-like arrangement of the scales. A few reach a length of two feet.

The "BLIND WORM" or SLOW "WORM," *Anguis fragilis,* of Europe, western Asia and Algeria, stands as the most snaky member of the *Anguidæ.* It is entirely devoid of limbs. The body is covered with smooth, round and polished scales. This species is not nearly so stiff and ungraceful in its movements as the glass "snakes"; the body is decidedly supple and suggestive of a serpent. In crawling it seemingly fits the uneven surface of the ground in that easy gliding fashion attending the motions of a true snake.

For this lizard the popular name is altogether inappropriate. The animal has keen, highly-developed eyes; and it is too large and prettily colored to be characterized as "worm-like." Adult specimens are often a uniform, metallic bronze, sometimes greenish bronze with a dark band on the back; on a few specimens there are scattered blue spots, a character distinct enough, according to some authorities, to warrant a varietal name—*colchica*.

Most interesting about the "Blind Worm" is the habit of producing living young. The young are born in August and September and are delicately pretty, being luminous silvery-white above with a jet black stripe on the back; beneath they are uniform black. The number in a brood ranges from a dozen to eighteen. A fourteen-inch female in the reptile house of the New York Zoological Park gave birth to sixteen young; the babies were three inches long. The latter fed upon termites—soft-bodied, ant-like insects to be found commonly in rotting logs. On this food they continued to thrive, yet their growth was so slow it appears several years would be required to reach maturity. Adult Blind Worms feed upon earthworms, slugs and the grubs of insects. The captives will eat raw beef mixed with beaten eggs; they exhibit a great liking for this diet. The food is masticated to some extent, a process utterly out of keeping with the reptile's snake-like appearance. Kept in a vivarium, the Blind Worm often burrows deeply in the moss and rich soil. A specimen may suddenly emerge from a damp spot, clean and shining, seemingly as immune to a stain from the soil as is a duck's back to water.

In one part of the structure the Blind Worm is singularly interesting. The teeth are recurved, fang-like *and show traces of a groove.* Here are actually indications of, with time, the formation of a poisonous lizard. The existence of such a character brings us directly to the only known lizards that are venomous, two in number.

The BEADED LIZARDS. Two strange American lizards form the family *Helodermatidæ*. In the ring-like setting of their tubercular scalation they show their near relationship to the *Anguidæ*. They are very stout of body with a short, fat tail. Above they are covered with close-set, beady tubercles; beneath with flat plates or scales. Their coloration is always vivid—pink and black, or yellow and black, arranged in irregularly blotched fashion on the body, in broad rings on the tail. The effect of the warty surface, together with the glaring combination of colors, is exactly like Indian beadwork.

From the character of the dentition, the present species are unique among lizards. The teeth are recurved, fang-like and swollen at the base; those on the lower jaw are strongly grooved on both the front and the rear surface. At the bases of these teeth is a chain of glands containing a venom very similar in its composition to that secreted by the poisonous snakes, and sufficiently powerful to produce death with man.

The Beaded Lizards dwell only in desert places; one in the United States and another in Mexico and Central America. Between the two lies a great stretch of country. The reason for such freak distribution of immediately related forms is rather a puzzle. The specific differences may be concisely outlined, thus:

Pink (or orange) and black, the pale hue predominating. Head marbled with the light color. *Tail very short.*

GILA MONSTER, *Heloderma suspectum.*

Distribution: Arizona and New Mexico.

Pale yellow and black, the black predominating. Head entirely black. *Tail much longer than with the preceding.*

BEADED LIZARD, *Heloderma horridum.*

Distribution: Mexico and Central America.

The GILA MONSTER, *H. suspectum.* The popular name is pronounced Hee'la Monster. In every way the animal looks poisonous. The pattern is so coarse and glaring the effect is like the conception of an impressionistic artist.

At no time can the Gila Monster get over the ground at faster than a spry crawling gait, seldom raising the fat body entirely clear from the surface. Despite its apparent sluggishness it is capable of surprisingly quick motions when annoyed, showing it to be a highly dangerous brute to tamper with. If annoyed while progressing in leisurely fashion, it stops immediately, evidently realizing the uselessness of attempted flight. Rearing the forward part of the body, the previously lethargic reptile displays a significant degree of vivacity, hissing sharply, while the forked, purple tongue protrudes from the lower jaw. If the hand of the tormentor ventures too near, woe to the possessor! With a side twist, like a flash, the lizard has made a snap in an endeavor to imbed its fangs. So agile are some specimens, they can, with a jump, entirely reverse their position, so the head occupies the spot where the tail has previously rested. If the jaws do reach their mark, the lizard's grasp is like that of a bulldog. It may retain its grasp for a good ten minutes. During this time the grinding motions of the jaws show a vicious desire to imbed the fangs as deeply as possible.

Within a few weeks of captivity, Gila Monsters become reasonably tame. For a while, however, they cannot be trusted, nervously turning their heads if startled in what might be termed involuntary preparations to bite. After a few months this nervousness wears away, when they are the personification of good nature, permitting themselves to be handled in the most unceremonious fashion, without the least show of temper. A warm sand bank, in undiluted outdoor sunshine, produces curious psychological phenomena. If left in a place like this for a few minutes they become different creatures, fiercely snapping from side to side, resenting the least hint of interference with sharp hisses, while they keep their jaws gaping, ready to close upon anything coming within reach. Several times when the writer wished to extract poison from his specimens, he has been unable to induce them to bite until they had a sun-bath on a warm sand bank. Then they bit with such energy it was difficult to disengage their jaws from the vessel in which the venom was collected Curiously enough, the temperature outside differed little from that of their artificially warmed cage. It is the sunlight which appears to produce the exhilarating effects.

In experimenting with the venom we find it dries and cracks in the same fashion peculiar to snake poison. Small animals injected with it die quickly, the poison appearing to particularly attack the heart. From the symptoms the animals display it is well to rate this species as among the reptiles highly dangerous to man.

The Gila Monster is an oviparous lizard, depositing smooth, tough-shelled white eggs that are large in proportion to the reptile's size. A specimen in the reptile house of the New York Zoological Park, measuring 19½ inches in length, deposited four eggs, each of which measured 2¾ inches in length and 1½ inches in diameter. All were fertile. One of them, opened for examination, was found to contain but a germinating spot to represent the future embryo. Incubation in warm, moist sand produced further development; at the end of a few weeks, however, all the eggs solidified, bringing the observations to a close.

While in a wild state the food of the Gila Monster is alleged to consist largely of ants. Captive specimens cannot be induced to take such food. They are fond of raw eggs, easily breaking the shell in their strong jaws, then lapping up the contents by means of their broad flat tongue. The writer improves upon this diet by mixing raw chopped beef with the beaten eggs. On this he has kept specimens in a flourishing condition for years. Many examples are fond of the soft, leathery eggs of snakes; such are gulped down entire. One Gila Monster consumed, in rapid succession, eight eggs of a Chicken Snake (*Coluber*). They will sometimes take mice, catching the animals by a quick turn of the head as they run by; the prey is shaken for a moment, then held in a tight grip in an evident wait for the venom to do its work.

The blunt tail of the Gila Monster is actually a reservoir for the storage of nourishing fat. When the animal has been steadily feeding the tail becomes much swollen. If food were suddenly and persistently denied the creature in this condition, it would live for many months upon the accumulated fatty tissue stored in the stumpy appendage. Thus has Nature provided for a slow-moving animal of the desert, where an erratic food supply is apt to be the rule. It is the writer's belief that the Gila Monster feeds principally upon the eggs of the desert snakes and lizards, cunningly digging these from the sand where they are placed by the mother to await incubation by the sun's heat.

The MONITORS, family *Varanidæ*. A single genus made up of twenty-seven species composes this, an isolated family. The distribution covers Africa, India, Malaysia and Australia. Among the members are the largest and heaviest known lizards, some of them reaching a length of 8 to 12 feet. The largest species attains a weight of at least 200 pounds. They are flesh-eating and voracious. Most characteristic about them is the extremely long tongue, as deeply forked as that of a serpent; in proportion to the size of the head the tongue is much longer than among snakes. As a Monitor is progressing, the tongue is kept constantly darting in an evident investigation of near-by objects. Another striking peculiarity of the structure is the very long neck. On this the head may be drawn back to a considerable extent, enabling the reptile to make a quick dart forward in catching the prey.

Monitors are covered with a fine, almost granular scalation, the scales being rounded and protruding in small, beady points. The abdomen is covered with smooth, square shields. The tail is usually very long; among the desert species it is round; others have a much compressed tail and are excellent swimmers.

The DESERT MONITOR OR YELLOW MONITOR, *Varanus griseus,* occurs in the arid portions of northern Africa, southwestern Asia and Arabia. In keeping with the sandy soil on which it lives, the colors are pale-grayish yellow, with obscure, darker transverse bands; even the long forked tongue is a pale flesh color. This is one of the smaller species, seldom growing over four feet long.

It is a rare thing nowadays for a large and important animal to be discovered as a new species, but one of the most spectacular of all the reptiles—in fact the most gigantic of known lizards—had not appeared on the lists of science up to 1914. The facts relate to the enormous monitor named *Varanus komodoensis* by Major P. A. Ouwens, late Director of the Buitenzorg Museum in Java.

There had been rumors of "dragons" inhabiting the small island of Komodo in the Dutch East Indies—also small islands to the west of Flores. Investigation in these modern days of science disclosed the abundant presence of a monitor attaining a length of over *twelve feet* and so massive in build that it attained the astonishing weight, for a lizard, of two hundred and fifty pounds or more. This extremely active, savage and carnivorous creature had long inspired terror among the natives. Living specimens have since been exhibited in Europe and America.

In 1926, with the habits of this creature remaining but little known, Mr. Douglas Burden organized an expedition to Komodo, and there made a series of remarkable observations. The great lizards were found to be quite common and when wild swine were shot and staked on rocky hills, would come to the bait and tear it to pieces. The Dutch government, from the time of discovery, had determined to preserve this remarkable species from extermination, but a permit was issued to Mr. Burden to capture a few specimens. This expedition enabled the American Museum of Natural History to prepare a mounted group of the monsters and two living examples were brought to the New York Zoological Park.

The next largest of all living lizards is a monitor inhabiting Ceylon, the Malay Peninsula and the greater number of islands in the Malay Archipelago. This is the KABARAGOYA of the Singhalese, a reptile known technically as *Va-*

ranus salvator, reaching a length of eight feet. The tail is much compressed. This powerful brute is partial to the jungles. Few sportsmen have been through such country without occasionally being startled by the rush of a monitor ahead, making as much noise as some hoofed animal as it tears its way through the undergrowth, away from danger. The species is an expert swimmer, employing the long tail in a series of undulatory motions while the limbs are kept folded against the sides.

The Kabara goya is one of the most interesting of reptiles in captivity. Its feeding habits are typical of all the species. The methods of attacking a small animal resemble more the actions of a warm-blooded animal than of a reptile. Rushing for the ill-fated creature at a gait rapidly overtaking it, the lizard seizes the prey and shakes it in the same violent fashion as a terrier treats a rat. If the animal's struggles become so violent its escape is rendered possible, the reptile holds it to the ground under its strong claws—as long as those of a fair-sized leopard—while the jaws take a better hold. Then the shaking process is renewed. The prey is soon dead. If it is small the monitor tosses it about in the jaws until the head points down the victor's throat. It is then swallowed in the same fashion as exhibited by an owl in bolting a scrap of meat or a mouse; that is, by a series of quick reaching gulps. Should the quarry be heavy and large, it is dropped to the ground after the struggles have ceased. The monitor rests a moment, wiping its jaws with the enormously long tongue. With perfect deliberation it begins an investigation of the prey, poking it here and there with the snout, finally seizing it by the head, when the swallowing process begins, in this case prolonged and difficult, but it is possible for a big monitor to swallow an animal as large as a two-third grown rabbit, entire.

A fine example of the Kabara-goya has lived in the reptile house of the New York Zoological Park for the past five years. It is often given a full-grown, freshly-killed pigeon, which is, with little difficulty, swallowed entire. Like all monitors this example is fond of eggs, taking eight to ten hen's eggs at a meal, swallowing them entire and with such rapidity the eggs come in contact with one another in passing down the throat, producing a clicking sound that can be plainly heard by one standing near by. Digestion is rapid. Within twenty-four hours the gastric juices have thoroughly disintegrated the shells, which are broken by compression of the stomach; subsequently, the shells are entirely dissolved. Lizards and snakes are also eaten by this monitor.

The big Kabara-goya described became wonderfully tame, crawling from its cage to cling to its keeper's body in a manner suggesting an embrace. Three other specimens of lesser dimensions evinced a similarly docile nature. It was finally decided to place them outside in a big sanded yard. Here the peculiar effect of fresh air and sunlight produced the same mental changes as noted with the Gila Monster.

On the day following the placing of the monitors in their new enclosure, Keeper Snyder entered with their food. He was surprised to hear a loud hiss from his big pet, the Kabara-goya, and behold that burly reptile puff up in angry fashion, then make a movement as if to deal a blow with the tail. Snyder dodged, but not quick enough. That instant of preparation had put the monitor in a position to lash the tail violently. It struck the pan of eggs carried by Snyder, sending most of the contents flying in all directions. Backing away in amazement, the keeper was astonished to see nothing but hostile glances from the other monitors, which lay hissing in surly fashion. Returning later to find whether the food had been devoured, Snyder was attacked by the big fellow, which rushed at him with open mouth, suddenly threw the body sidewise and with a wonderfully quick blow of the tail struck the man on the arm, inflicting as severe a welt as if dealt with a whip.

During their stay out of doors these monitors remained savage and wild. At the approach of autumn they were brought indoors, where, within a couple of weeks, they were as docile as before.

GOULD'S MONITOR, *V. gouldii,* is found in Australia and New Guinea. It grows to five feet in length and looks somewhat like the Kabara-goya, being blackish, with yellow dots and rosettes on the back.

Family *Teiidæ.* This is a New World family. The members vary from powerful, carnivorous, terrestrial species to degraded burrowing forms with rudimentary legs. Their scaly covering is just as variable as their size and habits. One character is fairly steady. This is the development of the tongue, which is a long, forked, flexible organ used continuously in examining the ground as the lizard progresses, or to inspect the food. Owing to the peculiar dentition, this family might be said to stand midway as regards the two well-defined phases of tooth structure among lizards. The teeth grow almost upon the edge of the jaw, but they are solid. Thus the dentition is neither strictly acrodont nor pleurodont. Some genera, such as *Tupinambis* and *Dracæna,* have molar-like crushing teeth in the rear.

The *Teiidæ* is analogous to the Old World *Lacertidæ.* Among several genera of each family there is a striking similarity, this appealing not only to form, but to the general scalation of the body, the plate-like scales on the tail arranged in rings and the large, regular shields on the head. The members of the *Teiidæ* are abundant from the southern portions of the United States throughout Mexico, Central America, South America and the West Indies. More than a hundred species are recognized.

The largest species of this family, three in number, compose the genus *Tupinambis.* They are popularly known as Tegus. The body and the round tail are covered with small square scales arranged in regular rings. On the head are very large, symmetrical shields. All of the species are similarly marked—black, with yellow or white crossing the back in bands. Their *habitat* is tropical America.

Tegus display a marked liking for clearings. They are

carnivorous, and swift runners. In the farming country they are an actual pest, repeatedly devouring young chickens and constantly eluding capture unless a dog is trained for the purpose or they are awaited with a gun. In many parts of South America they are hunted for their flesh, which is alleged to be tender and excellent eating. Largest of the species is the COMMON TEGU, *T. teguixin*. A fine example has lived for five years in the reptile house of the New York Zoological Park. This specimen is exactly four feet long; the head and body measure eighteen inches; the head terminates in big pouches or jowls like that of an old crocodilian and, measured across these jowls, is six inches wide.

The big specimen described is strongly marked with marble white on a dull black body. Its jaws are wonderfully strong, breaking hens' eggs or ducks' eggs at a single, nonchalant effort, when the contents are lapped up by means of the long, forked tongue. This lizard's favorite food consists of strips of raw beef mixed with beaten egg. It begins a meal by nosing about for the pieces of meat; after having consumed the last fragment it laps the dish fairly clean. When it first arrived at the reptile house it was lean and starved, ferociously eating small chickens and rats. It has since grown so fat it refuses to eat unless the food is prepared as described. Judging from the development of the cheek pouches this is a very old specimen, much thicker of body and consequently more sluggish than is normal with the species. Though its jaws have strength enough to crush a man's hand, the creature is so quiet the keepers handle it with no thought of caution. Younger specimens are dangerously vicious, actually chasing the keepers. They fight with other lizards, quickly killing them by a tenacious grasp, shaking and twisting. The species represented is found generally in South America from the Guianas to Uruguay, also in the West Indian Islands. A nearly allied species is the YELLOW-BANDED TEGU, *T. nigro-punctatus*. This has larger scales and looks more shiny. The cross-bands are dull yellow. The abdomen lacks cross-bands, being immaculate dull yellow or sprinkled with black spots. Confined to the continent, this species occurs over the same areas as the former one and is equally abundant. It is a vicious creature.

Ameiva and *Cnemidophorus* are closely allied genera, made up of a considerable number of species bearing a marked likeness to the European sand lizards and wall lizards of the genus *Lacerta.* These are slender lizards with an elongate tail. They have two folds of skin under the neck. The body is covered with fine, granular scales; the scales on the tail are coarse and in rings; on the head are large, regular plates. Few species of either genus grow over a foot long. The majority of them are marked with narrow yellow stripes running longitudinally. Some have rows of yellow dots. A few species of *Cnemidophorus* are boldly tessellated.

The nineteen species of *Ameiva* are confined to tropical America and the West Indies. *Cnemidophorus,* with its twenty-one species, is more extensively distributed. Its members occur plentifully in the southern portions of the United States, throughout Mexico, Central America and South America, though not in the West Indies. The species are strictly terrestrial, living in dry, usually sandy places, where they run with such rapidity they appear like a mere streak to the eye. Hence, in many parts of the United States they are called RACE-RUNNERS, the name also originating from their habit of basking on sandy roads, and, when approached, of darting ahead for a short distance, yet always keeping on the road, a trait causing the reptile to look as if inviting a race.

Cnemidophorus gularis and *C. tessellatus,* of the western United States and northern Mexico, are interesting from their transition in pattern from the young to the adult stages. The young of both species have three narrow, yellow longitudinal stripes on each side of the body. When specimens of *C. gularis* grow older, a row of bright yellow spots appears between each of the stripes; thus, the mature examples are both striped and spotted. The change of pattern is more pronounced with *C. tessellatus,* as the stripes entirely disappear and a bold, marbled pattern takes their place. The latter is one of the largest species of the genus, often reaching a length of a foot and a half.

The SAND LIZARD or STRIPED RACE-RUNNER, *C. sexlineatus,* is the only species of its genus ranging into the southeastern portion of the United States, whence it extends westward to California and into northern Mexico. It is common in South Carolina, Georgia and Florida, haunting sandy roads or dry fields, where it darts away from a pursuer at a gait defying capture unless strategy is employed. The best way to catch these lizards is to keep chasing them until they run into a little thicket of grass or leaves, where they remain in the imagination of being securely hidden.

The Race-Runner is insectivorous. Captives are fond of meal worms, which may be obtained at any bird store. This diet should be varied with the soft-bodied grubs to be found under the bark of rotting logs and with grasshoppers or crickets.

The present species retains the stripes through life. On the center of the back is a broad, dark band. Eight inches is the usual length of an adult.

As examples of the degraded forms of the *Teiidæ* we may take the species of *Scolecosaurus.* They are small, worm-like, have minute eyes, no ear openings, rudimentary legs and the scales smooth and arranged in regular rings. They exhibit burrowing habits and are often found in ant-hills. Through the courtesy of Mr. R. R. Mole, of Port-of-Spain, Trinidad, the writer received several specimens of the tiny but interesting *Scolecosaurus cuvieri,* found in tropical America and on the island of Trinidad. An accompanying plate shows the peculiar structure. The specimens mentioned were extremely active, immediately wriggling their way back into the wood pulp in their cage when exhumed for examination. Their tails were so fragile they would break from the body almost at a touch. The specimens lived for many months, appearing to feed upon termites from a nest sent North by Mr. Mole. These lizards were of a dull brown like that of the soil in which they lived.

Our next family of lizards forms one of the most remarkable groups in the Lacertilia. It is scientifically designated as the *Amphisbænidæ;* the members inhabit the warmer parts of the New and the Old World. They are the most degraded among all reptiles, leading an underground life, where they progress either backward or forward, exactly like a worm, by moving their segment-like rings of scaly integument—the scales being practically fused into rings. Owing to their external characters and certain features of the skeleton and the tongue, we may note similarity to certain forms in the *Teiidæ,* and rate these lizards as degenerate types of that family. The pectoral arch is reduced to a mere rudimentary condition. The species are stout; most of them have a stumpy tail.

The genus *Bipes* is composed of strange creatures. There are several species blind, exactly like a big worm in form and of a uniform brownish gray. *An utterly incongruous part of their make-up consists of a pair of well-formed front legs.* The species are often known as Two-Handed Blind "Snakes." They occur in Lower California and Mexico.

Most members of the family *Amphisbænidæ* differ from the preceding creatures only in having no limbs. They inhabit both the New and the Old World and are entirely worm-like, having no characters that might appeal to the popular observer as being like a reptile. When compared with other lacertilians it cannot be said they are covered with *scales.* The integument is separated into narrow rings or segments, these intensifying the worm-like aspect. The top of the head and the chin are covered with shields. It is by means of the segments (divided into numerous minute squares) that the members of this family are able to crawl. The segments are movable, carrying the lizard backward or forward with equal speed; they are employed in wave-like, peristaltic fashion, the body assuming slight, *vertical* undulations. The present lizards are persistent burrowers, and commonly found in ant-hills.

Among a dozen genera of the worm lizards *Amphisbæna* is the largest, with about thirty species, the members inhabiting tropical America and tropical Africa.

The WHITE-BELLIED WORM LIZARD, *Amphisbæna alba,* found in tropical South America and in Trinidad, is typical of its genus. A large specimen is two feet long, slightly over an inch in diameter and perfectly cylindrical for almost the entire length. The tail is just as thick and stumpy as the head; unless one examines the animal closely the two extremities cannot be told apart. Thus the reason for a popular name in some part of South America—Two-Headed Blind "Snake." If a specimen is carefully inspected, the eyes may be seen as two mere bluish spots sunk under the translucent skin. But we cannot say these queer lizards are absolutely blind. All of the writer's specimens showed a marked distaste for a strong light. They would display an immediate nervous movement if a match was struck in front of their cage at night. They were peculiarly sensitive to vibrations, moving uneasily if one stepped heavily across the room and twitching every time a finger was tapped on the glass of the cage. When a specimen was annoyed it would elevate the stubby tail in a fashion that caused the organ to look like a head reared in threat; at such times the head remained flat upon the ground unless the body was pinched, then the head swung about for the offender, while a tiny pink mouth gaped as widely as possible in a display of harmless bluff. The writer kept his specimens on a layer of damp wood pulp, too thin for them to burrow into, though through it they rooted vigorously. They shed almost entire skins, like snakes, and proved far more hardy than would be imagined with such subterraneous reptiles. During the several years they thrived their food consisted of earthworms and strips of raw beef. All became tame enough to take food from the fingers when it was held in front of their snouts. The food was subjected to a crude mastication. In proportion to the small mouth, large morsels were gulped down, practically entire.

The FLORIDA WORM LIZARD, *Rhineura floridana,* is the only species found in the southeastern United States, where it is restricted to the Florida peninsula. Its color is a uniform pale lavender, over which plays an iridescent bloom. Preserved specimens fade to a lusterless yellowish-white. A full-grown example is eight and a half inches long and a quarter of an inch in diameter at the thickest part of the body. The species bores long tunnels in soft ground through which it wriggles backward or forward. It is commonly discovered when the fields are ploughed.

The *Lacertidæ.* The pleurodont species of this strictly Old World family are analogous in general form and scalation with the *Teiidæ* of the New World. The tongue is long, deeply forked and frequently employed as an organ of investigation. All of the species have well-developed limbs and a long, gradually tapering, fragile tail. There are no strikingly degraded forms. One of the most pronounced examples of specialization involves the eyes of some species that live in sandy places and burrow to a considerable extent. This consists of a transparent disk in the lower eyelid, so that the eye may be protected while the animal is digging, yet the organ may be of use at the same time. This character will be found with the genera *Eremias* and *Cabrita,* of Africa and India. The species of *Ophiops* (Snake-Eyed Lizards), a genus represented by six species in northern Africa, southwestern Asia and in India, show this character carried to an extreme. The eye is permanently open and covered with a transparent disk like the eye of a snake, though both eyelids are present. Specialization has been carried forward until the disk in the lower eyelid—seen with *Eremias,* and notably large with *Cabrita*—has overspread the eye, while the lower lid has fused with the upper. The species so provided live in dry, sandy places and burrow with wonderful agility.

Like the *Teiidæ,* the members of the present family show practically no traces of the rapid and pronounced changes of color described in connection with several families of lizards. The scaly covering of the *Lacertidæ* varies greatly. The majority of the species have a fine, some a granular scalation; on the tail the scales are always coarse and arranged in rings. A few have large keeled scales on the back. All have large, regularly arranged shields on the head. The abdomen is covered with large smooth shields arranged in regular transverse rows. In their distribution these lizards cover an enormous area. They occur generally in Europe, Asia and Africa, being most abundant in number of species in the latter continent. None is found in Madagascar nor in Australia and but a few in the East Indies.

By far the greater number of species of the *Lacertidæ* are insectivorous. Some are cannibalistic. Most of them lay thin-skinned eggs, a few are viviparous.

The familiar European lizards are members of the genus *Lacerta,* which, in all, embraces over twenty species. The scales on the back are very small. On the throat a row of enlarged shields form a well-defined collar.

The GREEN LIZARD, *Lacerta viridis,* is an abundant and beautiful species of central and southern Europe and southwestern Asia. Most European specimens are of a vivid, uniform green. In southern Europe, thence westward, varieties are found that are dotted or streaked with yellow. Many examples have the lips and throat dyed with a rich dark blue. The abdomen is generally pale yellow.

A number of these attractive reptiles have formed a part of the writer's collection. His largest specimen was sixteen inches long. Ten or eleven inches, however, is the ordinary length. Kept in a vivarium that is not too damp, Green Lizards will live for years. They dig hiding places in the form of regular burrows or scoop out cavities under the rocks into which they always retire for the night, seldom becoming confused in their respective lairs. After a while their appetite prompts curiosity, even toward the human observer. They soon learn readily to take grubs and meal worms from the fingers and should be fed a diet of varied insect larvæ, as too many of the hard-shelled forms block the reptiles' intestines with hard chitinous fragments. Several of the writer's specimens took readily to a mixture of raw eggs and shreds of beef, well stirred together.

Care should be taken not to pick up a Green Lizard by the tail, for that appendage is very brittle. If the lizard is suddenly frightened, it is apt to give a quick twist and is instantly deformed. The new tail is seldom as long as the old one; it is covered with a rudimentary scalation, detracting much from the reptile's previously natty appearance.

Another pretty species of Europe is the EYED LIZARD, *L. lepida,* found from southern France through Spain and Portugal, also in northern Africa. The general hue is green or olive, over which are scattered yellow and black dots forming circular, eye-like spots or often running together in a fairly regular reticulate fashion. Old males have a broad, formidable-looking head and frequently reach a length of two feet, of which the tail forms two-thirds. This is also a hardy species for the vivarium. Big specimens should be excluded, however, as they are generally carnivorous and cannibalistic; they are fond of mice, eggs and young birds, as well as raw beef.

The COMMON LIZARD, *L. vivipara,* is extensively distributed. It is found in northern and central Europe and in Siberia clear to the eastern coast, where it occurs on the island of Saghalien. In Europe it does not occur south of the Alps, or, in the west, the Pyrenees. It is to be found throughout Great Britain and in Ireland. The colors of this species are not particularly attractive, though subject to much variation. It is brown or rusty above, sprinkled with light and dark spots. On some specimens a black band runs along the back and a dark, yellow-bordered band along each side. An adult is six or seven inches long.

The Common Lizard is noteworthy from its habit of producing living young—hence the technical specific name. The young are either born free or in thin membranous sacs, from which they soon burst their way. The litter may consist of from eight to a dozen young; these are less than an inch in length. As the mother leaves them immediately to shift for themselves, they hide among leaves or grass, living as do all young reptiles for the first few days after birth or hatching upon a portion of the egg yolk that has been absorbed through the abdominal opening. The first food consists of minute insects that are always to be found in crevices of the ground.

A closely related species, *Lacerta agilis,* ranges much like the preceding. Eastward, however, it does not extend beyond central Siberia, nor in the British Isles is it found in Scotland or Ireland. In England it is restricted to the southern portion. While the coloration appeals strongly to that of *L. vivipara,* the males show traces of green on the back and sides. During the breeding season some males are tinged with vivid shades of green, particularly on the sides. Female examples are invariably brown, with dark and light spots; each side of the back the dark spots fuse, producing a ragged, but well-defined band, this bordered by a whitish streak and causing the lizard to look as if having a striped pattern. On the males this character is seldom so distinct. Adults are eight inches long. From the allied species we may note a difference in habits, for *Lacerta agilis* is strictly oviparous, depositing 6–12 thin-skinned eggs.

Composed of ten species, inhabiting southern Spain and Portugal, southwestern Asia and Africa north of the equator, the genus *Acanthodactylus* contains some prettily-marked species that live in sandy places. The toes are fringed, which arrangement keeps the lizard's feet from sinking as it runs over the loose soil. On all of the species the scales of the back grow coarser toward the tail. This is especially pronounced with the SAND LIZARD, *A. boskianus,* living in desert portions of northern Africa and in Arabia.

In keeping with the sterile soil the colors are pallid. A photograph of an adult example, eight inches long, shows the pleasing pattern; the stripes are golden yellow; between them are traces of rusty red.

Seemingly intermediate between the *Lacertidæ* and a family to follow—the *Scincidæ*—is a strictly African family of lizards. This is the *Gerrhosauridæ.* The headquarters of the species are in South Africa and Madagascar. The members are characterized by a deep fold on each side of the body, the vicinity of this fold coated with granular scales as exists among the species of *Gerrhonotus* (New World members of the *Anguidæ*).

Some of the species of the *Gerrhosauridæ* have well-developed limbs; among others these members are rudimentary. The head is covered with symmetrical shields, the body with square or diamond-shaped, overlapping scales which are, among many, in regular transverse rows; underlying the scales are thin, bony plates, as exist with the *Scincidæ.*

Our next family, the *Scincidæ,* is cosmopolitan. Its members are popularly known as SKINKS. Among the vast majority of them there is a peculiar similarity of aspect, the scales being large, rounded and quite smooth, overlapping one another like extremely thin shingles.

Considered from a more technical point of view, the skinks may be described as pleurodont lizards, the body protected by thin, bony plates underlying the scales. The tongue is moderately long and feebly nicked at the tip. Most of the species have short limbs, but are fleet runners; others are snake-like of body and among the latter forms we may find all stages of degeneracy. Some have both pairs of limbs, these much reduced, and with them they drag their elongated body when progressing slowly, or wriggle away with limbs folded against the side of the body, when frightened; *others have a minute pair of hind legs only;* many species are entirely limbless. In no other family can we find such a mix-up of degenerating forms. In the genus *Leiolopisma*—containing over 160 species—are members with two pairs of fairly well-formed legs, others with two pairs of rudimentary legs, a few with but a pair of hind legs and several that are absolutely limbless. The intergradations of limb development run such riot in the face of absolutely no marked difference in the general scalation, we are compelled to place these eccentric forms under one generic head.

The FIVE-LINED SKINK, *Eumeces fasciatus,* is typical of that group of skinks having well-formed limbs. The scales are smooth, shining, almost glassy, producing an effect that is at once different from lizards of other families except certain members of the *Anguidæ.* This species ranges from Massachusetts to Florida and westward to Texas. It is rare in the Northern States, but swarms in the pine regions of the Southeast. Old males are ten inches long and have a wide, triangular head. The females seldom grow over seven inches long, are more slender and the head shows little swelling at the temples. From the youth to the adult state there is a strange transition in coloration. Young and old examples are so entirely different, they were at one time, not far remote, thought to represent well-defined species. The immature specimens are jet black with five bright yellow stripes running lengthwise on the body; the tail of such individuals is of brilliant blue and in wonderful contrast to the colors of the body. As the lizard approaches maturity the body assumes a brownish tinge, the stripes become less distinct and upon the males disappear altogether, while the head takes on a fiery red hue. This phase is known as the RED-HEADED LIZARD, or "Scorpion," and for a time was technically called *Eumeces erythrocephalus.* It is thought by the negroes to be very poisonous. Female specimens retain the stripes; these, however, are less distinct against the brown body hue than with the young; the red tinge on the head of the female is never so brilliant as on the other sex. The complete color transformation takes three or four years.

This handsome skink is difficult to capture. When basking it keeps a convenient hiding place in mind to which it instantly darts if frightened. The old males are very shy and cunning, living on pine trees, with always a snug retreat in the shape of a deep cavity, near by. Into this they rush as an intruder draws near, but from it is soon poked a fiery red head with wide, swollen temples and pointed snout, this member looking quite as formidable as the head of some deadly snake.

After fruitlessly trying to noose these lizards by fastening a piece of fine copper wire on a slender pole, the writer adopted new tactics. He was in the South Carolina pinelands at the time and as skinks were everywhere abundant, it was decided to obtain a good series of living specimens, showing the color transition. To obtain them dead would have been easy enough, as they could have been readily shot while basking. Owing to the persistently diurnal habits of the species, it was decided to hunt them just after daybreak, when they were yet in their hiding places. We hunted through a stretch of tall pine timber, where a tornado, years before, had felled a path of trees for a distance of several miles. The fallen giants were fast rotting and their bark had become very loose. By tearing away the bark we found the skinks in hiding. As it was disclosed, a reptile would be momentarily dazed; in that instant it had to be grabbed or it would recover its wits and dart away. In this fashion we obtained several, hundred examples, besides numerous small snakes.

Several species of *Eumeces* are found in the western parts of the United States. The genus is represented in the New and the Old World.

Another common member of the *Scincidæ* in the United States is the WORM SKINK OR GROUND LIZARD, *Leiolopisma laterale,* a tiny, elongated species with weak legs. It lives among leaves and under logs in the southeastern states, thence ranges into Mexico. When uncovered, it runs and wriggles away in such lively fashion it is apt to find a hiding place in the surrounding vegetation unless one makes a remarkably quick grab for the specimen. These little lizards look much like salamanders. The genus to which they belong is the largest of the family, embracing over one hundred and sixty species inhabiting North and Central America, China, the East Indies and Africa. It is in this genus that we find all stages of degradation; some of the species have well-formed limbs; others, mere rudimentary stumps and glide like a snake.

Tiliqua, made up of a moderate number of species, contains the giants among skinks. They inhabit Malaysia and Australasia. *Tiliqua gigas*—the GIANT SKINK—attains a length of two feet. It is found in New Guinea, the Moluccas and Java. The body is slaty gray crossed by dark bands; it is covered with large, smooth scales with a satiny luster. The tail is quite short. As a captive this species is hardy. It is fond of eggs and chopped raw beef, lapping up the former with its exceedingly broad and flat purplish tongue. Insects are also eaten as well as young mice and birds.

Scincus, composed of eight species that inhabit the deserts of northern Africa, Arabia and Persia, presents some particularly interesting examples of adaptation to a life in fine, dry sands. We may select the EGYPTIAN SKINK, *Scincus officinalis,* found in the Sahara and common in Egypt. The maximum length is eight to ten inches. The snout is flattened to such a degree it forms an excellent scoop, while the toes are so wide and thin they look like feathers. Thus these animals may walk over fine sand without the feet sinking and, if they wish to burrow, they employ the scoop-like snout. Their eyes are minute and beady and the ears are concealed by scaly flaps. Unless kept in a baking temperature, captives move as if paralyzed. A temperature of 90 or 100 degrees Fahrenheit produces normal vivacity. They are fond of meal worms. The species is beautifully marked, usually being a rich cream color crossed by blackish or dark red bands. The young are pale pinkish; as they grow older the transverse bands appear. Queerly enough, the abdomen is much flattened, forming an angle with the sides, as seen among many constricting snakes. In progressing over declivities in the sand the body follows the outlines of the soil, producing a sinuous, serpentine impression, even though the limbs are strong and well formed.

Allied to the preceding genus is *Chalcides,* with eleven species, found in southern Europe, southwestern Asia, Syria, Persia and northern Africa. The body is much elongated—snake-like, while the limbs are small and weak. The species are covered with smooth, shining scales; some have a conical snout; on others the snout is wedge-shaped. *Chalcides sepoides* is found in the reddish-yellow sands of the Sahara Desert and in Arabia. It is about seven inches long when adult. The long, cylindrical body is provided with four ludicrously small limbs. As the animal progresses it folds the legs against the body, moving in ophidian fashion. When frightened, it literally swims into the sand, the wedge-shaped snout greatly assisting in the process. The coloration is pale yellowish with faint brown longitudinal streaks.

Three families of worm-like lizards appear to be much degraded types of the *Scincidæ.* These are the *Anelytropsidæ,* with one Mexican and five African species; the *Aniellidæ,* with one Californian species, and the *Dibamidæ,* consisting of a single genus of two species—one in New Guinea, the Celebes and the Moluccas and another in the Nicobar Islands. *Dibamus novæ-guineæ* might appear to the popular eye merely as a long, slender worm covered with glassy scales. The head is blunt, conical and smaller than the neck, with a very large, cap-like shield on the snout, the rostral. It is almost needless to say this lowly reptile is blind and strictly subterraneous.

The CHAMELEONS. Lizards of several families are often called "Chameleons" owing to their involuntary habit of quickly changing their hues; such species are found in various parts of the world. The true Chameleons form an Old World family, essentially African; a large number of the species are found in Madagascar. Two occur in Arabia and Socotra; one species inhabits southern India and Ceylon and one of the African species is found in southern Spain. About fifty in number of species, these lizards compose a very distinct family, the *Chamæleontidæ*. The dentition is acrodont.

There is hardly any possibility of mistaking a chameleon. The body is high and compressed with a rather short, prehensile tail; the head is usually provided with a protuberance at the rear like a cap or hood. The body is covered with granules—sometimes studded with tubercular points. Most characteristic are the feet and the eyes. The foot is a *grasping* organ and shaped like a thick pair of pliers; the division of the toes consists of two on one side and three on the other. It is difficult to describe the eyes. To use popular language, the eyeballs bulge from the head though the eye opening itself is very small. Each eye is capable of independent and extensive motion; one eye may roll sharply upward and the other be directed forward; one may look up and the other down, or backward—in fact, the eyes perform all combinations. All of the Chameleons have an amazingly long, telescopic tongue which is club-shaped, sticky at the tip and capable of being shot at an insect to a length equaling that of the reptile's body. Lastly, in summing up the characters, it should be understood that while Chameleons undergo wonderful changes of color, they are rivaled by many species of the *Iguanidæ* and the *Agamidæ*.

The present family is composed of three genera, as follows: *Chamæleon*—45 species, inhabiting Africa and Madagascar, southern Spain, India and Ceylon—only two species occurring outside of Africa and Madagascar. *Brookesia*—3 species, in Madagascar. *Rhampholeon*—2 species, in tropical Africa.

The COMMON CHAMELEON, *Chamæleon chamæleon,* inhabits northern Africa, Syria, Asia Minor and southern Spain. A photograph delineates its characters better than words. This particularly interesting lizard is altogether arboreal, as are all the chameleons. On the ground it is ludicrously awkward. Among the slender branches of a tree or a bush it is a veritable acrobat, grasping branch after branch with its bifurcated feet, progressing in a nonchalant, slow fashion. When the lizard desires to steady itself, the prehensile tail grasps a twig firmly. While in this position the animal rolls its swivel eyes in all directions, squinting fixedly at any object that may seem in the least suspicious or interesting. The feeding affords a much exaggerated example of the way in which many of the sticky-tongued lizards obtain their insect prey. Grasshoppers, crickets and spiders are the favorite food. Approaching an insect with an air of perfect deliberation a chameleon regards it calmly for a second or two with one bulging eye, while the other may indifferently examine various objects. A sudden flash of the tongue follows to a possible distance of six or seven inches and the morsel is snapped back to the jaws, where it is well masticated by sharp teeth before it is swallowed.

Captive chameleons are not hardy. Few live longer than five or six months. They drink whenever the plants in the cage are watered, showing the necessity of this liquid nourishment. The feeding of captive specimens is often half-hearted and some fast with exasperating persistence. Some of the writer's specimens have become so thin they not only sounded quite hollow when their rough skin was rubbed by the fingers, but were actually translucent when held to the light. While these refused all food, they drank regularly. An occasional specimen feeds regularly, but it is one of fifty.

Many lacertilians have excited popular interest owing to their color changes. We have already noted these habits among the members of the *Iguanidæ* and the *Agamidæ*. Marked changes of color appear principally among species with a granular scalation. There are, however, many lizards with large, coarse scales, either smooth or keeled, that momentarily vary in hue. Usually, the variation among such examples consists of the intensification of a regular and permanent pattern, or the fading of this; as a good illustration we may take the Common Swift, *Sceloporus undulatus,* of the United States, and the allies of that reptile among which patches of pale gray on the abdomen and throat will assume really startling shades of blue and green, while the pattern on the creature's back varies from shades of gray into brown or yellow. Among the members of the *Chamæleontidæ* there are not only marked changes of the body hue, but strange patterns come and go.

Numerous experiments have been conducted in the Reptile House of the New York Zoological Park. Following is a partial list of these, the same relating to *Chamæleon chamæleon:*

Specimen A. Placed in the sunlight so that but one side of the lizard was exposed to the rays.
Specimen B. Placed in the sunlight at an angle to entirely suffuse the reptile with the rays.
Specimen C. Placed in a dark box—Temperature 75° Fahrenheit.
Specimen D. Placed in a dark box—Temperature 50° Fahrenheit.

After fifteen minutes these results were noted:

Specimen A. Was a dark brown on the side that had been exposed to the sun; the shadowed side was a pale brown, mottled with green.
Specimen B. A uniform brown, deeper than the dark side of Specimen A.
Specimen C. When the cover of the box was drawn the lizard emerged in a brilliant coat of green.
Specimen D. Crawled sluggishly from its cold quarters. Its color was a uniform, slaty gray.

Repetition of these experiments produced similar results, showing *light* and *temperature* to be among the factors responsible in changing the lizards' hues.

Another test was along lines to ascertain if the lizards responded to the colors of objects over which they moved or rested. The specimens were placed in separate cases, all with a uniform amount of illumination. One of the cases contained a branch of bright green leaves, another a bunch of dark, leafless twigs; in the third, a fine white sand had been spread. The results were humorously negative. All of the specimens assumed a shade of yellowish brown, causing each to appear sharply defined among its surroundings.

And a number of experiments in this direction went to show that the colors of chameleons have little to do with the hues of the reptiles' surroundings.

Excitement and fright bring marked results—usually paler shades. Specimens in a sickly condition are often splashed with pale hues; ragged patches of green appear which may give way to black immediately after death.

One curious effect of sunlight and shadow was observed. A specimen had been basking under a coarse wire grating. Becoming frightened at the approach of the writer, it changed its position. On the dark brown body was what had been the shadow of the grating, brilliantly imprinted in pale yellow. Within half a minute this pattern had entirely faded.

The common colors of captive chameleons are grayish or yellowish-brown, green with irregular spots and blotches or, when exposed to sunlight, brown with rings of green or yellow. Few specimens exhibit a definite pattern; obscure longitudinal bands, blotches and ocelli come and go with the varying shades of the body hue.

PART III

THE SNAKES

SUBORDER *OPHIDIA*

THE SNAKES: SUBORDER *OPHIDIA*

It is with the present great suborder of Scaled Reptiles that the writer begs leave to escort the reader within the portals of his favorite study. That many will encounter this subject with aversion is fully believed; but it is the writer's hope, ere this book is finally closed, a persistently reigning and unjust prejudice may be completely shattered by the explosion of a long train of erroneous theories; when snakes have been described as they truly are, and the clean, graceful and wonderful phases of their varied structure have been faithfully portrayed by the camera.

It is with a thoroughly sympathetic interest the writer compiles Part III of this book. While his studies have involved reptiles generally, his favorite creature in Nature has, from early boyhood days, been The Serpent. His home has always been the headquarters of an extensive collection of snakes large and small, innocuous and venomous. It was individual care, among restricted numbers of the various species, that elicited strange habits; and these, when fully comprehended, have been of the greatest value to the writer in successfully maintaining the many hundreds of serpents in the splendid Reptile House of the New York Zoological Park.

As compared with the closely allied suborder, the *Sauria,* the snakes exhibit even a greater variability of form. Take, for instance, a twenty-five foot python weighing three hundred pounds and compare this with a mature specimen of a burrowing snake but five or six inches long and not thicker than a goose quill; or place side by side a squatty, flat-headed viper and an enormously elongated tree snake—one secreting itself by shoveling sand over its back, the other darting away with the speed of an arrow!

In their general occurrence and distribution snakes are considerably more abundant than lizards though not so commonly seen, as the greater number lead a secretive life and the feeding habits of them all induce them to seek seclusion during the progress of the assimilation of food. Snakes also range much farther into the temperate regions than lizards; in many latitudes where lizards cease to occur, numerous species of snakes are common. As with the lizards, the number of species is especially high in the tropics, thence decreases north or south of the equator. Details regarding distribution will be treated under the heads of the respective families. A few points, however, should be primarily understood: The various species of Rattlesnakes are confined to the New World and the majority of them to the United States and northern Mexico; yet the family to which the rattlesnakes belong—the *Crotalidæ* (Pit Vipers)—is represented in both the Eastern and Western Hemispheres. The true Vipers—without head pits—are confined to the Old World. The famous Cobras are confined to the Old World and there are *twelve species;* not all of them spread a "hood." The family to which the Cobras belong—the *Elapidæ*—is represented in the New World by a single genus, *Micrurus*. The Elapine snakes swarm in Australia, forming the great majority of the serpent life; this is one of the few parts of the world where the poisonous species far exceed the harmless ones in number of species. Madagascar is the only large country in warm or temperate latitudes entirely free of dangerous snakes; it is, however, inhabited by a number of harmless kinds.

After the student has been referred to the great variety of limbless lizards that crawl in what appears to be typical serpentine fashion, a very natural question may arise—What are the points of differentiation distinguishing the true snakes from the legless lacertilians? The differences are not elaborate. The chief characters involve the bones of the head—particularly those of the lower jaw. Among snakes the lower jaw is not single, as with the lizards; it is composed of two elongated, nearly straight bones that are connected in the front merely by an elastic ligament. Besides this arrangement, the suspension of the lower jaw bones and the attachment of the upper ones, too, provide for great elasticity and enable a serpent to engulf its prey entire—often an animal four or five times the diameter of its neck. This swallowing apparatus of the serpent shows marked specialization among reptiles. The process of engulfing the prey is extremely simple and ingenuous, though little understood. About this characteristic has originated a string of ridiculous stories. Let us suppose a snake with a neck about as thick as a man's forefinger were about to swallow a large rat. This would be an easy task. Usually, the prey is grasped by the snout when the performance commences. One of the upper jaw bones and the corresponding lower jaw bone reach forward, the bones close upon the prey inserting the recurved teeth, when this side of head is pulled back drawing the animal a short distance into the mouth; the process is repeated with the other side of the head, each side working in alternation while the quarry is pulled into the mouth and forced into the throat, which, being very elastic, stretches to receive it. As soon as the prey reaches the snake's throat, a lateral undulatory movement of the neck commences, which literally seizes the creature in suctorial fashion, greatly assisting the now thoroughly distended jaws. At this stage of the feeding, the lever-like suspension of the lower jaw bones has been greatly strained from its normal setting and it is possible the lower jaw forms but a tight band about the prey, the upper jaw alone pulling in the animal—assisted by the movements of the neck; the eyes bulge and the skin of the neck is so distended as to widely separate the rows of scales; at frequent intervals the snake pauses to rest, when it forces, from between the animal and lower jaw, the tubular breathing appendage. One or two good breaths are taken, then commences again what seems like a most heroic task. Finally the sinuous movements of the throat engulf the heavy prey. The head quickly assumes its normal aspect, only a few flabby folds of skin denoting the astounding feat that has taken place. A yawn or two effaces all traces of the task except the distended portion of the body, slowly forcing the prey to the stomach by a combination of undulatory movements and an anterior pressure caused by drawing the muscles together.

In this swallowing performance we note one of the characteristics relating to the snake's anatomy that is markedly different from the structure of any of the lizards. Another ophidian character is the absence of eyelids. Thus, the eyes of a snake are always open and a sleeping serpent may be awakened by *seeing* a sudden movement. The eye is covered with a transparent cap which is shed at each casting of the skin; under this glassy cap the eye is capable of considerable movement. Yet another difference between snakes and most lizards is the absence, among all of the former, of any trace of an external ear. Internally, the serpent's ear consists of a thread-like bone and crude accessories. The ear seems to be in a state of degeneracy, but an ear is unnecessary, *for snakes hear with their tongues.* The delicate, nerve-supplied tips of this wonderfully specialized organ are highly sensitive to vibrations from even slight sounds. Besides, the tongue serves many purposes; vulgarly speaking, it is a "feeler" and of enormous value to the reptile.

In the osteological characters of the snake's body we find no marked difference from the limbless lizards. While all of the snake-like lizards have traces of internal limbs and the pelvic girdle, most snakes are devoid of such, but among the members of the older families, the *Boidæ* and some of the burrowing snakes, internal limbs are still present as well as bones representing the pelvic girdle—in fact, among some of the true snakes we find better developed limbs and pelvic bones than existing with some of the burrowing lizards. With the Boas and Pythons, the limbs are visible externally as bony spurs which are capable of vigorous movement.

Looked at from a concise standpoint, snakes may be described as the most specialized among all living reptiles, having originated from the lizards. Aside from the great modification of the jaws into an apparatus to engulf large prey entire, we find the most elaborate and remarkable structure pertaining to the dentition among all reptiles—the poison-conducting teeth or fangs of the venomous species. Hence, among creatures that man has seen fit to describe as lowly and repulsive, has existed for ages a perfect apparatus that man has discovered but yesterday, and this in the shape of an instrument of immense value to himself—the hypodermic needle. The viperine snakes possess these instruments in the greatest degree of perfection; their "fangs" are canaliculated teeth, in the forward part of the upper jaw, *rigidly attached* to a *movable bone*. On the front face, at the tip of the fang, is an elongated orifice for the ejection of venom. When the mouth is closed, the fangs of the viperine snakes fold back against the roof; as the jaws are opened they spring forward, ready for action. Each fang connects, at its base, with a canal, which extends back of the eye, thence fuses into an almond-shaped gland secreting a poison designed by Nature to be used in purposes of killing the creature's prey and which is thoroughly successful in its application. Secondarily, the venom apparatus is used for purposes of defense. From the situation of the fangs it can be immediately understood that the forked tongue is not a "sting" nor in any way related to the source of danger from the most deadly of snakes. Differing from the Viperine—the thick-bodied poisonous snakes—the Cobras and their allies, really comprising a distinct group in the family containing the harmless snakes, differ in having short, rigidly-set fangs that are not perfectly canaliculated, as they show strong traces of an external groove. A third group of snakes, the *Opisthoglypha,* have rigidly-set, *grooved* fangs in the *rear* of the upper jaw; a small proportion among their species may be rated as dangerous to man. We may take the members of the *Opisthoglypha* as types of poisonous serpents having the crudest venom apparatus—the fangs merely grooved; the Cobras and their allies, and the Sea Snakes, are the next highest types, the fangs having closed about the groove so as to form a canal within them, yet leaving a strong external trace of the groove. In the development of the viperine snakes' fangs, the canal is perfectly formed and the anterior surface of the poison-conducting teeth shows but a faint suggestion of a groove. It must not be taken for granted, however, that these "intergradations" show the three groups to have originated from a common source. The evolution of the Elapine and the Viperine snakes has sprung from quite distinct branches. The trend of evolution seems to point to the greater number of snakes becoming poisonous, and the elaboration of the fang mechanism among the forms now poisonous, even with the Vipers, if that be possible.

On account of the great array of serpent life and the peculiar external similarity of the smaller species in scale formation and arrangement of the head plates, technical writers have found it necessary to employ the dentition as the prime factor in classifying the ophidians. But in connection with the dentition, the rows of scales are counted, the structure of the head shields noted and the number of abdominal plates carefully taken. For the benefit of the beginner it is well to state that snakes have either *keeled* (carinated) or *smooth scales.* Examples of the former are the Water Snakes (*Natrix*) and of the latter, the North American Racers (*Coluber*).

The movements of most serpents are singularly quick and graceful. They depend largely upon the broad plates of the abdomen, the sharp, overlapping posterior edges of which offer a substantial purchase. In crawling slowly, a snake really walks upon these plates by bringing them forward in series along the body, then pulling them back again. Working in this fashion a serpent may progress in a perfectly straight line; a moment later it may be frightened, when it threads its way among twigs and stones, gliding swiftly in a series of lateral undulations. Most snakes are agile swimmers; the members of one family—the *Hydrophidæ*—have a vertically compressed tail, like a paddle; they pass their entire life in the sea. Many snakes are strictly arboreal and these are generally much elongated, really whip-like. Some snakes are quite subterraneous, boring their way into the ground like worms; larger species burrow at times in sandy places and often have a scoop-shaped snout.

The scaly covering of snakes is overlaid with a thin skin that is regularly shed, not in patches, as among most of the lizards, but carefully divested entire. Some time before this event the colors of the reptile fade decidedly and the eyes become white, like bubbles filled with smoke. This condition may last a couple of weeks. Then the reptile suddenly takes on a nearly normal appearance. The eyes look bright and the colors fairly intense. This change is caused by the attack of an oily secretion upon the under surface of the old skin, loosening that member preparatory to shedding. The snake soon rubs the epidermis back from the top of the head, shedding the eye plates, then rubs the skin from the lower jaw, after which preparation it crawls out of the old cuticle, turning it wrong-side-out for the entire length of the body and tail. Healthy and well-nourished snakes shed their skin at intervals of about two months apart, or at shorter periods.

The ophidians either lay eggs or produce their young alive. There is a much larger proportion of viviparous species than among lizards. The young of the poisonous snakes are provided at birth with perfectly formed venom-conducting fangs and glands; they are just as dangerous, in proportion to their size, as their parents. All young snakes at once shift for themselves after birth or hatching. The story of the female snake swallowing her young in time of danger is purely fallacious. It has originated from observations of cannibal species making a meal of young reptiles.

Though poisonous snakes are common enough in many parts of the world, the danger from them is not nearly so great as imagined. In India, where a large part of the population goes about bare-legged, the estimated number of human lives lost each year is about 20,000. Conditions are very different in the United States, though the various species of Rattlesnakes, the Copperhead Snake and the formidable Water Moccasin teem over vast areas. Records of snake bites are comparatively rare in North America.

Treatment of snake bite. With the progression of medical surgery, the treatment of snake bite has been much improved and the percentage of cures is substantially greater. The discovery of anti-venine, by Dr. Albert Calmette, of the Pasteur Institute, produced what might be called the first reliable *antidote* for the terrible virus of the Elapines and the Vipers. Anti-venine is manufactured along similar lines as the antitoxic serums for different diseases. A horse is repeatedly injected with small quantities of venom until strongly immunized. When in that condition a quantity of the animal's blood is drawn and the serous portion separated; the latter constitutes the valuable remedy. Antivenomous serum is now produced in India, Africa, South America and the United States for the respective types of poisonous snakes.

Aside from the hypodermic injection of anti-venine—if that is to be obtained—the treatment of snake bite involves several vigorous and absolutely necessary measures. Almost without exception the bite is upon some part of the arm or leg and the first thing to be done is to shut off the circulation between the fang wounds and the heart, to prevent the poisoned blood from gaining the general circulation. This is best done by applying a ligature (preferably a rubber one) a short distance above the injury. The next step is to drain away the poisoned blood from the vicinity of the fang punctures. This can be done only in one way —by generous laceration into the wounds. A cut should be made across each, at least as deep as the original wound, then a longitudinal cut at right angles across the first two incisions. The wounds should be drained thoroughly by suction. After every application the mouth must be rinsed with a wine-colored solution of *permanganate of potassium,* which chemical oxidizes the venom and destroys its action. Following these first precautions the wounds should be further drained with some suction device, if at hand. Such devices are regularly sold and should be part of a traveling kit. After the wounds have been drained of poisoned blood and washed, the ligature may be removed. Constitutional symptoms, in the shape of weakness and giddiness, should be met by small doses of brandy and hypodermic injections of strychnine. At this time it should be well understood that in blood, attacked by snake poison, the germicidal qualities for a time die out, the fighting corpuscles becoming entirely inactive. This condition renders the wounds liable to dangerous infection—possibly gangrene. Every precaution should be taken to keep the wounds clean and draining well. They should be packed with moist, antiseptic gauze and the dressing must be kept *continually* wet with some good antiseptic solution. If the serum treatment is possible, it should immediately follow the scarification and washing of the wounds. The wounds should be kept open and draining for at least two weeks, no matter how favorable may be the symptoms.

Following the writer's idea of indicating the size, classification and distribution of each Order and Suborder, a provisional list of the *Ophidia* is given: *

* This summary is presented mainly to indicate the scope of this division of reptiles. It is practically revised, but to keep such a list "up to date" with regard to scientific nomenclature is almost an impossible task, without constant access to world sources of literature by technical workers engaged in investigations of priority, relationships affecting grouping of species, elimination of disproved forms, and addition of new species.

	Number of Species	Distribution
Family *Typhlopidæ* (Small, degenerate, burrowing snakes. All *harmless*).		
Genus *Helminthophis*	5	Tropical America.
Genus *Typhlops*	100+	So. Europe; So. Asia; Africa; Australia and trop. Amer.
Genus *Typhlophis*	1	Brazil and Guiana.
Family *Leptotyphlopidæ.*		
Genus *Anomalepis*	1	Mexico.
Genus *Leptotyphlops*	27	So. U. S. to Brazil; S. W. Asia and Africa.
Family *Boidæ* (Embraces the giant constrictors; a number of the species are of small size. *All are devoid of fangs*).		
Subfamily *Pythoninæ.* The PYTHONS.		
Genus *Loxocemus* *	1	*Mexico.*
Genus *Nardoa*	1	New Ireland.
Genus *Liasis*	6	Timor, New Guinea and North Australia.
Genus *Python*	9	S. E. Asia; Africa; New Guinea and Australia.
Genus *Chondropython*	1	New Guinea.
Genus *Aspidites*	2	North Australia.
Genus *Calabaria*	1	West Africa.
Subfamily *Boinæ.* The BOAS. New and Old World.		
Genus *Epicrates*	8	Tropical America.
Genus *Boa*	6	Tropical America; *Madagascar.*
Genus *Enygrus*	4	Moluccas; Papuasia
Genus *Trachyboa*	1	Brazil.
Genus *Ungalia*	8	Trop. So. America: West Indies.
Genus *Ungaliophis*	1	Guatemala.
Genus *Eunectes*	2	Tropical South America.
Genus *Constrictor*	8	Tropical America; *Madagascar.*
Genus *Casarea*	1	Round Island, near Mauritius.
Genus *Bolieria*	1	Round Island, near Mauritius.
Genus *Eryx*	7	No. Africa; Southern Asia.
Genus *Lichanura*	2	Southwestern North America.
Genus *Charina*	2	Western North America.
Family *Anilidæ* (Small, *harmless,* constricting snakes that are closely allied to the *Boidæ*).		

* The only New World representative of the subfamily.

	Number of Species	Distribution
Genus *Anilius*	1	Tropical South America.
Genus *Anomalochilus*	1	Sumatra.
Genus *Cylindrophis*	3	S. E. Asia; Ceylon.
Family *Uropeltidæ* (Small, *harmless* burrowing snakes).		
Genus *Uropeltis*	1	Ceylon.
Genus *Rhinophis*	8	Southern India; Ceylon.
Genus *Silybura*	22	Southern India.
Genus *Pseudoplectrurus*	1	Southern India.
Genus *Plectrurus*	4	Southern India.
Genus *Melanophidium*	3	Southern India.
Genus *Platyplectrurus*	3	Southern India.
Family *Xenopeltidæ* (A *harmless*, burrowing species).		
Genus *Xenopeltis*	1	S. E. Asia.
Family *Colubridæ*. A grouping of related subfamilies, in two series, according to dentition.		
SERIES A. *Aglypha* (All the teeth solid; not grooved or canaliculated).		
Subfamily *Acrochordinæ*.		
Genus *Acrochordus*	1	Malay Pn. and Arch.; New Guinea.
Genus *Chersydrus*	1	Bays and coasts of S. E. Asia and Papuasia.
Genus *Xenodermus*	1	Java and Sumatra.
Genus *Stoliczkaia*	1	N. E. India.
Genus *Nothopsis*	2	Central America.
Subfamily *Colubrinæ* (The typical harmless serpents. Old and New World).		
Genus *Sibinophis*	12	Madagascar and Comoro Islands; S. E. Asia; Central America.
Genus *Liophidium*	1	Madagascar.
Genus *Dromicordyas*	2	Madagascar.
Genus *Xenochrophis*	1	S. E. Asia.
Genus *Prymnomiodon*	1	Siam.
Genus *Thamnophis*	11	United States and Mexico.
Genus *Natrix*	71	New and Old World.
Genus *Seminatrix*	1	Southeast United States—Florida only.
Genus *Macropisthodon*	3	East Indies.
Genus *Compsophis*	1	Madagascar.
Genus *Lioheterodon*	2	Madagascar.
Genus *Pseudoxenodon*	3	East Indies; So. China.

	Number of Species	Distribution
Genus *Helicops*	11	Trop. Amer.; S. E. Asia; Africa.
Genus *Hydræthiops*	1	Tropical Africa.
Genus *Tretanorhinus*	3	Central America; Cuba.
Genus *Opisthotropis*	4	Malay Arch.; So. China; West Africa.
Genus *Tropidoclonium*	1	Central U. S.
Genus *Storeria*	4	U. S. to Central America.
Genus *Amphiardis*	1	Texas.
Genus *Potamophis*	1	Eastern U. S.
Genus *Streptophorus*	3	Central America; Northern South America.
Genus *Geatractus*	1	Mexico.
Genus *Chersodromus*	1	Mexico; Guatemala.
Genus *Hydrablabes*	2	Borneo.
Genus *Trachischium*	5	Northern India.
Genus *Rhabdops*	2	India; Southern China.
Genus *Trirhinopholis*	1	Burma.
Genus *Plagiopholis*	1	Burma.
Genus *Oxyrhabdium*	2	Philippines.
Genus *Xylophis*	2	Southern India.
Genus *Brachyorhhus*	1	Malay Pn.; New Guinea.
Genus *Elapoides*	1	Malay Pn.
Genus *Achalinus*	3	China and Japan.
Genus *Haplocercus*	1	Ceylon.
Genus *Aspidura*	4	Ceylon.
Genus *Blythia*	1	Northern India.
Genus *Pseudoxyrhopus*	7	Madagascar.
Genus *Lycognathophis*	1	Seychelles.
Genus *Ablabophis*	1	Southern Africa.
Genus *Tetralepis*	1	Java.
Genus *Glypholycus*	1	Africa.
Genus *Lamprophis*	4	Southern Africa.
Genus *Gonionotophis*	3	Tropical Africa.
Genus *Bothropthalmus*	1	Tropical Africa.
Genus *Bothrolycus*	1	West Africa.
Genus *Cyclocorus*	1	Philippines.
Genus *Boodon*	9	Tropical and South Africa.
Genus *Lycophidium*	11	Tropical and South Africa.
Genus *Hormonotus*	1	West Africa.
Genus *Simocephalus*	7	Tropical and South Africa.
Genus *Lycodon*	15	Southern Asia.
Genus *Dinodon*	5	China and Japan.
Genus *Stegonotus*	10	Philippines; Moluccas; Papuasia and Northern Aust.
Genus *Dryocalamus*	5	S. E. Asia.
Genus *Pseudaspis*	1	Southern Africa.

	Number of Species	Distribution
Genus *Zaocys*	6	S. E. Asia.
Genus *Coluber*	27	New and Old World.
Genus *Masticophis*	12	So. U. S.; tropical America.
Genus *Salvadora*	3	S. W. United States; Mexico.
Genus *Phyllorhynchus*	2	S. W. United States.
Genus *Lytorhynchus*	3	Asia; Northern Africa.
Genus *Xenelaphis*	1	Malay Pn. and Arch.; Burma.
Genus *Drymobius*	8	So. U. S. to Northern South America.
Genus *Leptodrymus*	1	Honduras.
Genus *Phrynonax*	7	Tropical America.
Genus *Drymarchon*	1	So. U. S.; tropical America.
Genus *Spilotes*	2	Tropical America.
Genus *Elaphe*	43	New and Old World.
Genus *Synchalinus*	1	Central America.
Genus *Symphimus*	1	Mexico.
Genus *Gonyophis*	1	Central America.
Genus *Herpetodryas*	5	Tropical America.
Genus *Dendrophis*	10	S. E. Asia and Australia.
Genus *Dendrelaphus*	6	Malay Pn. and Arch.; India; Ceylon.
Genus *Chlorophis*	9	Tropical and South Africa.
Genus *Philothamnus*	5	Tropical and South Africa.
Genus *Gastropyxis*	1	West Africa.
Genus *Hapsidophrys*	1	West Africa.
Genus *Rhamophis*	2	Africa.
Genus *Thrasops*	1	West Africa.
Genus *Leptophis*	14	Central and South America.
Genus *Uromacer*	3	San Domingo.
Genus *Hypsirhynchus*	1	San Domingo.
Genus *Alsophis*	15+	West Indies.
Genus *Dromicus*	24+	West Indies; Chili and Peru.
Genus *Liophis*	21	Central and South America; West Indies.
Genus *Cyclagras*	1	South America.
Genus *Xenodon*	6	South America and Central America.
Genus *Lystrophis*	3	Southern South America.
Genus *Heterodon*	3	United States.
Genus *Aporophis*	5	South America.
Genus *Rhadinaea*	27	S. E. U. S.; Central and So. America.
Genus *Urotheca*	5	Cuba; Central and South America.
Genus *Sordellina*	2	Brazil.
Genus *Trimetopon*	2	Central America.
Genus *Hydromorphus*	1	Central America.
Genus *Dimades*	2	South America.

	Number of Species	Distribution
Genus *Hydrops*	2	South America.
Genus *Sympholis*	1	Mexico.
Genus *Coronella*	7	Europe; S. W. Asia; India and Africa.
Genus *Ophibolus*	7	U. S.; Mexico and Central America.
Genus *Diadophis*	3	United States and Mexico.
Genus *Hypsiglena*	6	United States to South America.
Genus *Rhinochilus*	3	United States; Mexico and Venezuela.
Genus *Cemophora*	1	Southeastern United States.
Genus *Simotes*	22	S. E. Asia; Malay Archipelago.
Genus *Oligodon*	18	So. Asia and Northern Africa.
Genus *Prosymna*	5	Tropical and South Africa.
Genus *Paraoxyrhopus*	2	Paraguay.
Genus *Leptocalamus*	3	Tropical America.
Genus *Arrhyton*	3	Cuba.
Genus *Simophis*	2	Brazil.
Genus *Scaphiophis*	1	Tropical Africa.
Genus *Opheodrys*	4	United States; S. W. Asia.
Genus *Liopeltis*	2	United States; S. W. Asia.
Genus *Contia*	15	United States; S. W. Asia.
Genus *Morenoa*	1	Mexico.
Genus *Ficimia*	3	United States; Mexico.
Genus *Chilomeniscus*	2	S. W. United States; Northern Mexico.
Genus *Oligolepis*	1	Africa.
Genus *Homalosoma*	4	Africa.
Genus *Ablabes*	12	S. E. Asia and Japan.
Genus *Grayia*	3	Tropical Africa.
Genus *Xenurophis*	1	West Africa.
Genus *Virginia*	2	Southeastern United States.
Genus *Abastor*	1	Southeastern United States.
Genus *Farancia*	1	Southeastern United States.
Genus *Petalognathus*	1	Tropical America.
Genus *Tropidodipsas*	6	Central America.
Genus *Dirosema*	4	Central America; Mexico.
Genus *Atractus*	23	Central America; South America.
Genus *Atractopsis*	1	Ecuador.
Genus *Geophis*	13	Central America; South America.
Genus *Agrophis*	1	Celebes.
Genus *Carphophis*	1	Eastern United States.
Genus *Stylophis*	1	United States—Florida only.
Genus *Geagras*	1	Mexico.
Genus *Macrocalamus*	1	Malay Peninsula.
Genus *Idiopholis*	1	Borneo.
Genus *Rhabdophidium*	1	Celebes.

	Number of Species	Distribution
Genus *Pseudorhabdium*	2	Malay Peninsula and Archipelago.
Genus *Calamaria*	36	S. E. Asia and Malay Archipelago.
Genus *Typhlogeophis*	1	Philippines.
Genus *Amastridium*	2	Northern South America.
Genus *Anoplophallus*	1	Tahiti.
Subfamily *Dasypeltinæ* (Number of teeth much reduced).		
Genus *Dasypeltis*	1	Tropical and South Africa.
Subfamily *Amblycephalinæ* (Bush snakes with slender body and lumpy head. Jaws capable of but slight extension).		
Genus *Haplopelturus*	1	India; Malay Archipelago.
Genus *Amblycephalus*	9	S. E. Asia.
Genus *Leptognathus*	21	Central and South America.
Genus *Dipsas*	1	South America.
Genus *Hererorhachis*	1	South America.
Genus *Pseudopareas*	2	South America.
SERIES B. *Opisthoglypha* (*Poisonous* serpents with grooved fangs in the *rear* of the upper jaw. Few of the species are really deadly to man).		
Subfamily *Homalopsinæ*. The River Snakes.		
Genus *Hypsirhina*	15	S. E. Papuasia; Northern Queensland.
Genus *Homalopsis*	1	S. E. Asia.
Genus *Eurostus*	1	Bengal.
Genus *Myron*	1	North Australia.
Genus *Gerardia*	1	India; Ceylon.
Genus *Fordonia*	1	Burma to New Guinea and North Australia.
Genus *Cantoria*	1	Burma; Malay Pn.; Borneo.
Genus *Hipistes*	1	Burma; Siam; Malay Pn.
Genus *Herpeton*	1	Cochin China and Siam.
Subfamily *Dispsadomorphinæ* (A great variety of forms—terrestrial, subterraneous and arboreal).		
Genus *Geodipsas*	2	Madagascar.
Genus *Hologerrhum*	1	Philippines.
Genus *Ithycyphus*	2	Madagascar and Comoro Islands.
Genus *Langaha*	3	Madagascar.

	Number of Species	Distribution
Genus *Allandina*	1	Madagascar.
Genus *Eteirodipsas*	1	Madagascar.
Genus *Stenophis*	8	Madagascar; Comoro Islands.
Genus *Lycodryas*	1	Comoro Islands.
Genus *Pythondipsas*	1	Tropical Africa.
Genus *Ditypophis*	1	Socotra.
Genus *Tarbophis*	8	S. E. Europe; S. W. Asia; Africa.
Genus *Trimorphodon*	4	S. W. U. S.; Mexico; Central Amer.
Genus *Lycoqnathus*	2	Tropical South America.
Genus *Trypanurgos*	1	Tropical South America.
Genus *Dipsadomorphus*	22	So. Asia; tropical Africa; Papuasia; Australia.
Genus *Dipsadoboa*	1	West Africa.
Genus *Rhinobothryum*	1	Tropical South America.
Genus *Himantodes*	7	Mex.; Cent. Amer.; South Amer.
Genus *Sibon*	9	Texas to Brazil; tropical and South Africa.
Genus *Chamætortus*	1	East and Central Africa.
Genus *Pseudoboa*	17	Central and South America.
Genus *Barbourina*	1	Ecuador.
Genus *Drepanoides*	5	Bolivia.
Genus *Rachidelus*	1	Brazil.
Genus *Rhinostoma*	2	South America.
Genus *Thamnodynastes*	2	South America.
Genus *Tachymenis*	2	Northern South America.
Genus *Hemihagerrhis*	1	East Africa.
Genus *Manolepis*	1	Mexico.
Genus *Tomodon*	2	South America.
Genus *Pseudotomodon*	1	Argentina.
Genus *Conophis*	3	Mexico to Southern Brazil.
Genus *Platyinion*	1	South America.
Genus *Amplorhinus*	2	Tropical and South Africa.
Genus *Pesudablabes*	1	Southern Brazil; Uruguay.
Genus *Philodryas*	13	South America.
Genus *Rhinodryas*	1	Argentina.
Genus *Ialtris*	1	San Domingo.
Genus *Trimerorhinus*	3	Africa south of the equator.
Genus *Cœlopeltis*	2	So. Europe; S. W. Asia; North Africa.
Genus *Rhamphiophis*	5	Tropical Africa.
Genus *Dromophis*	2	Tropical Africa.
Genus *Taphrometopon*	2	Central Asia and Persia.
Genus *Psammophis*	17	So. Asia; Africa.
Genus *Mimophis*	1	Madagascar.
Genus *Psammodynastes*	2	S. E. Asia.
Genus *Macroprotodon*	1	Spain and North Africa.

	Number of Species	Distribution
Genus *Dryophis*	8	S. E. Asia.
Genus *Thelotornis*	1	Tropical and South Africa.
Genus *Dispholidus*	1	Tropical and South Africa.
Genus *Oxybelis*	4	Mex.; Central Amer.; South Amer.
Genus *Dryophiops*	2	S. E. Asia.
Genus *Chrysopelea*	3	S. E. Asia.
Genus *Erythrolamprus*	9	Texas to South America.
Genus *Hydrocalamus*	1	Central America.
Genus *Scolecophis*	3	Central America.
Genus *Tantilla*	23	So. U. S. to tropical South America.
Genus *Agmius*	1	Mexico.
Genus *Stenorhina*	1	Mexico to Northern South America.
Genus *Xenopholis*	1	South America.
Genus *Diaphorolepis*	2	Ecuador.
Genus *Synophis*	2	South America.
Genus *Apostolepis*	9	South America.
Genus *Elapomoius*	1	Brazil.
Genus *Elapmorphis*	7	South America.
Genus *Amblyodipsas*	1	Mozambique.
Genus *Elapotinus*	1	Tropical Africa.
Genus *Calamelaps*	3	Tropical Africa.
Genus *Rhinocalamus*	1	East Africa.
Genus *Xenocalamus*	2	Tropical Africa.
Genus *Micrelaps*	2	Palestine; Somaliland.
Genus *Miodon*	5	West Africa.
Genus *Polemon*	1	West Africa.
Genus *Brachyophis*	1	Somaliland.
Genus *Macrelaps*	1	South Africa.
Genus *Aparallactus*	11	Tropical and South Africa.
Genus *Elapops*	1	West Africa.
Subfamily *Elachistodontinæ* (Number of teeth much reduced).		
Genus *Elachistodon*	1	Bengal.
Family *Hydrophidæ*. The SEA SNAKES (Strictly marine species, with vertically compressed, paddle-like tail. A pair of short, rigid, venom-conducting fangs in the front of the upper jaw).		
Genus *Pelamydrus*	1	Indian and Pacific Ocean.*
Genus *Thalassophis*	1	Coast of Java.
Genus *Acalyptophis*	1	Western tropical Pacific Ocean.

* Apparently the only species found in the New World—off the west coast of southern Mexico, Central and South America.

	Number of Species	Distribution
Genus *Hydrelaps*	1	Northern coast of Australia.
Genus *Hydrophis*	22	Persian Gulf to Northern Australia.
Genus *Distira*	18	Persian Gulf to Japan and New Caledonia.
Genus *Enhydris*	2	Coasts of India to New Guinea.
Genus *Enhydrina*	1	Persian Gulf to New Guinea.
Genus *Aipysurus*	4	Waters of the Malay Archipelago and the western tropical Pacific.
Genus *Platurus*	4	East Indian Ocean and western tropical Pacific.
Family *Elapidæ* (Terrestrial species with short, anterior, rigid fangs—the Cobras and their allies; the American Coral Snakes. Some of the most deadly of the poisonous snakes belong to this family).		
Genus *Ogmodon*	1	Fiji Islands.
Genus *Glyphodon*	1	New Guinea; North Australia.
Genus *Pseudelaps*	8	Papuasia; Moluccas; Australia.
Genus *Diemenia*	7	Australia; New Guinea.
Genus *Pseudechis*	8	Australia; New Guinea.
Genus *Denisonia*	21	Australia; Tasmania; Solomon Is.
Genus *Micropechis*	2	New Guinea; Solomon Islands.
Genus *Hoplocephalus*	3	Australia.
Genus *Tropidechis*	1	Australia.
Genus *Notechis*	1	Australia.
Genus *Rhinhoplocephalus* ..	1	Australia; Tasmania.
Genus *Brachyaspis*	1	Australia.
Genus *Acanthophis*	1	Australia; Papuasia; Moluccas.
Genus *Elapognathus*	1	Australia.
Genus *Boulengerina*	1	Central Africa.
Genus *Elapechis*	6	Tropical and South Africa.
Genus *Rhynchelaps*	4	Australia.
Genus *Bungarus*	6	Southeastern Asia.
Genus *Naia*	10	Southern Asia; Africa; Malaysia.
Genus *Sepedon*	1	South Africa.
Genus *Aspidelaps*	2	South Africa; Mozambique.
Genus *Walterinnesia*	1	Egypt.
Genus *Hemibungarus*	4	S. E. Asia.
Genus *Callophis*	5	S. E. Asia.
Genus *Doliophis*	4	Burma; Cochin China; Malay Pn. and Archipelago.
Genus *Furina*	3	Australia.
Genus *Homorelaps*	2	South Africa.

	Number of Species	Distribution
Genus *Micrurus*	28	So. U. S. to tropical South America (inclusive).
Genus *Dendraspis*	4	Tropical and South Africa.
Family *Viperidæ* (The thick-bodied poisonous snakes. The True Vipers, confined to the Old World. A pair of long fangs are on the forward part of the upper jaw *and fold against the roof of the mouth when jaws are closed*).		
Genus *Causas*	4	Tropical and South Africa.
Genus *Azemiops*	1	Upper Burma.
Genus *Vipera*	10	Europe; Asia; North and tropical Africa.
Genus *Bitis*	8	Africa.
Genus *Pseudocerastes*	2	Persia.
Genus *Cerastes*	2	Northern Africa; Arabia; Palestine.
Genus *Echis*	2	So. Asia; Africa north of the equator.
Genus *Atheris*	3	Tropical Africa.
Genus *Atractaspis*	11	Tropical and South Africa.
Family *Crotalidæ* (Vipers with a deep pit between the eye and nostril. New and Old World).		
Genus *Agkistrodon*	10	Eastern North America; Mexico and Central America; borders of the Caspian Sea; Asia.
Genus *Trimeresurus*	18	Indo-Malayan Region.
Genus *Bothrops*	20	Mexico; Central and South America.
Genus *Lachesis*	1	Central Am.; South America.
Genus *Sistrurus*	3	U. S.; Mexico.
Genus *Crotalus*	20	United States; Mexico; Central America and South America.

Family *Typhlopidæ*. The small, shining, burrowing members of this degenerate family are more like worms than snakes, looking like many of the degraded lizards we have previously noted. The entire body, both above and beneath, is covered with smooth, rounded, overlapping scales; the eyes are hidden, really buried under the head shields; the tail is short and stubby. As compared with other snakes, the skull is very simple—not at all fitted for the swallowing of large prey. The jaws are altogether toothless with the exception of a few teeth on the transverse edges of the maxillary bones—these situated almost over what corresponds to the palatine region; in consequence, the prey is restricted to insect larvæ and white "ants" or termites; gorged specimens are often dug out of ants' nests.

The average length of snakes of this family is from ten to twelve inches. Their prevailing coloration is pale to dark brown above, either uniform or longitudinally streaked; most of the species lack any trace of markings. They appear to be the surviving remnants of but little specialized ancient serpents; they tell the story of a once widely distributed group: for members of the present family are found in all semi-tropical and tropical parts of the world—even on isolated islands lost in vast stretches of ocean, these the probable points of former continents. TYPHLOPS is the largest genus, containing nearly a hundred species—queer little cylindrical, glassy creatures that look precisely alike to the novice, but may be easily separated by the technical herpetologist who considers the arrangement of the head shields and counts the rows of scales around the body. The species are found in Mexico, Central and South America, throughout the West Indies, in southern Europe, southern Asia, the Malay Archipelago, Africa and Australia. Despite their lowly form they are surprisingly quick when exhumed from their burrows. If dug out of sand a specimen must be instantly grasped, as it literally swims back into the soft medium. When an example is held in one's fingers the tiny mouth opens and shuts in a ludicrous attempt at intimidation. As captives, the various species are uninteresting. Unless provided with soil in which to burrow, they soon die; if thus provided, they at once bore their way out of sight.

The Family *Leptotyphlopidæ* is composed of little snakes closely resembling the members of the preceding family in external outlines, scalation and probable antecedents. Like the *Typhlopidæ,* the skull is simple; the lower jaw bones lack the lever-like suspension of most snakes; the skull is more like that of a lizard. From the *Typhlopidæ* we find a reverse in the situation of the teeth—very few in number. The only teeth are on the ends of the *lower* jaw bones. Among these little snakes we also find the least reduction of the pelvic girdle of any living serpents; even the bones of the hind legs are well formed (internally). The species—about thirty in number—belong mostly to the genus *Glauconia* and are found in the warmer parts of both the Old and the New World.

The YELLOW-HEADED WORM SNAKE, *Leptotyphlops albifrons,* represented in one of our illustrations by a specimen photographed on a man's hand, is mostly an inhabitant of ant-hills, where its burnished scalation apparently protects it from the bites of the insects while it feeds upon their larvæ. The specimen shown was sent to the writer by Mr. R. R. Mole, of Port-of-Spain, Trinidad. It was discovered in a termite nest and found to be gorged with the white "ants" of the tropics.

Here we have a good illustration of what comes from employing a preserved collection of reptiles and considerable theory, as has often been the case in describing these comparatively little known species. The scientific name—*albifrons*—literally means, white at the extremities, and the species has often been described as brownish, with the forehead and tip of the tail *white.* Alcoholic specimens are thus colored, but it seems probable that the writers describing such examples have never seen a living individual, which is lustrous blackish brown, all of the scales having narrow, pale edges that form longitudinal serrated lines, while the forehead, the lips and the tip of the tail are vivid *lemon yellow;* this latter hue, of course, fades to a dirty white in spirits, as do the bright colors of all preserved snakes. An adult is eight inches long. The *habitat* embraces Central America and South America to Argentina; also the southerly islands of the West Indies.

THE GREAT CONSTRICTING SNAKES—FAMILY BOIDÆ

Gigantic proportions over other creatures of their kind and brilliant colors woven into weird and symmetrical patterns place the Boas and Pythons among the most sensational of reptiles. It must not be imagined, though, that all members of the *Boidæ* are of massive proportions. The family is composed of but a moderate number of species and while it contains the huge pythons of India, Malaysia and Africa, and the great Anaconda or Water Boa, of South America, there are moderate-sized, arboreal species and a number of really diminutive, burrowing snakes, some of them living in the sterile sands of the desert regions.

One of the characteristics about the members of the *Boidæ* is the protrusion of a pair of internal hind legs in the shape of a pair of stout spurs, at the vent; internally, there are vestiges of pelvic bones, as well. This is a curious condition—true snakes with better developed limbs than some of the burrowing lizards. Moreover, the limbs of a boa or python are vigorously movable; the spurs are capable of inflicting an ugly scratch. A photograph shows the spurs of an Indian python.

All members of the *Boidæ* are clad in rather small scales above; on the abdomen is a row of enlarged crawling plates that are proportionately much narrower than among the greater number of snakes. The plates under the tail may be in one or two rows. Among the present serpents both upper and lower jaw bones as well as the palatine bones are well provided with recurved teeth; among the pythons, several species have lancet-shaped teeth that are of great value in aiding the reptile in securing a firm and instant hold of the prey while the coils of the body are thrown about it for constriction. Boas and pythons generally have the lower jaw suspension of the typical snakes, enabling large prey to be worked into the mouth and consequent enormous distension of the entire jaw mechanism.

Speaking from the standpoint of poison-conducting teeth

and glands for the secretion of a specific virus, all the species of this family may be termed entirely harmless, as they are absolutely lacking venomous properties. It would be inappropriate to describe the monster pythons, however, as quite devoid of harm. Most of them are vicious and can produce formidable lacerations with their long, recurved teeth. A few large individuals are bold enough to retain a bulldog grip upon a man and follow this advantage with a coil or two of the body that could crush out a human life. An eighteen or twenty-foot snake, if viciously inclined, could easily overpower a man and, if the latter had narrow shoulders, could swallow him. There are reliable records of pythons swallowing children—that is, in tropical countries, but no captive snake is bold or hungry enough to devour a human, clad in the garb of civilization.

The dimensions of even the largest members of the *Boidæ* have been much exaggerated. After careful investigation the writer feels satisfied that the Ular-Sawa, also called Regal or Reticulated Python, *Python reticulatus,* is the largest species of serpent, actually attaining a length of thirty feet. It inhabits Burma, Indo-China, the Malay Peninsula and Archipelago. Secondly we must rate the India Python, *P. molurus,* of southern India, China, the Malay Peninsula and Java, which grows to a length of twenty-five feet. A close third is the South American Anaconda or Water Boa, *Eunectes murinus,* occasionally represented by specimens over twenty feet long, and fourth, the African Python, *P. sebæ,* growing to a length of eighteen, sometimes twenty feet, and very stout in proportion to its length. These are the giants among snakes and the dimensions given are considerably in excess of the average. Following is the *average* length of what we may call large examples of the four species:

Regal Python, *Python reticulatus*	22 feet.
Indian Python, *Python molurus*	18 feet.
Anaconda, *Eunectes murinus*	17 feet.
African Python, *Python sebæ*	16 feet.

A thriving, twenty-two foot Regal Python weighs about 225 pounds.

There are many and ridiculous stories about the swallowing feats of the big snakes. The tales relating to giant pythons engulfing animals as large as an ox are utterly fallacious, nor do the big snakes ever wantonly attack large mammals. The limit of their swallowing capacity would be a moderate-sized antelope—an animal about the size of an American white-tailed deer—and nothing but an unusually large specimen could engulf such prey. A twenty-foot python has been observed by the writer to swallow a forty-pound pig and the process was by no means an easy one. This particular snake was ordinarily contented with two or three chickens at a meal, such being given her at bi-monthly periods. Almost without exception the members of the *Boidæ* live upon warm-blooded prey. Some are especially partial to mammals; others prefer feathered creatures. All kill their prey by constriction—squeezing it to death.

The *Boidæ* is divided into two subfamilies, the *Pythoninæ* and the *Boinæ*. It is a common idea that pythons may be told from boas by the presence on the labial plates of the former of a series of pits. This rule does not altogether hold good. Though the greater number of pythons have these pits and so prominently developed they would seem to be of some functional value, it should be explained that some species of boas also have the labial pits, which, in the genera *Epicrates* and *Boa,* are as sharply pronounced as among the pythons. An example of the latter genus is the Yellow Tree Boa, *Boa cookii,* a life-sized head of which is shown in a photograph. The real structural differences between the pythons and the boas relate to the bones of the head and the arrangement of the head plates; neither are any too definite in separating the two subfamilies.

With the exception of one small species, found in Mexico, the members of the *Pythoninæ* are confined to the Old World; the *Boinæ* occur in both hemispheres.

In the *Pythoninæ* we find a great variety of forms, among them the king of the big constrictors, the REGAL or RETICULATED PYTHON, *P. reticulatus,* called by the Malays the Ular-Sawa. A friend of the writer, much interested in serpents, whose observations are always calm and reliable, measured a dead specimen of this species that lacked a few inches of being thirty feet long.

The pattern of this splendid snake is difficult to put into words. It consists of an interweaving of rich yellow, brown and black like Oriental tapestry combined with an iridescence glowing in all the high lights of the folds. The markings on the head at once separate this snake from the other great Indian python, *P. molurus:* for the head of *P. reticulatus* is uniform brown with a narrow black line from the snout to the base; *P. molurus* has a blotch between and in the rear of the eyes shaped like the head of a javelin. A curious characteristic about mature specimens of the Regal Python is the ruddy hue of the eyes, these looking like russet shoe buttons and having, as with all the pythons, a vertical pupil.

Captive Regal Pythons prefer poultry and swine. A sixteen-foot specimen can swallow an eight-pound rooster, feathers, fighting spurs and all, within ten-minutes from the time the performance commences, when there is a hungry stare for more. One fowl of that size is all that is allowed for a snake of such dimensions in the Zoological Park; the twenty-foot specimens receive two chickens at intervals of about ten days apart. Some specimens prefer swine and are given freshly killed pigs. A twenty-five pound pig is considered the proper size for a twenty-foot snake. A fair-sized bathing tank should be in the cage. In this the big fellows coil and bathe for a week at a time while digesting a meal.

Most Regal Pythons are so nervous and irritable during the first few months of confinement, they steadily refuse food. Unless energetic measures are employed to nourish them they become badly emaciated. They are apt to deliberately continue the fast, actually starving to death, if not fed by force. When a big specimen is thus languishing, with the possibility of approaching a suicidal end, there is hope of awakening its dormant appetite by forcing food down its throat. In the compulsory feeding of the big snakes in the New York Zoological Park—say for a twenty-foot specimen—the writer kills four medium-sized rabbits, removes the skin, then ties the animals together—the hind legs of one to the neck of another; ordinary brown twine is used in this operation. A long bamboo pole is the accessory. This has a blunt tip and is forced through the neck of the leading rabbit of the string, the tip pressing against the roof of the skull for purchase. During lively work the monster is taken from the cage by a dozen keepers and held as straight as possible, the forward man holding it close to the head with both hands. By means of the pole the meal is forced down the throat for a distance of fully five feet. Food thus administered generally changes the snake's attitude toward captivity. Once the meal is digested, there generally comes an appetite, usually to be detected by a serpent's actions, and a sympathetic keeper will at once note such. Yet there are some pythons lacking sufficient courage to feed for months, even after repeated strings of rabbits have been administered and quickly assimilated, showing the digestive apparatus to be in good shape. The Regal Python Czarina in the Zoological Park was fed by compulsory methods for ten months before she took her first voluntary meal. Visitors to the few reptile houses of zoological gardens, possessing such buildings, seldom appreciate that the iridescent bloom on the folds of the big snakes denotes a state of perfect health brought about only after months of sympathetic care on the part of the keeper.

Unfortunately, a deadly mouth disease is a constant menace to the pythons, in fact, big snakes of all species. The writer believes this to be brought about by an enervated condition of the snake, robbing the blood of its germicidal qualities—and this during a period of a disordered stomach. As the mouth of a snake that is not feeding becomes stored with stagnant salivary secretions, and bacteria of many kinds always exist in the mouth, this is the region principally attacked. A slight sore—a bruise caused by striking at an annoying object—is generally the start of the trouble. The sore becomes at once infected; an intense irritation, attended with a sloughing of a white, cheesy matter, follows. If the disease is not immediately arrested, it works deeper, attacking the jaw bones; the teeth become loosened and fall out and necrosis of the bone develops. In this latter stage a cure is doubtful. Microscopical examination of the diseased tissues points to the existence of a specific bacillus, a thick, rod-shaped form. However, the disease does not seem to be in the least bit infectious. The mouths of all large snakes should be carefully watched for the appearance of a red spot. It is best to examine a specimen at least once a week—twice a week is better. If the dreaded "canker" spots are seen, the entire mouth should be washed with a mild antiseptic solution by rubbing the gums free of all slimy secretions, best done with a soft cotton wad on the end of a stick and followed by a generous flushing from a hard rubber syringe. One-third of listerine in boiled water gives the best results. If white flakes have formed, they should be removed, care being taken to make the gums bleed as little as possible. The treatment should be continued, once a day in mild cases, twice a day where the irritation is severe, until the mouth is perfectly white and clean of all traces of sores. Care should be taken to look for loose teeth; they may be removed by means of fine forceps (tweezers). In a very severe case of "canker" in the Zoological Park, this relating to a large Cobra, the writer found it necessary to clip away a large portion of the lower jaw bone. Necrosis had developed and a foul odor was noted. The operation had little effect. Determined to save the life of the valuable specimen—one of the single pair of Cobras on exhibition—the writer made an incision at the back of the head, disjointed the diseased jaw bone and drew it back through the orifice. With the infected bone removed, a strip of gauze, soaked in a mild solution of formalin, was drawn through the entire orifice made by the removal of the bone and left for fifteen minutes' time. This was removed and another strip, soaked in a solution of listerine, was inserted and left until the next day. The mouth was afterwards washed twice a day for a period of six weeks, until all traces of the disease had disappeared. Altogether, the Cobra was under treatment for three months and during this time was nourished by beaten eggs forced down its throat by a rubber syringe.

Considerably smaller—as represented among the greater number of specimens exhibited as captives—is the INDIAN PYTHON or BLACK-TAILED PYTHON, *P. molurus.* The largest specimens examined by the writer were respectively eighteen and nineteen feet long. There are two distinct phases of coloration—a dark, olivaceous phase with almost black markings, and a bright, tan-colored variety; with the latter variety the blotches are olive-brown and there is usually a pinkish band on each side of the head. The latter is the snake most commonly seen handled in traveling shows. It inhabits the western portion of the species' range. As a captive this snake is more hardy than the Regal Python. It is less particular in its feeding habits, taking fowls and large rabbits with a steadily good appetite. In its distribution the Indian Python differs materially from the preceding snake. It is common in India proper, is found on the Malay Peninsula, though it extends into but one of the larger islands—Java. *Python reticulatus,* it should be noted, is confined to Burma, Indo-China, the Malay Peninsula, thence extends well through the Malay Archipelago. It is common in the Philippines. *P. molurus* is distinguished from the Regal Python by the javelin-shaped mark on the top of the head—*P. reticulatus* having a narrow black line on the top of the head.

As a captive the India Python is at first inclined to be nervous and vicious, resenting all familiarity by hissing and striking. The recurved teeth—the edges flattened like a lance—are capable of inflicting ugly lacerations. This species, however, particularly the light examples, is susceptible to taming. Some examples become extremely docile. Owing to its ability to endure rough handling while traveling without being "thrown off its feed," the species is a general favorite among showmen. Large numbers are captured annually and shipped to various parts of Europe and America, where they arrive in the spring, selling to the shows for the proverbial and favorite "snake charming" act. In this new life the snakes' lazy motions provoke the general belief that the reptiles are drugged or hypnotized by the bespangled enchantress; but according to the latter's ideas —and snake charmers take a really sympathetic interest in their serpents—they are simply "well broken" specimens. They are cared for with the same tenderness as so many children. Each has a name, and when the big show packs up for the night, the snakes are tucked in many thicknesses of blankets to protect them from jar or chilling. Under these conditions they live for years, becoming actually affectionate. It is not unusual to find a specimen peevishly refusing to take food from any but the hand of its mistress.

In proportion to its length the Indian Python is a thick-bodied snake, with quite a small head—the small head relating particularly to the light phase. A coiled specimen, eleven or twelve feet long, looks to be bigger than a Regal Python sixteen or seventeen feet in length. Following are the dimensions of a fine example in the New York Zoological Park:

Total length	15	feet.
Length of tail	15	inches.
Girth of body	16	inches.
Width of head	2¾	inches.
Length of head	3¾	inches.

The specimen from which the measurements were taken easily swallowed large Belgian hares.

Another big serpent is the AFRICAN ROCK PYTHON, *P. sebæ*, an illustration of which is shown. This species attains a length of sixteen to eighteen feet. It inhabits Central and South Africa. Not many examples are shipped to America and the species is seldom exhibited with the shows. It becomes quite docile in captivity.

Species of the genus *Python* range over the greater parts of the tropics and semi-tropics of the Old World. Not all of them are of large size. The DIAMOND SNAKE, *P. spilotes,* of Australia and New Guinea, is full grown when six or eight feet long. It is a handsome creature, black above, with a yellow spot in each scale. On the sides are rows of spots or rings, producing a pleasing pattern.

Species of the genus *Python* have the plates under the tail—*subcaudals*—in two rows. Several closely related genera are recognized.

The Boas proper, forming the subfamily *Boinæ,* range in size from small burrowing species to gigantic serpents. The plates under the tail are usually in one row. The true boas are not, as is popularly imagined, confined to the New World. Most of the larger species inhabit Mexico, Central America, tropical South America and the West Indies. A single, small species occurs in the extreme western part of the United States, ranging as far north as Oregon. One genus, *Eryx,* is composed of small burrowing forms inhabiting southern Asia and northern Africa. Two fine members of the genus *Constrictor* are found in Madagascar. Several genera besides *Eryx* are confined to the Old World.

In the New World the largest of the boas is the ANACONDA or WATER BOA, *Eunectes murinus,* of Central America and tropical South America, a species alleged to grow twenty-five feet long, though individuals of such proportions seem to be so rare they never find their way to zoological institutions. Two fine specimens of this really aquatic snake are on exhibition in the Reptile House of the New York Zoological Park. The largest is seventeen feet long. She gave birth to thirty-four young, which were each twenty-seven inches long and an inch in diameter at the thickest part of the body. The coloration was the same as the parent, dark green with round black spots. Like their mother, they were vicious, resenting handling by quickly twisting from side to side in an effort to bite. They spent most of their time in a big tank, swimming slowly or massed in a dark corner with only their snouts protruding from the water. The birth of these youngsters illustrates a characteristic among the boas, the majority, or possibly all, of which bring forth their young alive. The pythons differ by laying eggs, coiling about them until they hatch after six or eight weeks' time—sometimes longer.

The writer has numerous records tending to show the progeny of boas to be numerous. One note relates to the brood of a big specimen of *Constrictor constrictor,* which gave birth to sixty-four living young; another relates to an Anaconda, fifteen and a half feet long, with a brood of thirty-seven young. Observations show the pythons to deposit from fifty to a hundred eggs. A twenty-foot specimen of *Python reticulatus* deposited sixty eggs. About these she coiled and fought off all intruders. Her efforts proved of no avail, owing to infertility of the eggs.

The birth of the Anacondas in the New York Zoological Park demonstrated another interesting fact, thus: Though popular supposition regards an *adult* Anaconda as a creature at least twenty-five feet long, we note a captive specimen perfectly mature and bringing forth a large litter (this signifying a well-matured adult), when the parent is but seventeen feet long. The writer believes the addition of a very few feet to this length would represent the maximum length of the great Water Boa.

In the Guianas is found another and smaller species known as the YELLOW ANACONDA, *Eunectes notæus.* The ground color is yellowish-green, over which are close-set, irregular and ragged blotches, imparting a quite different pattern from the round black spots of the commoner species.

The genus *Constrictor.* Eight showily-marked species form the genus. All are characterized by a series of large yellow saddles or transverse bands on the back. The distribution is curious. *Constrictor constrictor, C. occidentalis, C. orophias, C. imperator* and *C. mexicana* are found in the New World; *C. dumerilii* and *C. madagascariensis* inhabit Madagascar only. One of the most beautiful of serpents is a snake formerly best known by its scientific name, which was *Boa constrictor.* This is the COMMON BOA. Its name is now *Constrictor constrictor,* of tropical South America. Being a reptile of generally docile nature and taking readily to captivity, it is much sought by snake "charmers." Right here it is appropriate to straighten out the tangle about the term "Boa Constrictor." All the species of boas and pythons are constrictors, killing their prey by squeezing it to death. The student now understands that in scientific classification the boas and pythons come under the head of separate subfamilies. This being the case, it can be realized that the indiscriminate fashion of calling all big snakes "Boa Constrictors" is quite wrong, and the title is properly the technical name of the well-known South American species. While the theoretical "Boa Constrictor" is the giant among snakes, the actual *C. constrictor* is not an especially big serpent. A large adult is not over eleven feet long. The ground color is ruddy brown, becoming a rich brick red on the tail; on the back is a row of large, tan-colored saddles, gradually becoming lighter toward the tail, where they break into half rings of pale cream color and in vivid contrast to the red.

Closely allied is the WEST INDIAN BOA, *C. orophias,* inhabiting Dominica. The maximum length is about eight feet. In form and pattern there is a similarity to the common boa. The species may be distinguished by the darker hues and the considerably greater number of dorsal saddles which are necessarily shorter and more crowded than with *C. constrictor.* Specimens recently shed glow with an iridescent bloom, rivaling even the great pythons, a condition denoting a state of perfect health. *C. imperator* and *C. mexicana* are nearly related, besides similarly marked. The *habitat* of both embraces Mexico and Central America.

Epicrates, composed of eight stout species, is technically defined by the absence of the supraorbital bone. On the forward portion of both upper and lower jaw bones are several much enlarged teeth. By far the biggest and most powerful species is the CUBAN BOA, *E. angulifer*, found only in Cuba and Porto Rico. It is a pale, brownish reptile, with dark and irregular brown rhomboidal blotches on the back, and scattered dark blotches on the sides; the head is always uniform pale brown. The coloration is sinister; the large and dark, glittering eyes add to an effect which tallies perfectly with the actual disposition: for this is an absolutely diabolical creature, reaching a length of eleven feet. Captives strike their snouts sore against the glass front of the cage, never appearing to lose the slightest degree of hostility. As a snake strikes it emits a sharp, abbreviated hiss sounding like a sneeze—always startling to the novice.

This big, ugly snake has often been found in open, grassy places, where matted trails denote its whereabouts to the natives, who hunt it for the hide. Of recent years it has become scarcer. It is the only big snake found in either Cuba or Porto Rico, both of which islands are happily lacking any of the poisonous species.

The RAINBOW BOA, *E. cenchris*, derives its name from a gorgeous iridescence playing over the scales of a healthy example. The range is from Costa Rica to northern Brazil. In the pattern we find hues ordinary enough—pale brown or lead color, with dull brown or blackish spots or rings. Seen in the sunlight, however, the pattern seems to disappear under a blaze of peacock green, this merging into violet or red. The iridescence is particularly beautiful on specimens with a fairly strong pattern. Specimens received from Trinidad were almost uniform gray; they shone with a beautiful blue iridescence, but were not nearly so spectacular as the others. The species is very docile.

The BAHAMA BOA, *E. striatus*, inhabits the southern Bahama Islands and San Domingo. Little seems to be known about it. Eight specimens in the Zoological Park have been uniformly gentle and hardy. The largest is six feet long. The coloration is not gaudy, yet rather pretty, consisting of narrow, zigzag black and gray transverse bands producing a marbled effect. Compared with the two preceding species, this boa is more slender and has a longer tail.

The TREE BOAS form the genus *Boa,* six species in all. For members of the *Boinæ,* the body is much elongated with a long, prehensile, gradually-tapering tail. Considered from various points of view they are unique among members of their family. The neck is extremely long and slender, the head so large and broad it seems an incumbrance to the snake. Moreover, the head tapers to quite a point at the snout; the swollen outlines at the temples make it look wicked and venomous. With its compressed body wrapped tightly about a limb, the prehensile tail likewise employed and the long neck looped fantastically in support of the villainous head, an enraged Tree Boa appears far removed from its ponderous allies. The forward teeth on both jaws are enormously developed—quite as long as the fangs of a viperine snake. It is here, certainly, we have a good demonstration of how wrong it is to brand a snake as poisonous by the outlines of the head. Several photographs show the formidable appearance. Among examples of the various Tree Boas there is an unvarying amount of viciousness. The writer does not hesitate in branding them among the most mean-tempered of the non-venomous serpents.

The YELLOW TREE BOA, *B. cookii,* coils itself in a tight ball, well out on branches of trees along streams. Some specimens are yellow, with two series of diamond-shaped blotches; others, from eastern Venezuela and the island of Trinidad, are uniform yellowish. The maximum length is six or seven feet. Tropical South America and the southern islands of the West Indies form the *habitat.*

One species of *Boa* is remarkable in being found in Madagascar.

The SAND BOAS, *Gongylophis* and *Eryx,* burrowing species, seven in number, with a flat body, very stumpy tail, a small head, not at all distinct from the neck, and tiny eyes. The scales are small, either smooth or strongly keeled. A yard is the maximum length. Snakes of this kind are confined to sandy portions of north and east Africa, southern and central Asia.

The ROUGH-SCALED SAND BOA, *G. conicus,* of India, is the largest species. The body is incongruously stout, abruptly tapering to a blunt point, hardly worthy of the title of a tail; the head is small—not distinct from the neck. Anteriorly, the scales of the body are small and feebly keeled; toward the lateral part of the body they greatly increase in size and so heavily keeled as to make a squirming specimen really painful to handle, besides causing the front and rear parts to look as if belonging to markedly different reptiles; the tail terminates in a blunt, bony knob. The pattern is in keeping with the strange form. On a pale brownish body color is a wide, undulating band narrowly bordered with ruddy yellow. We find some specimens with this band broken into two series of rounded blotches; such look singularly like a deadly, thick-bodied snake of India, the Tic Polonga or Russell's Viper, *Vipera russellii.* To use the language of romantic writers of natural history, the sand boa might be said to "mimic" the deadly viper. A superficial examination will, however, readily distinguish the two apart: for the body of Russell's Viper terminates in ordinary, tapering fashion—lacking the curious, chopped-off outlines of the Sand Boa.

The writer has found specimens of the Rough-scaled Sand Boa to be hardy as captives, living for a number of years—providing they are given plenty of dry sand in which to burrow; in this they pass most of their time, often lying close enough to the surface to expose a portion of the back. Sparrows, mice and rats are taken as food. None of the specimens tried to bite when handled.

The EGYPTIAN SAND BOA, *E. jaculus,* occurs abundantly in northern Africa, also in the Ionian Islands, Greece, southwestern and central Asia. Two feet is the maximum length. Anteriorly the scales are smooth and shining; they are feebly keeled posteriorly; superficially examined, the entire snake looks smooth and glossy. The tail is longer than with *E. conicus,* though it terminates almost as bluntly as the head. Among several dozen examples in the writer's possession, the average length is twenty-two inches and the diameter at the thickest part of the body three-quarters of an inch. As a rule, the coloration is dull yellowish-gray, with irregular, yellow transverse blotches.

The INDIAN SAND BOA, BROWN SAND BOA or "TWO-HEADED" SNAKE, *E. johnii,* may be told by the almost uniform brown hue and the curious tail, that member looking as if it had been mostly amputated and healed in a rounded stump. A big specimen is two and a half feet long. Owing to the blunt character of the tail, the name, "Two-headed" Snake, has arisen. A novice might for a moment mistake the two extremities unless closely inspected and the tiny eyes discovered. The Hindoos practice a deception with this species by painting a mouth and eyes on the blunt tail and exploiting it as a serpent with two independent heads, explaining that while one sleeps the other watches in an endeavor to protect the animal from harm.

In its habits the Indian Sand Boa tallies with others of its genus, being persistently subterraneous. It digs its way into the burrows of small mammals, upon which it largely feeds. As a captive it is hardy, seldom attempts to bite and feeds upon small rats, mice and birds. It should be kept in perfectly dry sand at a temperature of at least 70 degrees Fahrenheit.

Two New World allies of *Eryx* belong to the North American genus *Charina.* The RUBBER BOA, C. *bottæ,* looks like *Eryx jaculus,* having a stumpy tail and small head. The scales are smooth and lustrous; a full-grown specimen is eighteen inches long. This snake is uniform yellowish-brown or lead color above, and yellow beneath. The range embraces the Pacific Coast region of the United States and this pigmy boa seems to be found farther into the temperate regions than any other species of the *Boidæ;* it occurs as far north as Oregon.

The Family *Anilidæ* contains a few burrowing species, separated as follows:—*Anilius*—1 species, tropical South America; *Anomalochilus*—1 species, Sumatra; *Cylindrophis* —3 species, southeastern Asia and Ceylon.

Anilius scytale, sometimes called the CORAL SNAKE, grows to a yard in length. It is of a gorgeous coral red ringed with black. The natives often keep it as a pet, twining it about their necks; such specimens cannot be induced to take food; after a suicidal fast of two or three months they die of starvation.

Among the species of the *Anilidæ* there are vestiges of the pelvis and the hind legs, the latter terminating externally in claw-like processes on each side of the vent, as with the pythons and boas; the scales of the body are small, smooth and iridescent; those on the abdomen are but slightly enlarged.

The *Uropeltidæ* contains a considerable number of small burrowing snakes inhabiting India and Ceylon. The body is short, with a stubby tail; the head of some members much pointed. Curiously enough, those species with especially pointed heads have particularly stumpy tails; when they move they look as if they were crawling backward.

The scales are smooth and shining; the abdominal plates but slightly enlarged. All have minute eyes. From the form and scalation there appears to be a relationship to the *Boidæ* and the *Anilidæ;* yet there are no vestiges of pelvic bones, or hind legs. Distribution is principally confined to damp forests, usually at some elevation. Many species are prettily colored.

The family *Colubridæ.* About seventy-five per cent. of all living snakes belong to this great, cosmopolitan family. We may term its members the Typical Serpents. Both jaws are well provided with teeth. The family not only includes an enormous number of entirely harmless species, but some with rather formidable fangs.

The variety of size and form is great; take, for example, the wonderfully slender Tree Snakes, so elongated and light of body they are able to dart like arrows over leaves and slender twigs, or, remaining motionless, might be mistaken for stretched tendrils; compare these arboreal racers with some of the stout-bodied terrestrial species—the American Hog-nosed Snakes (*Heterodon*)—the extremely short, thick body causing them to look like members of some remote family. As to the miscellaneous sizes among the *Colubridæ,* it is sufficient to explain that some of the species of *Spilotes*—South American—grow to a length of twelve feet and a great number of small ground snakes are quite mature when eight inches long. The coloration is just as varied. Some are of a dull, uniform hue; innumerable ones are prettily striped, longitudinally; a common pattern consists of rings of blazing colors.

As is natural among such an assortment of forms, every phase of serpentine habits is exhibited. We find arboreal, terrestrial, subterraneous, semi-aquatic and persistently aquatic.

As varied are the feeding habits; there are powerful constricting species, others that bolt the prey alive, and a whole division provided with fangs and a poison to benumb the prey, as it is being swallowed.

Viviparous species—those that bring forth the young alive—are common, but the oviparous species predominate, though among the latter are to be found all phases of egg development at the time of deposit—some laying eggs containing well-formed embryos, which hatch in two or three weeks, others mere germinating spots, the latter eggs not hatching before three months' time.

Colubrine snakes are distributed through all parts of the world where snakes of any kind are found, besides ranging farther north and south of the equator than serpents of any other family. They are classified principally by their teeth

—a necessary provision in the face of the great series of species monotonously alike externally. To the novice this system might seem beyond comprehension. A little study, however, unfolds the subject so it may be easily grasped, unless one wishes to delve into the intricacies of the more difficult genera, as the rows of scales round the body, the arrangement of the head plates, and the number of the abdominal and subcaudal plates are characters of great value. The coloration of a specimen and its locality are also important factors to the student taking up the subject in a general way.

Following is a bird's-eye view of the classification of the *Colubridæ:*

SERIES A. *Aglypha.* All the teeth solid—no grooved or perforated fangs. HARMLESS SNAKES.

Subfamily I. *Acrochordinæ.* Five genera. River Snakes of S. E. Asia; 1 in Central America. The scales are not overlapping as with most serpents.

Subfamily II. *Colubrinæ.* One hundred and seventeen genera. The typical harmless snakes. The scales are overlapping. Every graduation of form from extremely slender to very stout is represented. All parts of the world where snakes are found.

Subfamily III. *Dasypeltinæ.* A single genus with one species. A few teeth in the upper and lower jaw—an egg-eating snake. Tropical and South Africa.

Subfamily IV. *Amblycephalinæ.* So-called Bush Snakes. Five genera and about thirty species. The body is mostly compressed and very slender, the head wide and lumpy. The jaws are capable of but slight distension.

SERIES B. *Opisthoglypha.* One or more pairs of *grooved* venom-conducting fangs in *rear* of the upper jaw. While they are able to quickly benumb their prey, most of these snakes are but mildly poisonous to man.

Subfamily I. *Homalopsinæ.* Ten genera. Strictly aquatic. Found commonly in rivers and harbors of the East Indies, Papuasia and North Australia.

Subfamily II. *Dipsadomorphinæ.* Sixty-nine genera. The majority of the species rather elongate or exceedingly slender. Arboreal, terrestrial, burrowing and semi-aquatic. Found in all parts of the world but northern portions of the Northern Hemisphere.

Subfamily III. *Elachistodontinæ.* A single genus and one species found in Bengal. In relation to the *Opisthoglypha* the genus occupies a similar position as *Dasypeltis* (*Dasypeltinæ*) to the *Aglypha.*

The RIVER SNAKES, subfamily *Acrochordinæ,* form several genera of ugly-looking reptiles, most of them living in rivers and harbors of southeastern Asia and Malaysia; one remarkable exception is found on the Isthmus of Darien, Central America. Among the entirely aquatic forms the body is slightly compressed; there are no enlarged abdominal plates. One of the unique characters, as compared with other snakes (except the marine snakes) is the structure of the scales, which are so small with some as to appear granular, while they lack the usual imbricate (overlapping) arrangement of serpents.

The GRAY RIVER SNAKE, *Chersydrus granulatus,* a common species, ranges from southern India to New Guinea. Above and *beneath* the scalation is granular. The eyes and nostrils are on the top of the head. A full-grown example is three and a half feet long, dull grayish or olive above, paler beneath. Snakes of this kind are to be seen swimming in Manila Bay—sometimes a considerable distance at sea. They feed upon fishes.

The subfamily *Colubrinæ.* Here is contained the great majority of snakes. All are entirely harmless, so far as fangs or poison glands are concerned, for all of the species have perfectly solid teeth. Like in all families of reptiles we find species that are vicious, capable of inflicting severe lacerations; many never become tame in captivity. And there are others, large, powerful and beautiful reptiles, that are strangely gentle in their demeanor toward man, showing a real fondness for their master, never biting under the most severe mauling. They make veritable pets as captives.

In a wild state we find their habits widely different; slender forms dart through the trees in search of lizards;

in the same trees may stalk the big species of *Elaphe,* gliding slowly upon feathered prey beneath a leafy covering, their only quick motion being a flash-like dart of the head and neck when the quarry disappears in a mercilessly constricting series of coils. Leading a life on the ground are the swift Racers of the deserts or slow, bloated forms that grovel in the sand by means of an upturned snout. Far beneath the surface are subterraneous species barely larger than worms, while in the swamps and lagoons the water snakes bask in grotesque clusters on branches overhanging the water, plunging into the protecting element at the slightest alarm. Such is a *resume* of the *Colubrinæ.*

A well-known genus is *Thamnophis*—the STRIPED SNAKES. The *habitat* is North America and Mexico. Eleven species occur in the United States. They have coarsely-keeled scales and most of them show three yellowish stripes on a dark body color—one stripe on the middle of the back and a stripe on each side.

The Striped Snakes, sometimes called the Garter Snakes, are the commonest serpents of North America, inhabiting every part of the continent where snakes are to be found, literally swarming over numerous extensive areas. In cultivated districts, where other snakes have long since been exterminated, Striped Snakes are yet abundant. This may be explained from their power of multiplication. They are viviparous, giving birth to as many as seventy-five young in a litter; the usual number varies from thirty to fifty at a birth. The young are ingenuously secretive, and not at all particular as to food, thriving as well upon an unvarying diet of earthworms as upon small frogs and toads.

A key to the more common Striped Snakes of North America is interesting in showing the methods of separating them; also their distribution:

I. *Lateral (side) stripes on 3d and 4th rows of scales.*

a Very slender species.

Three vivid yellow stripes on a uniform, blackish-brown body hue. EASTERN RIBBON SNAKE, *T. sauritus.*

Distribution: U. S. east of the Mississippi.

Stripes pronounced on sides; center stripe showing only on neck. FLORIDA RIBBON SNAKE, *T. sackenii.*

Distribution: So. Car., Georgia and Florida.

Three vivid stripes on uniform blackish body hue; center stripe orange—lateral stripes much paler. WESTERN RIBBON SNAKE, *T. proxima.*

Distribution: Indiana and Illinois to Mexico.

b Body stout.

Center stripe orange; lateral stripes paler; body sometimes spotted. PLAINS GARTER SNAKE, *T. radix.*

Distribution: Indiana to Rockies; Canada to Texas.

Head not distinct. Three yellow stripes on a uniform blackish-brown body hue, the lateral stripes sometimes covering the 2d, 3d and 4th rows of scales. BUTLER'S GARTER SNAKE, *T. butleri.*

Distribution: Ohio, Illinois and Indiana.

Eye large; three narrow yellow stripes on obscurely spotted body color. ARIZONA GARTER SNAKE, *T. megalops.*

Distribution: Arizona, New Mexico and northern Mexico.

II. *Lateral stripe on 2d and 3d rows of scales.*

Scales usually in 21 rows; 8 upper lip plates or *labials—Thamnophis ordinoides,* an extremely variable species.

Three yellow stripes, generally on a uniform black or brown ground color. WESTERN GARTER SNAKE, *T. ordinoides.*

Distribution: Pacific Region; California to Oregon.

Subspecies carry the range into the Plains States southward to New Mexico.

A bright yellow crescent behind each eye. Body straw color, boldly tessellated with black. MARCY'S GARTER SNAKE, *T. marcianus.*

Distribution: Central Texas to S. E. California.

A bright yellow crescent on each temple. Stripes and spots indistinct. HAMMOND'S GARTER SNAKE, *T. hammondii.*

Distribution: Arizona to California.

Scales in 19 rows; 8 upper lip plates. Head very broad and distinct. A black patch on each temple. Body brown, spotted; stripes narrow. BROWN GARTER SNAKE, *T. eques.*

Distribution: Western Texas, Arizona and Mexico.

Scales in 19 rows—7 upper lip plates. *Thamnophis sirtalis.*

A variable species. There are several distinct subspecies. Sometimes tessellated with black—no stripes.

Distribution: Greater part of United States.

Three distinct stripes; spots in tessellated fashion between them; no red on sides. COMMON GARTER SNAKE, T. *sirtalis* (Typical).

Distribution: Eastern North America.

Stripes and spots present; a brick red tinge on sides. RED-BARRED GARTER SNAKE, *T. sirtalis parietalis.*

Distribution: Western North America.

Much red between the scales. PICKERING'S GARTER SNAKE, *T. sirtalis concinnus.*

Distribution: Northwest United States.

The EASTERN RIBBON SNAKE, *T. sauritus,* inhabiting the greater part of the eastern United States, is not nearly so common as some of the striped snakes. It might be called a water snake, because it invariably selects soggy meadows, swamp land or the borders of streams and ponds, taking to the water for protection and diving to the bottom, where it remains among aquatic plants until danger is supposed to be passed. If a Ribbon Snake were placed far inland, it might soon starve. Unlike most members of the genus, it does not feed upon earthworms. The food consists entirely of small frogs, toads, tadpoles and fishes. Thus the reason for haunting the immediate vicinity of water. A very large specimen is a yard long and half an inch in diameter at the thickest part of the body. It is difficult to imagine a prettier or daintier reptile. The body is exceedingly slender and the bright, sulphur yellow stripes impart an effect well worthy the popular name; between the stripes is a rich, velvety, blackish brown. The eyes are large, with golden-red iris. Closely related is the SOUTHERN RIBBON SNAKE, *T. sackenii,* on which the central stripe is represented merely by a pale streak for a short distance behind the head; on the sides the stripes are well defined. The form is exactly like the northern species. The writer found this snake fairly common in the low grounds bordering the Savannah River, in Hampton County, South Carolina.

Specimens were seen sunning on branches of bushes overhanging the water. When frightened, they dove into the coffee-colored water and swam out of sight. A larger and stouter species is the WESTERN RIBBON SNAKE, *T. proxima,* common west of the Mississippi River; also in the states of Illinois and Iowa. The dorsal or central stripe is much darker than the lateral ones, generally a rich ochre, while the side stripes are lemon yellow; on some the central stripe is red. Newly-born specimens are the most dainty of reptiles. A litter seldom exceeds twelve to fourteen; this is also the rule with the other slender-bodied species.

The PLAINS GARTER SNAKE, *T. radix,* abounds in the plains region of the United States. It is stout-bodied, but appeals to the ribbon snakes in having the lateral stripe on the third and fourth rows of scales, and particularly to the western ribbon snake, as the lateral stripes are paler than the central one. This species feeds upon earthworms, frogs, toads and fishes. A fondness for the latter prompts numerous snakes to lurk near "water holes," into which they will glide to evade capture.

Striped Snakes as a rule show considerable variation in their pattern and hues. Two species are particularly interesting in this direction. One is a western species technically recognized as *Thamnophis ordinoides.* The *habitat* covers most of the states lying west of the Mississippi River. In many portions of the plains region—especially to the west—large areas are overrun with one of the subspecies, *elegans,* sometimes grayish with narrow yellow stripes that are broken by black spots encroaching upon them from a tessellated pattern between the stripes.

A striking and pretty species is commonly found in Texas and Arizona. This is Marcy's Garter Snake, *T. marcianus.* The body hue is straw color with three narrow yellow stripes; at once pronounced are rows of square black spots, arranged in "checkerboard" fashion for the entire length of the body. A bright yellow crescent adorns each temple; the abdomen is marble white. Young examples are so boldly checkered they have excited formidable appellations —such as checkered "adders," spotted "vipers" and the like—very misleading titles.

Among the phases of *T. ordinoides* confined to the Pacific Coast region are specimens having a lemon-colored central stripe and red lateral stripes, making a pretty combination of colors; others are dull olive with a single, glaring stripe on the back; a few are uniform black or olive without stripes or spots. On account of these intergradations and a fairly constant scale formula, freak phases of coloration are unworthy of varietal names. All of the subspecies and phases of *Thamnophis ordinoides* have the lateral stripe on the second and third rows of scales.

The COMMON GARTER SNAKE, *T. sirtalis,* may be termed the most abundant of North American serpents, occurring in every part of the continent where snakes are to be found. Several varieties are recognized. Among the western subspecies are several looking like phases of *Thamnophis ordinoides.* Technically, they are to be separated by the lesser number of scale rows. A simple and good way to distinguish western examples of *Thamnophis sirtalis* from specimens of *T. ordinoides* is to examine the two large pairs of chin shields. With *T. sirtalis* the rear pair of chin shields is considerably longer than the front pair; *T. ordinoides* has both pairs of much the same size.

East of the Mississippi, the Garter Snake is everywhere the commonest serpent, stubbornly defying extinction even in the large city parks. The typical form itself evinces a puzzling degree of variation in pattern and in color. The commoner phase is dark brown above with three yellowish stripes, the lateral ones on the second and third rows of scales; between the stripes are two well-defined rows of alternating spots; beneath, the color is greenish, or yellow. The skin along the sides, when distended, shows numerous lineate spots of white or green—but this is a general character among the striped snakes. Specimens from mountainous districts are frequently blackish, without stripes or spots.

One rather common color phase is strongly spotted, but lacks traces of stripes; it is found from Maine to Florida and westward to the Mississippi.

In all conditions this snake is abundant from the Atlantic to the Pacific Coast, frequenting swamps, woods or high areas among rocks in the mountainous regions. The species will undoubtedly survive long after most other serpents have been totally exterminated by the ruthless slaughter an unjust prejudice inspires. Such appears probable from several conditions. First, it is viviparous, bringing forth exceptionally large broods of young; secondly, the young feed readily upon earthworms, grow rapidly and are cunningly secretive, gaining a livelihood without prowling into the danger zone of stone and clubs, as do the rodent-eating and actually the more useful serpents.

Adult Garter Snakes feed principally upon frogs, toads and earthworms—never upon warm-blooded prey. A large example is a yard long and an inch in diameter at the stoutest part. In confinement the species is hardy, living for years. Wild specimens, if handled, exude a foul-smelling secretion from glands near the base of the tail. After a few days in captivity, the trait entirely disappears. Examples in the writer's collection lived for over ten years; they were reared from the young, growing considerably larger than the average wild specimen. They seemed to have real affection and enjoyed being handled. During their ten years of existence they were kept in the writer's study, occupying a perfectly plain wooden case with a glass front. The entire collection of snakes was finally transferred to the fine Reptile House in the New York Zoological Park. Strangely enough, in spacious cages, with a profusion of plants and a gravel bottom, the snakes that had been longest in captivity began feeding indifferently and died within a few months. The result was attributed to the moisture attending the tropical decorations of the building. Ultimately, this theory was found to be entirely correct. A great number of snakes are unable to withstand any amount of dampness in captivity, their skins taking on a greasy look, finally breaking into ugly-looking sores which exude a cheesy matter. Most susceptible are snakes actually semi-aquatic in a wild state. To keep them in good condition, their quarters must be absolutely dry. It is consequently impossible to keep a number of species in the Reptile House on account of the humidity coming from the profusion of foliage. In the dry atmosphere of a living room, however, the species referred to will thrive indefinitely. Why this should be is difficult to explain. Even the boas and pythons, coming from regions notoriously humid, do better in a dry air than a greenhouse atmosphere. Yet to denude a reptile house of tropical foliage, would be to rob the exhibition of a certain charm almost involuntarily associated with sinuous, scaly life. The difficulty is met by selecting reptiles best calculated to withstand the conditions described.

The COMMON WATER SNAKES, genus *Natrix*. The members of this cosmopolitan genus are distributed abundantly in temperate and tropical portions of the Old and New World. Closely related to *Thamnophis,* they are told by the divided anal plate—the shield over the vent. Nearly all of them have coarsely-keeled scales; with few exceptions they are found in the immediate vicinity of water, to which they retreat in time of danger. The food consists largely of fish, also frogs, toads and tadpoles. As a rule, the body is stout, with a flat head and sinister coloration. Under the misleading title of water "moccasins" they are often and unjustly believed to be poisonous, an idea possibly strengthened by their uniform vicious display of temper when cornered.

Following are the more common species and subspecies of Water Snakes inhabiting the United States:

Longitudinally striped.

Leather Snake; Queen Snake, *N. septemvitta.* U. S. east of Mississippi.

Graham's Water Snake, *N. grahamii.* Mississippi Valley.

Two-Lined Water Snake, *N. rigida.* Pennsylvania to the Gulf.

Clark's Water Snake, *N. clarkii.* Louisiana to Texas.
Flat-Tailed Water Snake, *N. compressicauda.* Florida.

Transversely banded.

Common Water Snake, *N. sipedon sipedon.* N. E. United States.
Banded Water Snake, *N. sipedon fasciata.* Va. to Fla. and Texas.
Red-Bellied Water Snake, *N. sipedon erythrograster.* S. E. United States.
Blotched Water Snake, *N. sipedon transversa.* La., Texas and Arkansas.
Diamond-Back Water Snake, *N. rhombifera.* Mississippi Valley.
Green Water Snake, *N. cyclopion.* Gulf States.
Brown Water Snake, *N. taxispilota.* S. E. United States.

Probably the most familiar of the snakes in the preceding list is the COMMON WATER SNAKE, *Natrix sipedon,* the typical form, a dingy brown, rough-scaled serpent that may be seen sunning on the branches of bushes overhanging ponds and streams, and dropping into the water at the least fright. Except with the young and the smaller specimens, the pattern is not attractive. The brown body hue is crossed with ruddy brown blotches on the forward part of the body—on the latter portion these break into three series of alternating blotches—the point of differentiation from the typical form. The abdomen is prettily marked, being yellow or white with many bright red blotches. Old examples are uniform, dull and lusterless brown; they have a flat head, a thick body and look very ugly. A very big specimen is four feet long and one and a half inches in diameter at the thickest part of the body. From two and a half to three feet is the usual size. The Water Snake eats fishes, frogs, toads and tadpoles. As many as sixty young are produced alive during the later part of August or early in September.

The BROWN WATER SNAKE, *N. taxispilota,* found from Maryland to Florida and westward, along the Gulf States to the Mississippi, is the largest, most forbidding in aspect and the ugliest water snake of the United States. Above, the color is rusty brown with three rows of square, alternating chocolate brown spots or blotches. The body is proportionately stout, the head long, much swollen at the temples, with the eyes placed far forward. Old snakes look more dangerous than the deadly water moccasin (*Agkistrodon*), with which they socially bask on derelict timber.

Along the sluggish southern rivers the Brown Water Snake abounds, growing five feet long with a girth of six inches. During a collecting trip in the Savannah River low grounds, the writer found this the commonest snake. Friendly clusters, entwined with aquatic snakes of other species, were seen on the limbs of dead trees that had fallen into the lagoons. Our search was principally for the various water snakes and shy indeed are these creatures, many of them showily colored. They must be stalked in such cautious fashion that before the copper-wire noose —on the end of a long bamboo pole—is over the reptile's head and the operator has a chance to make a move of any consequence, the mosquitoes have settled in voracious clusters over his hands, face and neck. It is during these moments, when the snake is almost won, yet the torture from the fiendish insects is becoming unbearable, the snake catcher grinds his teeth in martyrdom to his work—sometimes to behold the coveted prize glide into the water and away some little distance, making a second stalking process necessarily more cautious than before. Well does the writer remember an instance when, advancing in snail-like fashion toward a particularly fine snake, that a mosquito imbedded its proboscis in his nose. Enduring the torment as best he could, there was a partial relief in observing the noose settle over the reptile's head, and utter chagrin immediately following in the discovery that a bramble, touching the sensitive wire, had caused it to tremble slightly and alarm the snake, which, before the writer could give a lightning-like pull at the pole to tighten the noose, pulled back its head with a motion as quick as the snapping of an elastic band and dove into the water to reappear at a spot inaccessible for noosing.

Discouraging it was to see these serpentine prizes, some

gaily decorated with bands of red and yellow, others golden-brown above with bright vermilion abdomen and all of large size, sunning in brilliant clusters over the muddy waters and realize that but one, at the most two, of the lot could be made captives. At the time of writing, clusters of these serpents adorn the cages of the Reptile House. What memories they recall of the luxuriant low grounds and days of fever-inviting labors!

Distributed throughout central Europe, western and central Asia and Algeria, the GRASS SNAKE, WATER SNAKE or RINGELNATTER, *N. natrix,* as it is called in various parts, is analogous, at least in distribution and abundance, to the predominating New World garter snake (*Thamnophis*). The scales are keeled. Above, the usual hue is olive gray with rows of small black spots. The typical European phase is characteristically marked about the head, having a broad yellow or white collar, generally intensified by a black border posteriorly. In southeastern Europe and Asia Minor is a variety having a pale band on each side of the back. Numerous phases, some without a pale collar, a few a uniform blackish brown for the entire length of the body, are found in southern Europe. Except that it is oviparous—egg-laying—the habits differ little from the near allies. Frogs, toads and fishes form the food. In captivity the Ringed Snake lives for years, becoming affectionately tame. Three and a half feet is close to the maximum length.

The TESSELLATED SNAKE, *N. tessellata,* derives its name from the longitudinal rows of small spots arranged in tessellated—"checkerboard"—pattern; the spots are blackish on a yellow or olive-gray body hue, hence in striking contrast. This pretty snake is semi-aquatic, occurring in Italy, Switzerland (south of the Alps), in the middle Rhine and Moselle Valleys, Bohemia, thence throughout southeastern Europe, southwestern and central Asia. An adult measures a yard.

One of the Indian water snakes, *N. macropthalma,*

spreads the neck in a fashion resembling the hood of the dreaded cobra. At a time when a bounty was offered for cobras, the heads of considerable quantities of these water snakes were brought in by the ignorant classes, who, much to their disgust, were told by the technically informed officials that the "hooded" snakes they found so plentifully along the streams and promised to be a source of generous revenue were but harmless imitators of the actual cobra.

Following *Natrix* in technical classification are several satellite genera, composed of small, retiring snakes, supposed to have originated from the water snake group and, by the adoption of burrowing habits, degenerated in size, structure and elaboration of pattern. *Seminatrix* contains a single species, *S. pygæa*—the MUD SNAKE, of Florida. Here is an excellent example of degenerate relationship to the water snakes. The length of an adult is a foot and a half. Above, the coloration is lustrous blue-black; the abdomen is deep red. Even when closely inspected, this highly-polished snake seems to have keeled scales, a delusion produced by a thread-like yellow line traversing the center of each scale. The lines seem to represent the location of the keels found among the ancestral forms and which have been obliterated to meet an underground existence. In the habits is also a hint of ancestral traits. Specimens are to be found hiding under chips of bark near the edges of ponds; but dry hammock lands are also selected as burrowing grounds. Some of the writer's examples were kept in cages provided with several inches of fine dry sand. They were always in hiding. When dug out of the sand, there was a frantic scramble to hide again, a specimen throwing itself from one's hand and burrowing with an agile swimming motion. The snake does not seem to go deeply into the sand—barely an inch below the surface. Once imbedded, it moves slowly, when its progress may be noted by a moving ripple in the yielding soil. Kept in all sorts of what would appear to be favorable conditions, none of the examples could be induced to eat. A trait appealing to the water snakes is the habit of producing living young. One snake gave birth to nine active youngsters on the twenty-first of August. They were colored precisely like the parent and just as persistent in digging their way out of sight.

Storeria seems to be another genus made up of degenerate descendants of the striped snake and water snake group. The viviparous habits point significantly to such relationship. The scales are roughly keeled. Four species are known. Two are generally abundant in eastern North America, where they are known as the BROWN SNAKES or GROUND SNAKES. Of these DEKAY'S SNAKE, *S. dekayi,* is most familiar. It lives principally in stone piles or under flat rocks, where there is plenty of its favorite food, earthworms. The color above is brown, with an obscure pale streak on the back, bordered on each side with a row of black dots; the abdomen is pink. A large specimen is but fourteen inches long. Twelve to fourteen young are produced at a birth. The babies are altogether different from the parent, being black with a white collar. They mature within a year.

STORER'S SNAKE or the RED-BELLIED SNAKE, *S. occipitomaculata,* despite its formidable scientific name, is smaller than its near ally. Elevated places, where there are plenty of stone piles and flat rocks, with an abundance of earthworms, are the localities frequented. From DeKay's Snake we may easily tell the present species by the gorgeous vermilion of the abdomen. Two phases are equally common:—one, brownish on the back with a pale streak, the other dark slaty gray. The tiny young form a litter of ten to fourteen. One of them could comfortably coil on a penny, leaving a margin all around. Both DeKay's and Storer's snake are interesting for the vivarium. Living peaceably among the smaller kinds of lizards, they are satisfied with an earthworm diet. At the same time they are so good-tempered it is possible to handle even wild specimens without provoking an intimation of hostile symptoms.

The RACERS. *Coluber, Ptyas* and allied genera of both hemispheres are smooth-scaled, highly active serpents, obtaining the small mammals and reptiles forming their prey by hunting boldly in the open. Contrary to stubborn supposition, they are not constrictors. All are oviparous. As a rule, they are vicious and untamable. Among the structural points we may mention the large eyes, elongated tail and divided anal plate.

The INDIAN RAT SNAKE, *P. mucosus,* familiar in southern Asia, the Malay Peninsula and Java, may be taken as a typical Old World species. Nine-foot specimens represent the maximum length. Imparting an emaciated look, the back rises as a sharp ridge for the entire length of the body. Uniform pale olive or brownish, sometimes with dark transverse blotches on the posterior part of the body, forms the prevailing coloration. The popular name comes from a useful habit, this species preying largely upon rodents. Over a considerable portion of the range there is a sensible inclination to protect it from the slaughter waged among harmless snakes, and in several parts of India a fine is imposed for the killing of Rat Snakes.

As a captive, the average Rat Snake resents all attempts at familiarity by a curious habit, this in opposition to the actions of the great majority of Colubrine snakes. It rears the head and neck slightly, then flattens the latter *vertically;* in this position it hesitates for a few seconds, strikes wickedly at the annoyer for a distance of fully a third the length and, finding the bluff without result, dashes away. Against the glass of the cage it may blindly rush, thumping the snout painfully, when it throws itself into an hysterical coil, again flattening the neck in an endeavor to look as formidable as the slender body will permit. Nervousness so controls the majority of captives, they cannot be induced to eat unless the keeper veritably stalks to the cage, drops in the most tempting of morsels—a very young rat or a bird out of the nest—then makes a stealthy retreat. Two fine specimens in the Zoological Park so constantly hit the glass of the cage in striking at visitors, their snouts were battered bare of skin and shields, smearing the glass with blood at each blow. Evidently devoid of pain in their rage and excitement, they were necessarily removed from exhibition, whence they paid the penalty for bad temper in making a meal for the pair of cannibal King Cobras.

Rather an exception among the Racers in displaying a sharply-defined, blotched pattern is a north African species, *C. diadema,* shown in the series of illustrations. The scales are glossy; so vividly contrasted are the brown and creamy hues, the pattern looks as if painted in enamel. Fourteen adult examples arrived in a shipment of African reptiles from the Cairo Zoological Gardens. Though uniformly gentle when handled, none could be induced to eat; young rats, mice, birds, frogs, lizards and young snakes, everything on the ophidian *menu* was offered, without a single response. A suicidal fast, lasting over seven months, terminated the life of the last survivor.

The AMERICAN BLACK SNAKE or BLACK RACER, *C. constrictor,* stands prominent among serpents inhabiting the United States. Contrary to the specific name, this species never constricts the prey, but holds it firmly to the ground under a portion of the body, deglutition proceeding at the same time; the swallowing motions of the jaws are quicker than with constricting snakes; besides, the Black Snake generally feeds on animals of smaller size in comparison with other snakes.

Wonderfully agile, the Black Snake lurks in open, rocky places, foraging for small rodents, birds, frogs and the young of other snakes. It is not nearly so courageous as is generally supposed, nor is it the enemy of the rattler or the deadly copperhead snake, the cannibalistic habits relating to the smaller, weaker species. When surprised by man it will always take to flight, if escape be possible. Few snakes can show the agility in getting over the ground as this black meteor, which darts off to disappear as if by magic, as it threads its way into undergrowth or among rocks. If cornered—its escape be cut off—it will fight savagely, darting for half the length of the body at the aggressor. Before biting it pauses momentarily to slightly open the mouth; at such times the tail is vibrated, producing a distinct whir if among dry leaves. The slightest opening is instantly noted, the reptile making a dash for cover. If it should bite, the needle-like teeth can cause nothing but mere scratches on the skin. Nevertheless, the Black Snake is generally feared—and everywhere slaughtered. This is unfortunate, for the species is of real value to man in destroying the smaller mammals injurious to the woods and fields.

There is no mistaking a Black Snake. The smooth, satiny black scales impart a gun-barrel luster to the back. The abdomen is a lustrous slaty black; on the chin and throat is a patch of milky white, this occasionally showing on the upper lip plates. *Large* Black Snakes are six feet long and an inch and a half in diameter at the heaviest part of the body. The species is oviparous, laying elongated white eggs that look as if they had been sprinkled with coarse grains of salt. Young "Black" Snakes are strangely different from the parent, being pale gray with a series of brownish blotches on the back; the head and sides are irregularly spotted with black. When a year old, the body color becomes very dark, though close examination will reveal the blotches. During the second year the snake takes on the uniform pitchy black of the adult. Such is the typical form found east of the Mississippi River. In the Central States, thence westward, is a pale variety, *flaviventris,* which is greenish-gray with a yellow abdomen—often bluish above and popularly known as the BLUE RACER. From this it will be appreciated that *Coluber constrictor* is found from the Atlantic to the Pacific Coasts.

Covering as extensive an area of country in longitude, but restricted to the southern United States, is the COACH-WHIP SNAKE, *C. flagellum.* The eastern or typical form is blackish about the head and neck, brownish posteriorly. Greatly elongated, with a slender, tapering tail and rather large scales, giving the impression of a braided whip, the popular name is a good one. Texas representatives are paler —greenish or clay color. In the West is a distinct variety, the RED RACER, *C. flagellum piceus,* which is ruddy brown above and coral pink on the abdomen.

The Coach-Whip Snake and all its phases are quick, nervous serpents, feeding upon small mammals and birds. They are too high-strung to endure captivity for more than a few months. Even more slender is the STRIPED RACER, *C. tæniatus,* figured among the illustrations. Texas and the Southwest form the *habitat.*

Drymarchon, containing but a few, though large and fine species, inhabiting southern North America, Mexico, Central America and South America, approaches *Coluber* in most of its characters. The anal plate, however, is single. The species have either smooth or keeled scales; they look much like the racers. The only North American representative is a variety of a Central and South American form. It is restricted to the southeastern portion of the United States, inhabiting the coastal regions of South Carolina and Georgia; in Florida it is most abundant, being found in all parts of the state, thence ranging westward to Texas. This fine reptile—the largest serpent of the eastern United States—grows to a length of nine feet and is known as the GOPHER SNAKE or INDIGO SNAKE, *D. corais couperi,* the former title coming from a habit of seeking retreat, when pursued, in the burrow of the gopher tortoise; the latter name originates from the shining blue-black of the entire upper and under surface, except the chin and throat—those portions are dull red. To see one of these glittering brutes trailing its black length across a stretch of pale sand is a startling spectacle, even to the seasoned collector.

In captivity the Gopher Snake becomes perfectly tame, displaying what might be truthfully called affection in its toleration at being handled. The shining scales of the back, and the polished plates of the abdomen, the latter as clean as glass and reflecting all the prismatic colors, are points in strong opposition to the popular idea of a serpent's "slimy" coat. This powerfully-formed reptile is not a constrictor. Rats, birds, toads, frogs and snakes are eaten; as the prey is being swallowed it is held firmly to the ground under a portion of the snake's body.

In Texas and Mexico is a greenish phase of the Gopher Snake. The typical form—the CRIBO—occurs in Central and tropical South America. On this, the forward part of the body is olive, giving way to orange yellow posteriorly. Over a considerable part of the range the Cribo is recognized as a useful serpent, a reputation bringing it comparative immunity from harm.

Largest of the members of *Spilotes,* really one of the longest of all Colubrine snakes, is the BLACK RAT SNAKE, *S. variabilis,* a native of tropical America. Twelve feet is the maximum length. However, a twelve-foot specimen looks hardly bigger, when coiled, than a six-foot cribo, as the form is decidedly slender. The scales are proportionately large. As there is a pronounced ridge on the back, we again note the same permanently emaciated look as existing with the Indian rat snake. Incidentally, it is appropriate to mention that the species of *Spilotes* are in several localities called Rat Snakes. *S. pullatus* is black, with white or yellow blotches; on the abdomen the markings assume a tessellated pattern. This is a bad-tempered snake.

Grouped among the genera of large Colubrine snakes feeding principally upon warm-blooded prey is *Elaphe.* The members are quite nearly related to *Coluber* and *Spilotes.* They are commonly called rat snakes, and it might be explained they are powerful constrictors, feeding entirely upon mammals and birds; they have a peculiarly flattened abdomen, forming a sharp, angular border with the sides of the body; the half a hundred species inhabit both eastern and western portions of the Northern Hemisphere from the temperate latitudes to the tropics. The average species of *Elaphe* is a powerfully-built snake, about five feet long, with a squarish head distinct from the neck, quite large eyes and feebly-keeled scales. The flattened abdomen and glossy scalation are good characters for gross identification. For the most part, they are prettily colored, agile climbers and may lead a partly arboreal life. In the stubborn slaughter of such snakes, the agriculturist little realizes the economic value of the reptiles in destroying injurious mammals. The appearance of numerous snakes in fields of grain and about the barns excites but one idea, a determination to eradicate the "plague" of reptiles. In reality, the presence of the snakes is significant. They instinctively congregate in places where rodents are becoming numerous—the wild mice and rats, and the ground squirrels, each capable of causing the farmer much trouble and loss. Traps are of little avail when pitted against the sagacity of the small, gnawing animals. Farmers fume about the damage done to their grain and the ineffective work of the traps; meanwhile, they continue to slaughter every snake they find about the bins or seeking seclusion under some stray bundle of fodder, not caring to realize that every one of these harmless creatures is equal to half a dozen traps. It would be an easy matter for an intelligent farmer to learn the gross differences between poisonous and harmless snakes, then permit the latter to go unmolested. The foolish prejudice against reptiles, however, overrides all desire for argument. Frequent times, when the writer has gone to some pains to explain the subject to an inveterate snake-killer, he has elicited nothing but a sarcastic attitude. During a collecting trip he stopped on a farm where the rats were becoming an alarming menace to the owner's scanty profits. Several species of the larger, harmless snakes were common, entering the barns, where they coiled on the girders. The sight of a snake never failed to produce a commotion, the gathering of clubs and immediate murder. Poisonous snakes were not found in the neighborhood. Knowing the harmless species to be of economic value to his host, besides in every way inoffensive, the writer ventured to expostulate. His remarks excited caustic replies. Nettled at the result, he suggested each snake killed be brought to him for dissection. This arrangement elicited an interesting fact:—Nearly every reptile killed contained either a full-grown rat, several smaller individuals, or an entire brood of young. After many such emphatic demonstrations the farmer was asked if he were at last convinced of the snake's usefulness. His stubborn reply was to the effect that a snake was a snake and as such fit only to be hammered to death with a club.

Of the several fine rat snakes found in the United States, the most widely distributed is the PILOT BLACK SNAKE, *Elaphe obsoleta,* a shiny black species, with feebly-keeled scales. It ranges from southern Massachusetts to Florida and westward to the Mississippi. In the Northern States it occurs principally in high country and is known as the Mountain Black Snake by the bright country lad who goes to pick huckleberries. The pitchy black of the upper surface resembles the coat of the common black snake or racer (*Coluber*), but the Pilot is to be recognized by the keeled scales and glossy, not satiny luster. The name Pilot Black Snake comes from an erroneous idea; it is thought this serpent warns the rattlesnake in time of danger, leading the slower, venomous reptile to a safe retreat. The theory has probably arisen from the fact that the Pilot Black Snake frequents the same localities as the timber rattlesnake, the two species, in the Northern States, hibernating in the same dens. A large specimen is six feet long—well able to swallow a squirrel or a half-grown rabbit.

In the Southeastern States is an interesting ally of the former species—the CHICKEN SNAKE, *E. quadrivittata.* A yellow body-hue with four dark bands extending the entire length of the animal has elicited the specific name, meaning four-banded. With this variety we have an admirable example of the transformation of pattern from the young to the adult, existing among several serpents. The young, hatching from eggs, as do all rat snakes, are pale gray, with dark *oblong blotches.* During the latter part of the first year the stripes appear as smoky lines, connecting the blotches, while the ground color becomes more tawny; the snake is now both striped and spotted. As the stripes grow stronger, the blotches become fainter, the pattern finally becoming as originally described.

The popular name, "Chicken Snake," is an unfair, misleading title for a useful reptile. Snakes of this kind may be occasionally found prowling about poultry houses, where they may take toll for their rodent-eating services in the shape of several eggs or a very young fowl. As is usual with snakes, however, the little evil they do is the only point of their habits considered by the farmer. It is the same as the war waged against hawks. Over the proverbial fireplace of the farmhouse is a loaded shotgun, ready for a hawk. A chicken stolen by a bird of prey is but one to a hundred as compared with the injurious rodents caught and eaten by the feathered ratter.

Among the handsomest of the rat snakes is the CORN SNAKE, *E. guttata,* also of the Southeast, occurring from southern North Carolina southward. A full-grown specimen is five feet long. The coloration is reddish-yellow with a series of large crimson saddles on the back and smaller, alternating blotches on the sides; the head is red, with chevron-shaped markings; all of the large blotches of the body are bordered with black. The abdomen is boldly tessellated with black and white.

This beautiful creature lives well in captivity. Queerly enough, it prefers mice to any other prey. In widely-separated parts of its range the writer has heard it called the Mouse Snake, showing the persistence of a useful habit when in a wild state.

In Europe, the most familiar related form is ÆSCULAP'S SNAKE, *E. æsculapii,* a brownish or blackish, glossy serpent common in southern France, in Italy and southeastern Europe generally. Northward, it occurs in well-separated, restricted areas, which freak distribution is alleged to have been caused by the Romans introducing these snakes as inmates of the temples erected to Æsculapius.

The most attractive of the European species is the LEOPARD SNAKE, *E. leopardina,* a small and slender species of southern Italy, southeastern Europe and Asia Minor. Yellowish-brown is the body color, decorated with reddish, black-edged blotches—one series on the back and a smaller, alternating row on each side. The abdomen is tessellated with black. Mice form the greater part of the food. Another European ally is the FOUR-RAYED SNAKE, *E. quatuorlineata.* Southern Europe is the *habitat.* This is one of the largest of the European snakes, reaching a length of six feet. A yellowish ground color with a black band on each side of the back and a similar band beneath it on each side make this reptile look quite like the American *E. quadrivittata*—the Chicken Snake. From the eye to the angle of the mouth is a black bar. The young are blotched.

We must necessarily skip many genera of the Colubrine snakes, containing a great assortment of species—some stout, others excessively slender, terrestrial, arboreal, subterraneous in habits, their patterns embracing an amazing display of design and hues. We pick our next genus as representative of Colubrine forms living entirely upon the ground, lacking any constrictive powers, while they are so stout of body as to look really formidable; at times they assume threatening attitudes, prompted by pure bluff. Such are the three species of *Heterodon*—the HOG-NOSED SNAKES, BLOWING "ADDERS," or FLAT-HEADED "ADDERS," their striking titles coming from eccentric looks and actions. North America is the *habitat.*

The Hog-nosed Snakes live in dry, sandy places, where they burrow by means of the sharply-upturned, shovel-like snout. Short, thick, with keeled scales, a flattened, wicked-looking head and stubby tail, their make-up is sinister, immediately suggesting venomous properties. To add to a bodily appearance, causing terror among the misinformed, is a formation of the anterior ribs, which are elongated, lying close to the body when the snake is in a passive mood, but spreading laterally when the creature is annoyed; this movement flattens the forward part of the body to a great extent, in a fashion resembling the well-known trait of the cobras. As the body flattens, the head takes on a villainous, triangular outline, the pattern of the neck becomes much intensified, and the snake hisses loudly, wriggling the tail convulsively in alternation to vicious darts of the head—incidentally with closed jaws.

The average farmer refuses to be convinced that the Hog-nosed Snake or "Puff Adder," as he may choose to call it, does not combine everything fiendish and deadly among serpents. One uninitiated cannot be blamed, when it is considered a reptile of this kind causes the dreaded copperhead snake, the moccasin and rattlesnake to appear quite angelic in the latters' respective fighting attitudes. An excitable idea points to the "hissing breath" of the "Puff Adder" as frightfully poisonous.

Gross examination of the genus shows *Heterodon contortrix* to have the widest range, occurring from the southern New England States to the Missouri River, thence southward through Florida and into Texas. *H. simus,* the smallest species, is found from South Carolina and Florida to the Mississippi. *H. nasicus,* having the most pronounced snout, ranges from Montana to Texas and Arizona into northern Mexico. *H. browni* is confined to southern Florida.

The COMMON HOG-NOSED SNAKE, *H. contortrix,* reaches a maximum length of three and a half feet. Difficult to describe, the coloration may be given as pale brownish, yellow or gray, with coarse, irregular darker blotches on the back; the lower part of the sides and the abdomen are thickly powdered with black dots. Markings and colors vary into all sorts of blotched and marbled designs; we find snakes with brick red on the anterior part of the body; numerous ones, from mountainous regions, are entirely black, forming the variety *niger.*

One of the interesting traits of the Hog-nosed Snake is the habit of feigning death if it finds its vigorous imitations of a poisonous snake are of no avail in frightening the enemy away. During the entire episode the actions seem carefully studied. Some scientists insist that the snake is frightened into a convulsion or faint. The writer is of a directly opposite opinion. After hissing, striking and going through all sorts of alarming manœuvres, the snake suddenly *rolls on its back,* opening the mouth and thrashing the head from side to side until the jaws are smeared with earth or dust, then becomes utterly limp and motionless. If one remains near, making an occasional motion, the snake continues in the same condition, possibly for fifteen minutes or more. Let the observer hide. Something interesting happens at once. The reptile cautiously rears the head, darts out the tongue as if feeling for suspicious sounds, when it rolls over on its crawling surface, making away with as much speed as its stubby form will permit. Suddenly approached, it flops over on the back again, as if this were the only position to be assumed by a correctly dead snake. In spite of all such airs, a Hog-nosed Snake cannot be induced to bite, not if one's finger be forced into its mouth. Few snakes, among them the most peaceable species, will absolutely refrain from biting when first caught; so we must consider this ugly-looking but wholly good-natured serpent as unique among members of its family and give it credit for seeking to frighten away its enemies by a display of ingenuous, purely harmless bluff.

While collecting in the South, the writer had an amusing experience with the negroes, this involving a Hog-nosed Snake. The negroes regarded the species as exceptionally poisonous. They had never lingered by a performing specimen long enough to discover the habit of "playing possum." On the way to the savannas, across a cotton-field, a big "Blow Adder" was found crawling along a sun-baked furrow. The writer's colored guides and assistants shouted in terror, urging that this kind of snake be excluded from the collecting bags and instantly killed. They were asked to pause, to form a large circle and witness the writer's powers in snake hypnotism. The writer explained he could slay the snake by a few waves of his hand, without touching it. Walking up to the snake, a few motions of the hands convinced the creature its hostile airs were of no use, so it soon rolled on its back, becoming apparently lifeless. A murmur of surprise came from that staring circle. The writer insisted the "dead snake" be passed from one to another to convince his assistants of his powers. With many uneasy motions, nervous laughter and shouting, the snake was handed around by the tail. Then the circle was told to remain perfectly quiet for a minute more, to witness a restoration to life. This provoked a heated argument that the serpent be permitted to remain dead, but the "hypnotist" was adamantine; he wanted a *living* specimen for his collection. Placing the snake upon the ground, he made a few eccentric motions, then, removing his hands, kept perfectly quiet. Thinking danger past, the reptile rolled over, starting away. It was caught and put in a bag. The writer's idea had been to promote respect for himself in a wild, almost lawless region. But the effect was too pronounced. His assistants at once decided his powers of black art as suspiciously dangerous. They dropped away, one by one, until the ludicrous situation was presented of necessarily changing the location of collecting in order to leave a bad reputation behind and secure men to carry the snake bags.

The three species of *Heterodon* feed exclusively upon toads and frogs, principally the former. To aid them in holding the struggling prey is a pair of fang-like teeth in the rear of the upper jaw; these teeth are entirely solid and not connected with glands for the secretion of poison.

Our examination of the *Colubrinæ* brings us again to several constricting species, thoroughly terrestrial, aggressive, tremendously strong in proportion to their size, smooth-scaled, cylindrical of body, in fact, experts in forcing their way into the burrows of small animals as well as in hunting down other snakes in their hiding places. Veritable terrors among all species of serpents, they do not hesitate in attacking the deadly species, exhibiting a perfect immunity against the venom of the latter. This interesting group contains several genera—native of the New and the Old World. In the United States the species are called KING SNAKES; they represent the genus *Lampropeltis*. Five members of this genus are found in the United States, of which the best known is the COMMON KING SNAKE or CHAIN SNAKE, *L. getulus*. The typical form occurs from southern New Jersey to Florida and westward to the Mississippi; varieties extend westward to the Pacific Coast.

The Chain Snake is a lustrous pitch black with narrow white or yellow lines crossing the back and forking on the sides, where they unite to form a chain-like pattern.

King Snakes are surprisingly gentle in their attitude toward man, making beautiful and interesting pets. They are hardy, not at all particular as to the character of their food—eating dead animals or strips of raw beef—and live for years in confinement. As long as snakes of the same species are kept in the cage together, all goes well; immediate trouble begins when reptiles of other kinds are introduced. The docile attitude of the King Snake vanishes as if by magic. Several individuals invariably grasp the newcomer, winding coil after coil of their bodies about it. There is soon a tight ball of squeezing, viciously-chewing reptiles, all fighting to swallow the now lifeless victim. The climax may combine comedy and tragedy. One of the smaller—and livelier—snakes possibly manages to seize the victim's head, when a swallowing feat commences; a larger snake soon begins at the tail, engulfing the victim and working up toward its smaller cage mate; here it arrives, snout to snout, pauses but an instant, then swallows the now writhing victim of its kind. Unless prompted by such disputes, King Snakes will live together for years. It is best not to awake their cannibalistic temperament by placing snakes of other species in their cages; they feed readily enough upon small rodents. At feeding time it is well to watch them, preventing an entanglement that might accidentally crush the weaker members.

Surprising indeed is the amount of pugnacity displayed by even a small King Snake toward serpents of other species. The writer was once assisting a half-grown specimen to shed its skin. Relieving the King Snake of the old epidermis, he turned to show this to some friends. The snake meanwhile glided along the tier of cages and quite accidentally worked its way through the ventilating apparatus into the cage of a water moccasin fully four times the thickness of the wanderer; incidentally, the moccasin was a deadly snake. A thrashing of bodies in the moccasin's cage attracted the writer's attention. He discovered the King Snake to have seized the moccasin in its miniature, bulldog hold and coiled its body three times about the bulky adversary. Twice the moccasin turned, burying the fangs in the body of its relentless combatant. The attack provoked never a flinch, but several more wraps of the glittering yellow and black body. Embraced in the mercilessly squeezing spiral, the moccasin turned again, biting savagely. The light, scintillating along the King Snake's folds, showed it to have tightened its hold. In desperation the moccasin sought to wound once more with its fangs. Its strength was fast failing. The head wavered from side to side. It opened its mouth in a helpless gasp for air. Two or three minutes more and it would have been dead. As it was an exceptionally fine specimen, the writer decided to save its life. Pressing a stick across the head of the poisonous snake, he grasped it by the neck. An assistant, with difficulty, unwound the coils of the King Snake. The moccasin soon recovered its breath and strength.

Deeply wounded by the fangs of the poisonous serpent, the King Snake became an object of much interest. The average reptile would have died within a few minutes after receiving such injections; not so with this creature. A blood-stained, serous oozing was noted at the wounds, the skin about which was slightly raised in a soft swelling.

Within forty-eight hours the swelling had subsided, while the wounds became quite dry. The snake refused food for a couple of weeks, when it regained its normal appetite and vigor. Since that time the writer has made some experiments with King Snakes. He finds them apparently immune to the venom of such deadly species as the rattlesnakes, the copperhead, moccasin and the South American lance-headed snakes—*Bothrops;* injected with the poison of the Old World Cobras, they evinced marked symptoms of distress, usually dying within an hour.

With all its pugnacity and immunity against the virus of most serpents, the King Snake is not the sworn enemy of the rattler. It does not prowl for the mere purpose of starting a duel to the death. Summing up the habits, we might explain the King Snake to be cannibalistic, feeding largely upon other kinds of snakes and lizards; gifted with a quarrelsome disposition, it fights with any of the larger snakes crossing its path. It is fond of small rodents and young birds. Why it should be immune to the bites of poisonous snakes is difficult to explain, although here is a romantic field for theory. Most cannibalistic snakes exhibit a similar immunity, among them, kinds that never attack the venomous snakes. Another odd characteristic has been appreciated by the student:—The docile attitude of the King Snake toward man when it is such a notorious fighter among all kinds of serpents.

A large King Snake is two inches in diameter and six feet long. In the lower Mississippi Valley is SAY'S KING SNAKE, *L. getulus sayi,* blackish, with a pale green spot in the center of each scale. In the southwest United States may be found another variety—BOYLE'S KING SNAKE, *L. g. boylii;* the coloration is attractive:—dark brown or black, with chalky white or pale yellow bands crossing the back and widening on the sides.

As an object of ridiculous stories, we may take the MILK SNAKE, *L. triangulum triangulum,* alleged to steal milk from the cows. The length is about a yard, the color gray with chestnut saddles on the back. Throughout the northeastern portion of the United States it is abundant.

A farmer once told the writer one of the cows had been giving a small quantity of milk. On an evening just before milking time, the "cause" of the trouble, a large Milk Snake, was seen gliding from the yard and immediately killed. From that time, the farmer explained, the cow was giving her expected quantity. When the man was asked how a snake a yard long and less than an inch thick could steal enough milk from a cow to produce a noticeable effect, he paused in some embarrassment, when a happy thought caused him to exclaim that snakes were queer things and capable of performing strange feats. Suffice it to say, the capacity of a reptile this size would be not more than an ounce of fluid if it were to feel comfortable, which amount should not produce any great effect upon the poorest cow that ever grazed on sterile soil. In reality, the presence of "Milk" Snakes about farms and the like comes from the prevalence of mice in such places.

In Europe and Asia are serpents closely allied to *Lampropeltis,* having a cylindrical body, smooth scales and a head but little distinct from the neck. They are constrictors, evincing cannibalistic habits, but also feeding upon lizards, small rodents and birds. The SMOOTH SNAKE, *Coronella lævis,* may at times resemble the European viper by the two rows of black spots on its brown body fusing into a zigzag band. From the poisonous snake it may be told by the smooth scales. The *habitat* is southern England, through the most part of temperate Europe to Asia. Two feet is the length of an adult; occasional examples exceed this by a few inches. Kept for observation, the Smooth Snake is sullen, not feeding well. If handled, it exhibits deliberate treachery, quietly running its snout over the skin until finding a particularly soft spot, when it takes a sudden hold, chewing alternately with each side of the head until the tiny teeth draw spots of blood. The bite, of course, is entirely innocuous. Very young mice—just out of the nest—are eaten by captive snakes; but a diet of this kind is not easily obtained. Contrary to the habits of most *Coronelline* snakes, this is a viviparous species; the number of young is small.

Diadophis, a North American genus, embracing four species, is much like *Coronella.* Its species are generally called the RING-NECKED SNAKES, each uniform gray, except at the neck, where a brilliant yellow color forms the only marking. The abdomen is orange yellow, sometimes with a row of black spots. Scale rows and the number of plates on the abdomen are employed as distinguishing characters to separate the species. *D. punctatus* is familiar in eastern North America, ranging well into Canada; *D. regalis* occurs from Illinois to Arizona and southward to Vera Cruz; *D. amabilis,* a western reptile, may be found from Texas to the Pacific Coast, thence into Sonora, Mexico. A phase of the latter has a coral red collar and abdomen. When frightened, it curls the tail upward in the form of a conical spiral and in a way to show both the bright abdominal hue and the dark color of the upper surface. The little creature appears thus seeking to intimidate the enemy.

Ring-necked Snakes seldom grow to a length of two feet, except *D. regalis.* They are secretive, hiding under flat stones or the loose bark of dead trees. The young of other small snakes, young lizards, salamanders and earthworms form their prey. A partial constriction is employed in subduing the quarry. These may be described as oviparous snakes, yet the eggs are extremely thin-skinned, hatching in less than half the time required by most snake eggs under the most favorable of circumstances. Small openings in timbered regions, scattered with flat stones, are good localities for Ring-necked Snakes. The writer remembers a large flat stone lying close to a trail leading up a mountain, in New York State. He seldom turned this stone without finding a specimen. The stone was always turned back into the same spot and propped up slightly over another stone as an inducement for shelter. Never more than a single snake was found under it at a time, but the trap seldom failed. Once, while going up the trail, a snake was bagged and four hours later, on returning, the stone disclosed another snugly coiled beneath it. The snakes came from a growth of almost impenetrable timber, brush and tumbled rock.

Cemophora contains a single species, C. *coccinea*—the SCARLET SNAKE—of the southeastern part of the United States. This is a beautiful little creature, about one and a half feet long when fully grown. From above, the pattern seems to consist of broad scarlet rings, separated by yellow rings that are bordered on each side with black. On the lower part of the sides these colors abruptly give way to the immaculate white of the abdomen. The novice is apt to mistake the species for a poisonous snake of the southeastern United States—the Coral Snake, *Micrurus fulvius.* The latter reptile has much the same coloration, but the arrangement of the hues is different, thus:—The poisonous snake has the black rings wider than the yellow and *narrowly bordered on each side with the latter hue.* Several harmless snakes, brilliantly ringed like the *Micrurus,* may be readily separated by the differences in pattern described.

The Scarlet Snake is a constrictor, feeding upon lizards, small snakes and very young mice. It is oviparous, like most of the smooth-scaled American snakes. One in the writer's collection deposited eight eggs and remained coiled about them for several weeks, when they were nearly ready to hatch. Then she performed the most eccentric of deeds. Though food had been constantly offered her, it was discovered she had eaten her entire brood of eggs.

During a collecting trip a queer observation was made. A heavy rain had fallen the night before, enticing the burrowing snakes from their hiding places. Evidently the Scarlet Snakes had been conspicuous objects during the early morning. On the ends of dead twigs and stems, right and left, were the weird souvenirs of the shrikes, or butcher birds, consisting of partially-eaten bodies of snakes. The reptiles were securely fastened by forcing the tip of the twig into the body cavity like a finger into a glove. The shrike is a carnivorous bird, notorious in having eyes too big for its stomach; its half-eaten prey is thus jauntily deserted. The number of Scarlet Snake bodies left by the shrikes was a tip to the writer. We started in to tear the bark from every dead tree in our way. In such places do these little snakes pass most of their time. When the day closed we had a bag well filled with the desired specimens. As the bark is torn away from a rotting trunk, uncovering the dark, mouldy pulp beneath, a Scarlet Snake is the most inappropriate of objects for such surroundings, appealing to one, as a romantic assistant declared, like a fairy's lost necklace.

Opheodrys and *Liopeltis,* genera represented in Asia and North America, contain mostly uniform green species. Two of the most dainty of the serpents of the United States are the GREEN SNAKES, *Opheodrys æstivus* and *Liopeltis vernalis.* The former has keeled scales and is restricted to the Southern States; the latter ranges from the New England States to the South and over a large part of North America; its scales are smooth. A uniform, livid leaf green renders a specimen difficult to see. Stone piles and the bushes at the edges of meadows are the favorite lurking places. Curious among snakes are the feeding habits of both *Opheodrys* and *Liopeltis;* they are insectivorous. Smooth-bodied caterpillars, crickets, grasshoppers and spiders are preferred. They will not eat earthworms. In the vivarium the Green Snakes are easily fed and hardy. They cannot be induced to bite. Both are oviparous. The young of *L. vernalis* are blue-black for the first few months.

Before leaving the *Colubrinæ* it is appropriate to mention a beautiful serpent of the southeastern United States. This is the RAINBOW SNAKE, *Abastor erythrogrammus.* Five-foot examples, two inches in diameter, are common in Florida. On a lustrous purplish body-hue are narrow vermilion stripes; the sides are banded with orange, the scales red-tipped. Beneath, the pattern is reversed, the abdomen being red with rows of purple dots. This beautiful, glittering reptile leads a subterraneous life. It is the only species of its genus. In captivity, mature individuals cannot be induced to eat; very young examples take earthworms. A closely-related species—also the only member of its genus —*Farancia*—is known as the RED-BELLIED SNAKE, *F. abacura*. The *habitat* embraces the Southeastern States. The back is iridescent pitch black, the abdomen brick red, which hue extends upward on the sides in the form of bars. While specimens six feet long are not rare, the structure of this handsome snake at once indicates subterraneous habits. The head is flat and not at all distinct from the neck, with small, dull eyes, the pupil barely larger than a pin-hole. As markedly degenerate is the structure of the tongue; this organ is incongruously small and incapable of the rapid vibratory movements to be noted among most snakes. Red-bellied Snakes are lively enough when handled, but seldom attempt to bite. The tail is armed with a minute spine as sharp as a needle. In thrashing about a specimen may try to scratch one's hand with this spine. Owing to this characteristic a story has arisen to the effect that snakes of the species sting with the tail. More ridiculous, however, is the belief of the negroes that the Red-bellied Snake often takes its tail into the mouth and rolls along at a lively gait; hence another popular name, the Hoop Snake.

Subfamily *Dasypeltinæ*. One genus, containing a single species, is known. The *habitat* is tropical and South Africa. Characterized by the presence of only a few teeth on the rear part of the jaw bones, the food of the species is restricted almost entirely to eggs. To aid the snake in cutting through the shell is an ingenuous development in the throat. Several of the vertebræ have strongly-formed, knife-like points extending into the æsophagus, these cutting through the egg as it passes into the throat. *Dasypeltis scabra* is the scientific name of this interesting reptile. It is full grown when less than a yard long, yet a specimen two and a half feet long can swallow a hen's egg. During the process the neck is enormously distended, the scales forming widely-separated rows. The egg moves a short distance down the throat, when the sharp processes described are brought to bear upon it by a constriction of the muscles; the swelling suddenly collapses when the snake rears the anterior part of the body slightly to permit the contents of the egg to run down its throat. Some examples disgorge the crumpled mass of shell soon after; others swallow and dissolve this part of the meal. If the feast consists of the soft, leathery-shelled eggs of some other species of snake, the integument of the eggs is invariably swallowed. The EGG-EATING SNAKE is a common species; its coloration is pale brown with three rows of darker blotches. The eye has an elliptical pupil and the body scales are keeled.

Amblycephalinæ. About three dozen species form the present family of *harmless* snakes; they inhabit tropical America and Asia. The members are sometimes called CHUNK-HEADED SNAKES, as nearly all of them have a lumpy head with very large eyes (pupil elliptical), mounted on an extremely slender neck. The body is slender and generally compressed. Some of the species have a row of enlarged scales on the back.

The Snakes of this subfamily are related to the *Colubridæ,* looking like the Dipsades of the *Opisthoglypha,* but may be recognized by the absence of a longitudinal groove in the center of the chin. The development of recent studies rendered possible by accumulation of specimens for comparison indicate that this family, alleged to represent ancestral stock of the vipers, can no longer stand as distinct, and must be included in the listing of Colubrine snakes. Their jaws are capable of but slight distension.

The OPISTHOGLYPHA. A study of this Colubrine division will dispel a number of pet theories. Venomous snakes are far more numerous than they are supposed to be. The old, popular supposition has it that poisonous serpents may be instantly detected by their thick bodies and wicked, heart-shaped heads. This is altogether wrong, even when applied to the vipers themselves—they constituting but one family of the venomous serpents. An imposing aggregation of entirely innocuous serpents exhibit just these outlines. The snakes of the present, extensive division have every indication in outline and external structure of the typical harmless species, a large portion of them being really much elongated —whip-like—which is in distinct contrast to the popular notion of a poisonous reptile. Let it be well understood, before we go farther, that the present big group is entirely distinct from the cobras, the coral snakes and their many allies, all of these, too, looking like the harmless snakes in their configuration.

Until a comparatively recent date, the members of the *Opisthoglypha* were classed with the wholly innocuous snakes. Even now they are not regarded with due significance. We find references, describing them as "slightly poisonous to small animals, but harmless to man," or "capable of producing bites little worse than a bee's sting." The truth of the matter is, the Opisthoglyph snakes are, as a rule, shy and active; besides, their fangs are so placed the reptile would inflict a wound only with the harmless anterior teeth if dealing an ordinary bite. Thus, in the absence of records to show what their venom is capable of doing, numerous writers have filled the gap by theoretically declaring the reptiles' harmlessness. A considerable number of the species are of diminutive size, consequently possessing almost microscopic fangs. Such may be unhesitatingly described as incapable of doing much harm to man. Compared with the Elapine and Viperine snakes, the majority of the Opisthoglyph serpents might be termed mildly poisonous. In spite of this argument, though, there can be no excuse in placing snakes having perfectly developed poison-glands and grooved fangs to conduct the virus, under any other head but that of *Poisonous Serpents*. By so doing, we remove from what has been termed in the past the "great family of harmless snakes," nearly a third of the members.

The anatomy of the poison apparatus is reversed from

that of the other kinds of venomous snakes, the fangs being furrowed or grooved instead of canaliculated, while they are in the extreme rear of the upper jaw. The pair of poison glands is situated in the labial region, independent of the suprelabial gland and immediately above the fang, not occupying the temporal region, as is the case of the Elapine and Viperine snakes. Opisthoglyph snakes may have one or several pairs of fangs. Boulenger believes them to connect the Colubrine and Viperine serpents, the highly specialized venom apparatus of the latter seeming to have been derived from that of the *Opisthoglypha* by the reduction of the forward portion of the maxillary bones and subsequent loss of the small solid teeth, thus bringing the venom fangs to the front; during the process the fangs have closed about the furrows, becoming perfectly canaliculated—like hypodermic needles.

To imbed its fangs, an Opisthoglyph snake must advance its jaws in a series of chewing motions; when the fangs are brought into play, the jaws grip hard. The retained hold enables the poison to flow down the furrow of the tooth and well into the wound. Thus it may be understood why such snakes are not well able to inflict a dangerous bite unless they grip hard with the jaws. The Elapine and Viperine snakes may "strike"—bite rapidly—and during the manœuvre the fangs, entering the flesh, discharge the poison from the orifice at their tip, leaving the fluid deeply imbedded. By deliberately biting their prey, the Opisthoglyph snakes kill the quarry in significantly quick fashion, even with neater dispatch than some of the vipers. The venom seems to act entirely upon the nerves, benumbing the victim. An Opisthoglyph snake can kill a lizard quicker than an Elapine or Viperine snake of the same bulk.

The *Opisthoglypha* is a cosmopolitan division. In the New World the members are confined to the warmer latitudes—from the extreme southern part of the United States through the tropics. In the Old World they range farther into the temperate regions.

POISONOUS RIVER SNAKES, *Homalopsinæ.* In relation to the *Opisthoglypha,* this subfamily occupies the same position as the Aglyphous *Acrochordinæ.* The species are entirely aquatic, with valvular nostrils on the upper surface of the snout, and small eyes—the pupil vertical. The greater number have very narrow abdominal plates. All are viviparous. Their aspect is as ugly as their temper. Rivers and bays of the East Indies from Bengal throughout Malaysia to North Australia are inhabited by representatives of the twenty-three species. In the harbors of Cochin China and Siam is found the most interesting of these serpents, *Herpeton tentaculum,* having two tentacles on the snout. Occasional members of the *Homalopsinæ* are seen well out to sea. They may be told from the deadly representatives of the *Hydrophidæ* by the rounded tail—not broadly compressed or paddle-like. The various species feed upon fishes. When the prey is seized, the jaws grip it in chewing fashion until the fangs have been well imbedded. Thus holding the prey, the reptile sinks leisurely to the bottom. Within a few minutes the fish is helplessly benumbed by the poison. Even though it be provided with long, spiny fins, the muscles of these become perfectly inert. Seizing it by the head, the snake swallows it without difficulty, as the bristling fins fold against the body of the prey as deglutition goes on.

The *Dipsadomorphinæ.* This extensive subfamily contains, to a moderate extent, groups analogous to those of the *Colubrinæ.* A considerable number of the species are much elongated—whip-like—with an extremely slender tail; among such, except the typical tree snakes, the head may be sharply distinct from the neck and the eyes large, with elliptical pupil—characters imparting a venomous look notwithstanding the slender body. Terrestrial, subterraneous, strictly arboreal and semi-aquatic habits are displayed in the subfamily. Some of the tropical species are dangerously poisonous to man.

As examples of extremely slender form we may take the

seven species of *Imantodes,* inhabiting Mexico, Central America and tropical South America. *I. cenchoa* ranges over the entire area given for the genus. The body is about a yard long, strongly compressed and terminating in an extremely elongated neck not thicker than a goose quill, which surmounts a lumpy, wicked-looking head with huge eyes having vertical pupils. The tail tapers to an almost thread-like point. Snakes of this kind live on trees, not leading the active life of the typical tree serpents: for they are rather sluggish and nocturnal. They hide under strips of loosened bark or in thick clusters of leaves, gliding stealthily forth under cover of darkness in search of sleeping lizards, tree toads, the fat-bodied grubs of insects or the eggs of small species of birds. Fruit steamers, coming to our northern ports, bring many specimens hidden in bunches of bananas. A stowaway of the kind came into the writer's possession, living for three years. During the day it persistently hid under a strip of bark. During the night it roved steadily through the branches in the cage, doubling back the neck into fully half a dozen fantastic loops, when disturbed, glaring steadily at the intruder with its big, cat-like eyes, but never offering to bite. Frogs were regularly eaten, a small one, at intervals of about ten days apart. Freshly-hatched sparrows elicited the greatest interest, two of them constituting a meal. Regularly each year, in August, this snake deposited from ten to twelve elongated eggs, placed in a carefully scooped-out hollow of the gravel under the strip of bark. While infertile, the eggs were white with a perfectly-formed firm shell and retained their shape for several weeks, when they solidified from a constant absorption of moisture.

Thicker of body, but appealing to *Imantodes* in form, particularly by the distinct head and elliptical pupils, are several genera, forming a fairly well-defined group, the DIPSADES. *Sibon* is one of the genera. Nine species are known, all with a sharply-defined, poisonous-looking head, but plated in typical Colubrine fashion. The distribution includes tropical and South Africa and the New World from southern Texas in the United States into tropical South America. The ANNULATED SNAKE, *S. septentrionalis,* is the only species found in the United States. The *habitat* is southwest Texas and northern Mexico. It is rusty brown above with transverse black blotches extending down the sides almost to the borders of the abdominal plates; examined from above, the snake seems to be boldly ringed—hence the popular name. The combination of flattened, distinct head with large shields, the elliptical pupils and strong pattern should distinguish the reptile among others in the country it inhabits. Lizards are the favorite food. Judging from the way they become quickly benumbed by the poison, snakes of this kind should be handled with caution.

With *Tomodon,* a South American genus of two species, there are two very long fangs on each side of the upper jaw—directly beneath the eye. *T. dorsatus* reaches a length of two feet. The head is distinct from the neck with a short, very convex snout. The body is cylindrical with smooth scales. With this species the eye is of moderate size, having a round pupil. *Coloration:* Olive or brownish, with a yellow stripe on the back—sometimes only distinct on the neck; a dark band from the eye to the angle of the mouth; yellowish or greenish beneath, sprinkled with dark spots. Snakes with such fang development must be rated as dangerous to man.

Tantilla, with its twenty-three small species, is in opposition to the preceding genus. The maxillary teeth are small and followed by a pair of feebly-enlarged fangs; as the snakes themselves are diminutive, the fangs are almost miscroscopic. We may term them harmless to man. Several species occur in southern portions of the United States. They are smooth-scaled, opalescent and lead a burrowing life. *T. coronatum,* ten inches long when fully grown, inhabits the Gulf States. The head is black with a yellow collar, the latter black-bordered. *T. gracilis* is pale brown, the top of the head black, but lacking the pale collar; the abdomen is salmon red. This snake is found from Missouri to Texas.

Dryophis, with eight species in southeastern Asia and Malaysia, is made up mostly of beautiful leaf-green Tree Snakes that are excessively slender. The LONG-NOSED TREE SNAKE, *D. mycterizans,* grows four to five feet long. It inhabits the Malay Peninsula and Archipelago. Its color may be described as uniform, rich leaf-green; when feeding and the body is distended, a beautiful effect is produced. The scales are separated, forming green bands between which the skin is intensely black and showing, at regular intervals, broad bands of white in lineate streaks.

This attractive snake has a much elongated, conical snout. The eyes are large and golden, with a *horizontal* pupil. All of the writer's specimens have fed exclusively upon lizards. The prey becomes quickly paralyzed after the serpent's fangs have been imbedded. Snakes of this kind have a habit of stretching out the anterior third of the body, sometimes a greater part of the length, straight forward into space from their arboreal roosts; in this position they peer about for a good fraction of a minute's time. The feat shows remarkable strength. All of the Dipsadomorphine tree snakes evince this habit.

A New World species of similar structure is found from Mexico into tropical South America. This common reptile might appropriately be termed the PIKE-HEADED SNAKE; the technical name is *Oxybelis acuminatus.* The head is elongated, terminating in a sharp snout. Specimens may be green, gray or brown; the latter hues are commoner and the bodies of such specimens look like the remains of slender, dead vines loosely twined among the foliage. As captives, examples of this species exhibit much vivacity and intelligence. They should be given a generous supply of branches. On these they spend most of their time, seldom coiled, but resting lightly in graceful undulations with upraised heads, watching for food. They will remain for hours, motionless, apparently glaring at nothing until the introduction of several lizards into the cage produces an immediate effect. A snake instantly discovers the prey, stalking it with the slender neck drawn back into an S-shaped loop. This position is retained until the snake is within striking distance. The movements of the reptile are as slow and deliberate as the actions of a cat after a bird. Just prior to a dart for the food, the snake's head and neck will be seen to tremble in tense preparation, then comes a dart, lightning-quick and surely aimed. The lizard is firmly seized when one side, then the other of both upper and lower jaw alternately hook it back to within reach of the fangs. As these instruments are imbedded, the snake holds the struggling prey tenaciously. The action of the venom is speedy. The violent efforts to escape become irregular convulsions, soon giving way to an occasional twitch. Without releasing its hold, the snake works the prey about in the jaws so that the head of the lizard points down the serpent's throat. The swallowing motions of the jaws now quickly engulf the meal. It takes but one or two minutes' time for the poison of this kind of snake to render a lizard inert, in fact, apparently lifeless.

When a snake of the present species is crawling it has the habit, as have all the tree snakes, of thrusting out the tongue in straight and rigid fashion, the forked extremities lying close together instead of spreading; this causes the tongue to look like a thin spike; nor does the tongue of a tree snake often describe the rapid oscillations to be noted with this important organ among most serpents.

If angered, the Pike-headed Snake acts as though reluctant to bite, yet appears to threaten and thus frighten away the cause of annoyance. A captive, when disturbed, will sometimes open its mouth and follow, with quickly-turning head, every motion of its observer. Occasionally it may strike, but in a hesitating fashion, with no trace of the agility displayed in catching the prey.

Wild tree snakes of this or any other species are difficult to catch. They exhibit a wonderful similarity to the colors of the vegetation in which they live, their slender bodies being easily mistaken for the stems and tendrils of vines. If surprised, they dart away with speed and grace, scarcely rustling the leaves over which they pass.

The PROTEROGLYPHA. In this division of Colubrine allies are two families—the *Hydrophidæ,* marine serpents, and the *Elapidæ,* containing the cobras and their numerous allies, besides the New World coral snakes. In this division we find many of the most deadly known species of snakes. As compared with the *Opisthoglypha,* the fangs are scarcely larger. They are canaliculated, however, and have an orifice at their tips for the discharge of poison; moreover, they are connected with venom glands secreting a far more virulent poison and in greater quantities. The situation of the fangs differs as well from the preceding division. They are on the forward portion of the upper jaw, where they are rigidly attached—not folding against the roof of the mouth when the jaws are closed, as is the case with the Viperine snakes. Few examples of the *Proteroglypha* are found in the New World.

It is with the *Proteroglypha* that we arrive at the actually deadly snakes. The vast array of serpent life treated in the preceding pages shows the wholly innocuous snakes to be in the great majority. A study of the pages to come, however, will convince the student of the imposing series of terrible-fanged creatures existing upon this earth, some of them strangely beautiful in coloration, others eccentric of form. They cause greater loss of human life—where the population is ignorantly incautious—than do the fierce beasts of prey. As an example we may quote a paragraph appearing in the London *Times,* September 19, 1906, thus:

"A statistical paper on India issued to-day shows that in 1904 there were killed in that country by snakes and wild beasts 24,034 persons—21,880 by snake bites, 796 by tigers, 399 by leopards, and the rest by other animals. The number of cattle killed was 98,582.

"The other side of the account shows that 65,146 snakes

and 16,121 wild animals were killed, for which rewards of £7,313 were paid."

The division of the *Proteroglypha* into two families may be summarized as follows:

Tail vertically compressed—paddle-shaped. Habits—marine. The HYDROPHIDÆ; Sea Snakes.

Tail cylindrical. Habits—terrestrial or semi-aquatic. The ELAPIDÆ; Cobras, Kraits and their allies; the New World Coral Snakes.

The SEA SNAKES, family *Hydrophidæ*. The serpents of this family are strictly marine and very poisonous. They abound in the Indian Ocean and the western tropical Pacific. A single species occurs in tropical waters of the New World, off the west coast of Mexico, Central America and South America.

While the existence of marine monsters, such as are occasionally noted upon the logs of leisurely-moving vessels, must be open to speculation, there exist many species of true *sea serpents;* though these actual creatures do not attain the length usually cited in the average newspaper yarn, exhibit the outlines of a dragon or spout like a whale, they grow to a fair size for snakes—six to eight feet. They are, for the most part, of striking coloration and provided with fangs and a venom so virulent, their rank must be among the most deadly of the poisonous snakes. All are viviparous.

The species of *Hydrophidæ* are most nearly allied to the Elapine snakes. As a rule, their scales are small and not overlapping, as seen among most snakes. Many of the species lack the abdominal scutes so characteristic of the terrestrial snakes; on a few these scutes are well developed. The eyes are usually quite small with a round pupil. With the Sea Snakes the tongue is but slightly employed, only the forked tips being protruded from the mouth.

In the development of the poisonous fangs the Sea Snakes are quite similar to the members of the *Elapidæ*. The fangs are very short; while they are permanently erect and show a well-defined groove on the anterior surface, the venom is conducted through an interior canal and discharged through an orifice at the tip. The poison produces a strong benumbing influence on the nerve centers, which characteristic is associated with the poison of the deadly cobras (*Naja*) and their allies.

The Sea Snakes have no gills; they come regularly to the surface for air. Their methods of breathing are much like those of the marine turtles, enabling them to remain under the surface for a considerable time. If removed from the water their movements are very erratic. The awkward attempts at crawling show them to be much out of their element. At such times their vision seems to be defective; they show considerable viciousness, biting wildly at moving objects or shadows. As captives they are nervous and delicate, generally refusing all food amid a stubborn inclination to hide in the darkest corner of the tank.

In the Indian Ocean and waters of the Malay Archipelago, Sea Snakes may be seen swimming in schools of several dozen individuals. My friend, Mr. Rudolf Weber, informs me that when nearing the coast of Sumatra upon one of the regular steamers, he was treated to an interesting spectacle. The sea appeared to become suddenly alive with brightly-banded snakes, swimming in every direction in graceful lateral undulations.

After the typhoons the bodies of many of these reptiles are cast upon the beaches, a condition possibly demonstrating that the specimens are killed by the heavy seas when venturing to the surface for air. While practically safe in their marine existence from extermination by man, the Sea Snakes have many enemies in the shape of the larger fish and the sea birds. Several captains of steamers that ply through the Molucca and the Sunda Straits have informed the writer that they have observed large birds drag these serpents from the waves, and flying to the rigging of the ship engage in battle with the reptiles, beating them with their wings and tearing with the beak until the prey is dead, when it is partially eaten.

Ten genera of the marine serpents are recognized, the same comprising over fifty species. Of these but one is known to occur in the waters of the New World. This is the YELLOW-BELLIED SEA SNAKE, *Pelamydrus platurus,* a reptile to be seen off the west coast of Mexico, Central and tropical South America. Its form is rather eel-like, the body much compressed, covered above and beneath with small round scales. The head is long, flattened and moderately distinct from the neck. The tail is very wide (vertically) and paddle-like. In its coloration the species is quite striking, being jet-black or rich brown above—on the upper half of the body—while the lower half is bright yellow. The tail is yellow with upright black bars.

This is one of the smaller species of the marine serpents, seldom reaching a length of more than a yard; the average specimen is considerably under that length. To impart an idea of the proportions, the dimensions of an adult specimen are given:

Total length	24 inches.
Vertical diameter	$\frac{7}{8}$ inch.
Lateral diameter	$\frac{9}{16}$ inch.
Length of tail	$2\frac{7}{8}$ inches.
Vertical breadth of tail	$\frac{5}{8}$ inch.
Width of head	$\frac{11}{16}$ inch.
Length of head	$1\frac{5}{16}$ inch.

The specimen measured was taken off the coast of Panama. At the lower edge the tail was a quarter of an inch in thickness, whence it gradually became flat toward the top —the upper edge being sharp and fin-like.

The Yellow-bellied Sea Snake is widely distributed. It is common in the Indian Ocean, the waters of Malaysia and the tropical and semi-tropical Pacific generally. The species is dreaded by fishermen, who often haul up specimens in their nets.

Some of the Sea Snakes have the body decorated with bright transverse bands, imparting a ringed effect. One of these is technically known as *Hydrophis obscura.* The colors are dull olive and yellow. Three feet is the average length. The form is extremely eccentric—a stout body and broad, paddle-shaped tail, but anteriorly stretching into a long, whip-like neck and singularly small head. Most of the species of *Hydrophis* are brightly colored.

The ELAPINE SNAKES, family *Elapidæ*. The members of this important family are treacherously deceptive in appearance; largely so in actions. Here we have admirable illustrations of how incorrect it is to believe that the venomous snake may be told by a thick body and a heart-shaped head. Such is certainly not the case with the cobras, their numerous Old World allies, and the coral snakes of the New World. Many of the most deadly known serpents belong to this family. The most diabolical in temper and terrible of them all is as slender of body with a head as innocent in appearance as to be noted among well-known genera of wholly innocuous snakes, *Drymarchon, Lampropeltis* and *Coronella.*

The cobras and their immediate allies throw their bodies into a weird posture of defense, striking viciously when annoyed. The greater number of the Elapine snakes evince the nonchalant demeanor of innocuous serpents. If handled, they turn and bite treacherously with a chewing motion, making a series of perforations with the fangs. Their slender, shining bodies and pretty colors are unfortunately liable to mislead the novice as to character. The New World is singularly free of such reptiles, a single genus representing the family; while all of the members are so similarly colored it is not difficult to recognize them. India, Malaysia and Africa are infested with Elapine snakes, but their headquarters must be given as Australia and New Guinea. They constitute the ophidian fauna of the former great island with the exception of a few burrowing snakes, small pythons and several species of *Colubrinæ*.

It would be practicably impossible to construct a key enabling the student to recognize the Old World *Elapidæ* as compared with the many harmless snakes. The former, however, are usually lacking in the *loreal* plate, a small shield on each side of the head between the anterior eye plate (or plates) and the plate bordering the nostril to the rear; it should be understood, though, that many harmless snakes have a similar scalation.

The fangs of the Elapine snakes are short, stout, always erect, and situated on the forward part of the jaw.

Prominent in interest among the *Elapidæ* are the COBRAS, *Naja,* ten in number and widely distributed, as will be be seen by the following list:

Egyptian Cobra; *Naja haje.* Africa.
Yellow Cobra; *Naja flava.* Africa.
Black-Lipped Cobra; *Naja melanoleuca.* Africa.
Black-Necked Cobra; *Naja nigricollis.* Africa.
Yellow-Headed Cobra; *Naja anchietæ.* Africa.
Gold's Cobra; *Naja goldii.* Africa.
Guenther's Cobra; *Naja guentheri.* Africa.
King Cobra; Hamadryas; *Naja hannah.* India; Southern China and the Malay Archipelago.
Spectacled Cobra; *Naja naja.* India; Southern China and the Malay Archipelago.
Philippine Cobra; *Naja naja samarensis.* Philippine Islands.

It is not alone from their deadliness and almost hysterical disposition that the present reptiles have acquired notoriety. The habit of many of them of spreading the neck into a "hood" when angered, is, to say the least, spectacular. It should be realized, though, that not all the species of *Naja* spread the neck so widely as does the Indian *N. naja.* With some, the characteristic is but slightly developed. Members of several allied genera show a like habit, particularly *Sepedon,* the single species of which—the Ringhals—is as much a hooded snake as *Naja naja.*

The SPECTACLED COBRA OR COBRA-DE-CAPELLO, *Naja naja,* might well be termed the most sensational of poisonous snakes. The species swarms over India and the larger islands of the Malay Archipelago, causing a fearful loss of human life. When annoyed it rears the anterior portion of its body, usually a third the length, from the ground, spreads the "hood" and discloses a weird marking on the distended skin which might be likened to a pair of huge, glaring eyes connected by a figure similar to a pair of spectacles; on the hood of some cobras the design is similar to a death's-head. Though not a big or bulky snake the Cobra-de-Capello must be ranked among the most deadly of all serpents. Its diminutive fangs inflict wounds more speedily fatal than the enormously elongated venom-conducting teeth of the big vipers—unless the bite of the latter type of reptiles involves the wounding of an important blood vessel.

Spectacled Cobras are the stars of a reptile collection and the most vicious snakes to be seen in captivity. They will remain for an hour or more in an upright position if steadily annoyed. Upon discovering a failure to vent their anger upon the object of annoyance, they will fight fiendishly among themselves. Fortunately, they are immune to each other's poison, so their combats terminate with little damage. Specimens from the Indian peninsula and Ceylon are typical in their markings, showing on the "hood" the staring aspect of two large eyes enclosed in spectacles, which strange ornamentation has led to the popular name. Examples from Sumatra and Java exhibit pronounced variation from the mainland form. One of the varieties is technically known as *Naja naja semifasciata;* popularly, it has been called the Masked Cobra. The figure on the extended neck looks like a grotesque mask.

When annoyed, the Cobra actually hurls itself into an upright position, the neck dilating simultaneously. The action is accompanied by a sharp hiss, and if a moving object is within reasonable distance the snake strikes immediately. The writer has never observed Cobras to strike without first rearing into the characteristic position with the neck spread widely—unless darting for their prey. In a wild state their only warning would be a sharp hiss which generally accompanies the instant of preparation in getting into fighting attitude; this warning so slight, though, that unless he who seeks to evade the blow be possessed of great agility, the damage may be done before he has time to realize what has happened. In a country like India, where a large part of the population goes about bare-legged, the danger from Cobras may be imagined.

Compared with other snakes, both dangerous and innocuous, the Cobra appears to be the most untamable. After years in captivity the average specimen remains as frenziedly hostile as when first received from the native wilds. The tales of Cobras attacking men have been generally condemned as fallacious, but are not entirely devoid of truth. On several occasions the writer has noted signs of real aggressiveness on the part of angry Cobras, clearly indicating a more dangerous type of serpent than the thick-bodied and sluggish viperine snake. Two specimens of the Sumatran Cobra have been in the reptile house of the New York Zoological Park for over three years. They are fully as vicious to-day as upon their arrival at the Park. The opening of the cage door, even a slight wave of the hand, is sufficient to throw these specimens into a frenzy of anger. When rearing to strike they are extremely nervous. A slight movement of a stick will cause them to start like a fractious horse at a gun-shot. They strike forward and downward, often with such force as to slide them bodily forward. Each successive dart brings them nearer the observer, when they rear higher, hissing with such vigor as to be heard for seventy-five feet or more. Not infrequently, when near the intruder, they display a bold habit of suddenly dropping from their rearing posture, darting forward, then flinging the body again into the fighting position. This is an action devoid of fear and may be seen among all Cobras in a state of perfect vigor. It is commonly enacted by the King Cobra, an extremely bold creature, refusing to take a bluff and, on the whole, the most dangerous in habits and venomous properties of all poisonous snakes. Concerning this snake in a wild state there are many stories relating to hostility toward man—aggressiveness carried to the point of actual attacks. Judging from the habits of captive specimens the writer is inclined to believe such statements.

When biting the Cobra displays a different series of movements than those of the long-fanged viperine snakes. The latter, when striking, throw the jaws open to an enormous angle, the fangs literally stabbing the object aimed at. At the instant of penetration there is a biting movement to imbed the fangs as deeply as possible, but the two processes are practically simultaneous and the effect to the eye is simply a lightning-like dart of the head. With the Cobras, such actions would be productive of little result owing to the shortness of the fangs. When the Cobra's jaws reach the offending object they grasp it tenaciously, then the peculiar *chewing* motion characteristic of snakes advances the fangs in a fashion producing a series of wounds from each. The duration of the biting movements may be from two to five seconds, this depending upon the reptile's irritability. A man wearing ordinary summer underclothing and a thin suit might consider his limbs fairly well protected from a Cobra's fangs unless the garments fitted tightly and the snake secured a firm hold. A viperine snake, to the contrary, in *striking* for a man's leg could drive its long fangs through several thicknesses of clothing and inflict a fatal stab. Thus we understand there is much difference between the stabbing stroke of the long-fanged snakes and the bite of a Cobra, the latter, in nine cases out of ten, harmlessly gripping the loose part of one's clothing. An ordinary pair of army leggings will produce perfect immunity from Cobra bites—not so against the fangs of another deadly serpent of India and Malaysia, the Tic Polonga or Russell's Viper. The writer has noticed that a Cobra is unable to kill an Angora guinea pig unless the snake grasps the animal by the leg or nose. When the animal is seized by the body the poison is expended in the fur, the fangs being too short to reach the flesh. Bitten animals die quickly from what appears to be a general paralysis; during this there are but slight struggles and the victim seems to suffer little pain. Occasionally, the writer has witnessed the ability of Cobras to eject their venom when in a coiled and defensive position. It seems that in striking the snake simultaneously compresses the poison glands by a contraction of the jaw and muscles and ejects the poison, though quite accidentally, in the direction of its annoyance. If the fluid should enter the eyes, blindness or death are probable consequences. The habit is common with a South African hooded snake, *Sepedon,* and with the latter species seems to be quite voluntary.

Like all the species of *Naja* the Spectacled Cobra is hardy as a captive, feeding readily and if given proper care, particularly as regards the shedding of its skin, will live for years. As to the skin-shedding process there is often negligence on the snake's part; the old epidermis hardens; unless the reptile is bathed and the skin removed by hand, the snake sickens and refuses all food. The process of removing the skin is not particularly dangerous. A stick is placed across the serpent's head; pinned to the ground it is helpless and the operator grasps it firmly by the neck; while holding the snake in a straightened position an assistant easily removes the old cuticle.

Cobras feed upon small rodents, birds and eggs. The latter are swallowed entire. Some specimens evince a fondness for frogs. The food is grasped and *chewed* until several times wounded by the fangs, the snake steadily retaining its hold until the prey is dead or so benumbed by the poison as to offer no voluntary struggles.

A large Spectacled Cobra is six and a half feet long and two inches in diameter at the thickest part of the body.

Another well known species of *Naja* is the EGYPTIAN COBRA or Asp, *N. haje,* a reptile sharing with an Egyptian viper, *Cerastes cornutus,* the reputation in history of being the serpent concerned in the suicide of Cleopatra.

The Egyptian Cobra is fully as vicious as its Indian ally, spreading a "hood" in a like manner. It is, however, a smaller snake and of a dull brown hue with no markings showing upon the neck when extended. Consequently, it is a less dramatic creature than the spectacled snake. The intelligence of this serpent, nevertheless, is marked, while its motions are wonderfully quick. The following experiment, conducted in the New York Zoological Park, demonstrates the vivacity and reasoning power of the species:—

A small wooden box with thin sliding top was placed in the serpent's roomy cage. The lid of the box was left partially open, and into the box, for the greater part of the day, the snake retired to hide. The box was left in the cage for a week with the idea of permitting the reptile to become thoroughly familiar with it. An opportunity was then awaited of finding the snake prowling about the cage, when the box was taken out and placed in a room twelve feet square. The snake was taken from the cage, placed in a bag and carried to the room, where it was liberated on the floor about six feet from the box. For a moment it dilated its hood and assumed the fighting posture, when, as usual with Cobras suddenly transported to strange surroundings, dropped to the ground and began gliding about to discover a place of retreat. The box was moved slightly to attract the snake's attention to it and the result awaited. It will be appreciated that this box opened at the top by means of a sliding lid so that the snake as it glided about the floor could see no opening. At the slight movement of the box the snake changed its course and made directly for it. A bright colored cloth was fluttered in its path at which it rose and struck promptly. Persistently continuing its course toward the box it reached this, reared the head and neck over the top and in a fashion characteristic of the lively asp, literally flung itself into the hiding place, its tail striking the wooden side of the box with a slap like that of a whip's end. This test was convincing enough to the writer to demonstrate substantial reasoning power, but to prove it to be not mere accidental wandering of the reptile it was repeated, again and again, with the same result. A dozen times, on different days, the snake made for the box, reared upward and glided in from the top. The test showed the reptile to recognize its hiding place, though the box had no openings on the sides that could be seen from the level of the floor on which the Cobra was crawling.

Similar experiments were tried with snakes of the genus *Elaphe, Drymarchon, Lampropeltis* and *Natrix*—all harmless reptiles. They incidentally discovered the box and sought shelter in it when it was placed in the cage, but when in a bare room and annoyed as was the Cobra, dashed stupidly about, rooting into corners and trying to escape in an erratic, uncertain fashion, never succeeding in finding the hiding place, though often passing in close proximity to it.

Following are the measurements of an adult Egyptian Cobra:—

Total length	5	feet.
Length of tail	9	inches.
Greatest diameter	1½	inches.
Width of head	1¼	inches.
Length of head	1¾	inches.

The present species is common in countries bordering the Sahara Desert and in Arabia.

Apparently the most deadly of the Old World poisonous serpents is the KING COBRA or HAMADRYAS, *Naja hannah,* attaining the great length, for a poisonous snake, of twelve feet. It is a slender, graceful serpent with a narrow head that looks anything but poisonous. An example of large size, when coiled, shows so little bulk it might be mistaken for a serpent of but seven or eight feet long. The coloration is pale olive, crossed by darker olive bands. Toward the latter part of the body there is considerable black, the scales of the tail usually showing little of the pale hue except a spot in the center of each. Looked at from directly above, the King Cobra appears to be ringed. When angered, there is a marked flattening of the neck and the serpent rears the head and neck from the ground—but only to a slight extent, as compared with the position assumed by the former species. When the hood is spread, and not to the width of a man's hand even with a large specimen, the pattern evinces vivid transverse bands, while the skin bordering the scales is white, thus intensifying the markings.

Of all species of snakes observed by the writer, the King Cobra is the most intelligent. Its certain, snappy actions indicate good reasoning powers. A slight vibration at the door of the cage will bring a specimen rushing to the opening, where it searches about, inserting its tongue along the frame in a search for food. Wild King Cobras have a diabolical temper, coupled with a dangerous degree of intelligence. Their movements appear well premeditated—not so hysterically nervous as the smaller cobras. Moreover, the King Cobra becomes fairly tame as a captive, but can never be trusted, as its touchy nature flames into anger upon slight provocation and the fearlessness of the snake prompts it to actually attack one. This has several times happened to the writer.

As an illustration of the intelligence of the King Cobra it might be explained that the specimens in the Zoological Park, prior to their feeding time, come to the door of their cages, where they assume the graceful cobra position—head and neck upraised to the level of the small glass window in the door, when they follow intently, with turning head, the movements of the keepers in the passage behind the cages. Among snakes such actions are unusual. They appeal more to the mental faculties seen among mammals. In a number of other instances the writer has witnessed the unusual intelligence of the King Cobra. Its apparent sagacity, large size, the possession of stout fangs and probably the most virulent poison of all snakes, well merits the popular title, though that actually comes from its feeding habits, herewith described.

It has been alleged that the King Cobra, while strictly cannibalistic, feeds but seldom upon the long-fanged, poisonous snakes, evidently having an instinctive dread of the deep wounds liable to be inflicted by such reptiles. To test the truth of this statement, the writer made the following experiment:

A large, thick-bodied, *harmless* water snake, *Natrix taxispilota,* and a *poisonous* water moccasin, *Agkistrodon piscivorus,* of much the same proportions and coloration, were selected for the experiment and at a time when the King Cobras were voraciously awaiting their weekly meal of a snake apiece. The door of the cage was opened and the poisonous snake thrown in. There was the customary rush for the food. Upon reaching it, both snakes abruptly paused. This was the first time in their feeding they had failed to immediately seize and fight over a snake thrown into their cage. The moccasin was permitted to remain in the cage for about five minutes, during which time the cobras reared well above it out of harm's way, regarding it intently. To find if they were hungry, a common striped snake was thrown to each. The little snakes were grasped and swallowed at once. The moccasin was again introduced. There was the same rush and inspection of the newcomer, and the pit viper, thoroughly annoyed by the rough treatment, showed fight. At this display the cobras backed off warily, spreading their "hoods" and rearing higher. The moccasin was finally removed unharmed and the big water snake substituted so quietly the cobras for the moment failed to note what had been done. To the human observer, the innocuous water snake looked more villainous than the poisonous moccasin; it showed emphatic signs of temper as the cobras drew near, but they attacked it without hesitation. Satisfied with the result and seeking to avoid a combat, the writer threw in a smaller water snake and forced the smaller King Cobra to release the snake used in the experiment; upon doing this it glided over to the newly introduced specimen, when each of the cobras swallowed their respective morsels and coiled contentedly in their favorite corners. On repetition, the same result was elicited, the cobras appearing to instantly recognize the dangerous character of the long-fanged viperine snake. While deadly and of great size, they were far less courageous than the harmless King Snake, *Lampropeltis,* described in pages preceding.

Captive King Cobras usually refuse everything but snakes. When feeding, they exhibit considerable cunning and agility. When the prey is placed in the cage, it may be seized by the middle of the body and, like a flash, the fangs have done their work. The serpentine prey is rather slow, however, to succumb to the poison and there is generally vigorous opposition on the part of the victim. The cobra regards the superficial wounds inflicted by the struggling quarry with stoical indifference, working the body of the snake along in its jaws with an idea of getting to the head. At such times it may have much trouble, the victim twisting about its neck. It is then that the larger reptile pauses and awaits a chance of seizing its prey near the head. If the quarry makes an attempt to bite the cobra on the neck or head, the body is released and the approaching head seized with astonishing agility; after this performance the engulfing process begins without further trouble.

The King Cobras in the Zoological Park have no aversion to taking snakes that have been freshly killed. This saves much fighting, as a snake may be tossed directly in front of each specimen. It also affords opportunities to practice economy: for the snake supply stops abruptly during the winter months. Consequently, during the cold months, each snake killed is stuffed to the utmost capacity of the elastic body with frogs or young rats and thus made to equal in bulk and nourishment a half dozen snakes. A meal like this lasts the cobras for a good two weeks.

Before leaving the genus *Naja* it is well to understand just how the cobras spread their necks so widely. In this portion of the body they are provided with extremely long, movable ribs lying closely against the backbone when the snake is in a quiescent mood. When annoyed, the reptile spreads this series of ribs laterally, forming the well-known hood. With a dead cobra it is impossible to spread the "hood" unless the ribs are pushed forward. In mounting alcoholic specimens in the characteristic fighting position, the writer makes an incision in the skin beneath the neck, thus uncovering the ribs, pushes these forward with the tip of a scalpel, then pins them into shape against a sheet of cork in much the fashion of stretching a butterfly. The body is reared upward against a form of wire, plentifully injected with a strong solution of formalin, when the entire snake is placed in a large jar of that preserving solution for about a week's time. By that time it has rigidly set, is removed from the form and placed in the permanent museum jar, containing alcohol.

Among the poisonous Colubrine snakes the writer's observations of the breeding habits have been restricted as to species, but nevertheless of importance. They have demonstrated, despite the general assertion to the contrary, that the cobras are egg-laying—*oviparous*—snakes. Not only has he succeeded in breeding the representatives of two species, but has hatched the eggs by placing them in layers of damp *sphagnum* moss. A batch deposited by a fine Spectacled Cobra consisted of twenty perfectly smooth, tough-shelled, creamy-white eggs, which were one and a quarter inches long and seven-eighths of an inch in diameter. About 50% of the eggs proved fertile. They were kept in an average temperature of 75° Fahrenheit, increased slowly in size, assuming spherical outlines and began hatching seven weeks after time of deposit.

Snake Charming. Before leaving the species of *Naja* let us look into a performance involving these snakes and surrounded by much sensational theory.

Under the trees of a public square, the idlers gather about a solemn Hindoo, whose shrill-toned reed has attracted their attention. Sitting cross-legged before two round, flat baskets, he begins a refrain upon his flute. The music is strange and crooning, suggesting something strange to follow. With a bamboo stick he presently removes the covers of the baskets and several strange apparitions arise into view from a mass of tangled bodies within. These are specimens of the deadly cobra-de-capello, their hoods spread widely. While the reptiles' eyes stare with a glassy monotony at the Hindoo, the spectacle markings upon their distended necks seem to cast ghastly grimaces upon those assembled for the exhibition. Seemingly imbued with a frenzy at the appearance of the snakes, the performer quickens the strains upon his flute. His body sways from side to side in time to the music, when the spectators behold the dreaded snakes are alike swaying to the refrain. The celebrated cobra dance is on.

With bated breath the onlookers witness this juggling with the serpents, when there is a sudden murmur of horror.

Sinuously gliding from one of the baskets is a snake of Oriental hues and a head so flat and cruel that a glance would instinctively suggest its deadliness. It is a "Tic Polonga," known among the more learned as Russell's Viper, a reptile with a fearful reputation as regards the destruction of human life. With the same undisturbed expression of solemn dignity, the Hindoo quickly reaches forward and grasps this object by the neck. With the other hand he produces a fluttering fowl. Applying the snake's mouth to the squawking creature, he permits the reptile to do the rest.

There is a flash of cottony-white jaws and the fowl is cast upon the pavement, where it batters its wings for a moment, then lies pulsating and dying. Before the snakes have been again enclosed in the baskets, the fowl is dead. In silence the Hindo gesticulates to his observers his willingness to demonstrate as well the power of his cobras. But there is a general shaking of heads, the jingling of a few coins and the exhibition is over.

To most of us comes a feeling of awe and fascination attending the performance of a snake charmer. In this instance we have seen a man associating intimately with two species of snakes that have increased the death-rate of India about twenty thousand a year. The performer was apparently in perfect control of the reptiles. Thus follows the question: Is snake charming an art, and if so, how is it acquired?

The greatest requisite of the snake "charmer" is nerve; this must be backed by a thorough knowledge of snakes. No hypnotism figures in the business. The handling of poisonous snakes is a reckless performance. Not infrequently the snakes are "fixed"—that is, their fangs have been extracted. This treatment does not render them entirely harmless: for poison flows from the wounds left by the extraction of the venom-conducting teeth, and the palatine and teeth of the lower jaw are liable to produce lacerations through which the virus may gain the circulation. But it must be acknowledged that snakes in this condition are not so liable to bite, and if they do, there is considerably less danger.

Well does the Hindoo know that if his cobras become accustomed to handling and teasing, they will "dance" with less energy: so he keeps a supply of fresh and undisturbed serpents on hand. The cobra's natural attitude of defense is, as has been previously explained in detail, a rearing posture with "hood" spread widely. From this position it follows with swaying motions every motion of its aggressor. The Hindoo's swaying body elicits a like motion on the part of the snake, as it alters its position in aiming to strike. Thus is the "dance" explained. The shrill notes of the reed appeal only to the imagination of the spectators and, were the weird intonations to cease, the dance would continue without interruption: for snakes exhibit absolutely no interest in music of any kind, an unfortunate condition for the writers of romantic stories.

The RINGHALS, *Sepedon hæmachates,* a South African cobra, differs from the species of *Naja* in having strongly-keeled scales. The popular name is that of the Boers and relates to markings on the neck. It is a sooty black serpent, the back crossed by narrow, grayish bands. The abdomen is mostly pitch black. When rearing into a fighting pose, one or two broad white bands may be seen on the under portion of the anterior part of the body—hence the popular name. A five-foot specimen must be considered a large adult.

Captives are hardy, feeding upon small rodents, birds, eggs and frogs. Their actions are as quick and vicious, while they rear from the ground into the same position as the species of *Naja*. They are particularly dangerous from their habit of persistently ejecting fine jets of poison for a distance of six or eight feet, these dangerously well aimed at the observer. As the snake rears upward to fight, it opens the mouth slightly, contracts the lower jaw, thence closes the jaws in a fashion that leaves the fangs uncovered —overlapping the lower jaw. At a movement of the adversary the snake instantly arches the neck, a movement momentarily throwing the head backward and bringing the fang tips to bear. Simultaneously the muscles over the poison glands are contracted and a thin stream of venom leaves each fang. The aim is formidably accurate and one is liable to receive the deadly spray directly in the eyes. The amount of poison expended is surprising; the writer has seen the entire lower portion of a large panel of glass peppered with tiny drops after an enraged Ringhals had been rearing for but a few minutes' time. When transferring or in any way handling snakes of the kind, the author wears a large pair of auto goggles to protect his eyes. In procuring the photograph which shows a fine Ringhals in characteristic striking position, the front of the camera was well spattered with poison and the lens necessarily protected with a plain glass cap until the moment of exposure.

The Mambas, Genus *Dendraspis,* are tree cobras occurring in Central and South Africa. They are whip-like, extremely active, and attain a length of ten to twelve feet, although the average length is six to eight feet. *D. angusticeps* is the most common of four species. There are two color phases, greenish and black. The black phase appears to grow the larger. These snakes are extremely dangerous during the breeding season, as some specimens actually attack. Their venom is of high toxicity.

Closely allied to the genera containing the hooded snakes is *Bungarus,* with several species in southeastern Asia and the Malay Archipelago. Most familiar is the dreaded KRAIT, *B. cæruleus,* a common Indian reptile attaining a length of four feet. It is alleged to cause a terrible loss of human life. Like all the species of *Bungarus,* its scales are smooth. A strong characteristic is the prominent backbone and much-enlarged central row of scales. It does not spread a hood. The color is purplish black or dark brown, with yellow cross-bands—the latter sometimes broken into spots; the abdomen is immaculate white.

Several of the Australian snakes, among them the species of *Pseudechis* and *Notechis,* spread the neck slightly in cobra fashion. The BLACK SNAKE, *Pseudechis porphyriacus,* growing to a length of five and six feet, is an abundant species. The smooth scales are blue-black, the first row on each side of the abdomen, red. This is a very dangerous snake—sometimes called the Purple Death Adder; the effect of its venom is much like that of the cobras. A beautiful specimen lived in the reptile house of the Philadelphia Zoological Gardens for over eleven years, feeding upon small rodents and birds.

The TIGER SNAKE, *Notechis scutatus,* is another of Australia's deadly serpents. The scales are smooth and the markings somewhat variable, usually olive or brown with dark cross-bands. The plates under the tail are in a single row. The distribution covers the greater part of western Australia.

Quite different in outline from the great array of dangerous members of the *Elapidæ,* found in Australia, is the DEATH ADDER, *Acanthophis antarcticus;* nevertheless, this is an Elapine snake. The body is short and stout, with keeled scales, the head flat and distinct from the neck; the eye has a cat-like, vertical pupil. Most characteristic is the tail, the tip of which is *laterally* flattened, provided with enlarged, overlapping scales and terminating in a long, thin spine. This villainous-looking snake is abundant in Australia, where it is widely distributed; it also occurs in New Guinea. Above, it is variegated with brown and yellow, crossed by darker bands.

Among other Old World Elapine snakes is *Doliophis,* composed of several species in Indo-China and Malaysia. They are small, with smooth scales and lead a secretive life. *They are remarkable for the development of the venom-secreting glands, which, instead of being confined to the temporal region of the head, extend a third the length of the body, terminating in club-shaped tips.* Owing to this incomprehensible development, the heart has actually been pushed farther down the body than with any other serpent.

NEW WORLD ELAPINE SNAKES

A single genus, *Micrurus,* represents the *Elapidæ* in the New World. About twenty-six species are known. Two occur in the southern United States. The others are distributed throughout Mexico, Central America and tropical South America. Owing to their brilliant colors, a rich red nearly always figuring in the pattern, we will call these reptiles the CORAL SNAKES. They are not so highly organized as the cobras, being rather addicted to a burrowing life. The form is cylindrical, with small, blunt head. The usual markings consist of red, black and yellow disposed in rings, a pattern rendering the species generally distinguishable, though various harmless snakes evince striking similarities of pattern. In Mexico is a variety of *Micrurus fulvius,* with narrow black rings separated by very wide red spaces, the black narrowly and obscurely bordered with yellow; it is wonderfully like a non-venomous snake known technically as *Lampropeltis micropholis* and closely related to the little red king snake of the southern United States, *L. triangulum.* The harmless serpent in question has the narrow black rings separated by wide red spaces, but close examination will show a faint and very narrow yellow ring within the black. Hurriedly examined, the poisonous and harmless snakes might be pronounced identical. To add to the deception, the head of each is black with a yellow band crossing the temples. Such conditions point to some definite provision of Nature, but it would be a bold assertion and mere theory to declare that the harmless snake has acquired the coloration of the poisonous reptile in order to inspire respect among its several enemies. It appears certain, though, that this similarity of pattern, color and form, between creatures widely separated in classification, indicates no uncertain process of evolution, but one which is governed by conditions as yet unknown to Science.

Despite emphatic assertions to the contrary, the species of *Micrurus* are highly venomous. In proportion to the reptiles' size, their fangs are capable of inflicting damage equal to the Old World allies. Few of the Coral Snakes, however, attain a length of more than a yard. *Micrurus corallinus, M. lemniscatus* and *M. marcgravii,* of tropical South America, cause frequent loss of human life. These species reach a length of three and a half or four feet.

Occasional examples of *Micrurus lemniscatus,* the SOUTH AMERICAN CORAL SNAKE, are four feet long. It is common on the mainland and occurs in several of the islands of the Lesser Antilles. This is a gorgeous snake, the pattern consisting of glaring brick-red rings separated by very wide rings of purplish black, each of the black areas containing two narrow rings of yellowish-white. The polished scales are highly opalescent. The tip of the snout is dull red; behind this is a black band followed by a red band as broad as those on the body. The measurements of a fine specimen from Trinidad are:

Total length	3 feet, 10½ inches.
Diameter of body	1 inch.
Width of head	⅞ inch.

But two species of *Micrurus* occur in the United States, their red, yellow and black-ringed coloration causing them to look rather alike. There is also a strong resemblance to several harmless snakes, particularly the following species: Arizona King Snake, *Lampropeltis multicincta;* Western Milk Snake, *L. triangulum gentilis;* Scarlet King Snake, *L. elapsoides* and the Scarlet Snake, *Cemophora coccinea.* Careful examination will demonstrate a valuable character that may be generally employed in distinguishing the venomous from the harmless reptiles. It will be noted in the case of the poisonous snake that *the black rings are single and bordered with a pair of yellow rings.* With the harmless species *the yellow rings are single and bordered with a pair of black rings.*

The species of Coral Snakes found in the United States may be easily separated, as follows:

Snout black; a yellow band across the head, followed by a *black* ring. HARLEQUIN SNAKE; CORAL SNAKE, *Micrurus fulvius.*
Habitat: Southeastern United States into Mexico.

Snout black; a yellow band across head, followed by a *red* ring. SONORAN CORAL SNAKE, *Micrurus euryxanthus.*
Habitat: Arizona and northern Mexico.

The HARLEQUIN SNAKE or CORAL SNAKE, of the southeastern part of the United States, is a common reptile in South Carolina, Georgia and Florida, where it is dug up in sweet potato fields during ploughing. Specimens are found wandering about, after heavy rains. The scales are highly polished and opalescent; the pattern consists of regularly-disposed, broad scarlet and black rings, separated by narrow rings of yellow. The snout is black; a wide orange band crosses the head. It is not unusual to find specimens with the scarlet much obscured by a scattering of black spots; on the abdomen the coloration is more brilliant. A big example is a yard long and three-quarters of an inch in diameter at the thickest part of the body. The head is blunt and flattened, but little distinct from the neck and has minute, beady eyes.

Ranging into Mexico, the Coral Snake undergoes a considerable variation in pattern. One phase of *M. fulvius* shows the red rings of great breadth, a constriction of the black ones and almost total obliteration of the yellow.

Among the species of *Micrurus* generally, the blunt head, minute eyes, absence of the loreal plate, cylindrical form and brightly ringed pattern are strong distinguishing features.

The species of *Micrurus* rank rather low in mental powers. They appear stupefied by captivity. The prevailing idea is to avoid the light and observation, and this they do, if there are any facilities for burrowing or coiling beneath some object. Once secreted, all ideas of food seem to vanish among the majority of specimens. Like many of the Elapine snakes addicted to burrowing habits, the Coral Snakes are cannibalistic, feeding upon other species of snakes and lizards. The method of feeding is similar to that of the king cobra, though these smaller serpents display less ingenuity in overpowering the prey. It is quickly grasped and worked along in the jaws until the head points down the throat, when swallowing commences. Upon the cold-blooded prey the poison is slow in taking effect; and, while the fangs are observed to be repeatedly employed, the subtle fluid seems to aid the snake but little in subduing the quarry, which usually struggles vigorously during the entire swallowing process. The Coral Snakes consume serpents of surprising proportions in comparison to their own bulk and length. Several times the writer has observed *Micrurus fulvius* eating snakes that were but a few inches shorter than the feeding reptile and of greater thickness of body. After engulfing a meal of this size, the gorged snake is rendered too rigid to properly coil. The scales are so widely separated as to appear like well-separated rows of shining spots. All the species of *Micrurus* show a liking for lizards, especially such smooth-scaled species as the *Scincidæ*. A big example of *Micrurus corallinus* swallowed a stout-bodied, red-headed lizard (*Eumeces fasciatus*) that was fully nine inches long. Lizards are more susceptible to the action of the poison than the smaller harmless snakes.

It is fortunate, though, if one succeeds in inducing a single specimen of *Micrurus fulvius* out of a dozen to take food. The food may be regularly placed in the cage or left with the specimens, yet in the midst of plenty, after fasts lasting from six to ten months, they slowly but deliberately starve. While utterly disregarding the presence of food, they exhibit an interesting desire for water. For this they regularly search their cage and, when it is found, drink long and copiously.

It has been stubbornly alleged that the species of *Micrurus* are mild in disposition, seldom attempting to bite. Such assertions are not only fallacious, but dangerously misleading. They tend to invite accidents from reptiles that are highly formidable. Observed closely and sympathetically, the Coral Snakes will be found to exhibit habits that are unique in comparison with the other poisonous snakes. They do not "strike" at an offending object, but twist and snap from side to side with the rapidity of motion of a well-tempered steel spring suddenly released from tension. So energetic are these actions that some species, touched lightly with a stick, will instantly turn and grasp their own body. They *bite,* as do the cobras, when once they have seized the offending object, advancing the fangs in a series of chewing motions and producing four or five separate wounds with each. The truth is that occasional specimens appear to be quite gentle, if handled. The writer has experimented with such examples, protecting his hands with heavy buckskin gloves. The results were interesting, as they showed with what degree of safety a reckless person might handle these apparently quiet and pretty, though poisonous, reptiles.

An example may be handled for some time without a show of temper on the serpent's part—providing the operator employs no resisting motions. A slight pressure of the fingers may cause the snake to turn without warning, seize a finger and chew viciously, staining the glove with venom. The larger, tropical species are much more "touchy" than the common species of the United States.

Yet they never "strike" unless pursuing their prey. A child running about bare-footed would certainly be bitten if treading upon a snake of this kind, but we may remove the Coral Snakes from the more dangerous class—those serpents that *strike* at a passing object. The writer has never observed a specimen of *Micrurus* to bite unless actually touched on the body. Especially nervous specimens will thrash from side to side, but do not attempt to seize an object near by, even though it should be in motion. Their fangs are so short that ordinary clothing would insure good protection—a pair of canvas leggings over thin clothing producing perfect immunity from the largest specimens.

The breeding habits of the Coral Snakes seem to be comparatively unknown. Until two years before the time of writing, the author's efforts to note definite results were unavailing. A specimen of *Micrurus fulvius* finally deposited eleven eggs, which were placed in finely-ground wood pulp. Though these eggs were kept moist and warm, they required the lengthy period of *thirteen weeks* for incubation. The young were marked like the parent, but the scarlet, yellow and black rings were in more vivid contrast. In form they were proportionately more slender and dug like earthworms into the hatching medium. Compared with the dark hue of the latter, they were in brilliant contrast, their lustrous, beautiful hues causing them to appear as if freshly squeezed from a paint tube.

The VIPERINE SNAKES; *Viperidæ* and *Crotalidæ*. The families of long-fanged venomous serpents are the most specialized among snakes in the development of the poison apparatus. In place of the elongate and horizontal maxillary bone, existing with the snakes we have examined, the maxillary of the present reptile is reduced to a small, *vertical*, movable bone on each side of the anterior part of the head and bearing an enormously elongated, canaliculated fang, provided with a narrow orifice at the tip like a hypodermic needle. Connecting with each maxillary is a bone extending from the rear of the head, its function lever-like in raising or lowering the fang at the will of the snake. Here we find several differences from the formidable elapine snakes, thus:—(1) There are no teeth in the upper "jaw," except the two rows of palatine teeth and the pair of huge, venom-conducting fangs; most of the elapine snakes have a short row of small teeth behind each fang. (2) The fangs of the Vipers, rigidly attached to *movable* bones, fold flat against the roof of the mouth when the jaws are closed.

By far the greater number of Viperine snakes are thick-bodied, with a distinct flattened head, while the eyes have a cat-like pupil. They exhibit the outlines popularly accredited to poisonous snakes and are markedly slower in their motions—except in striking—than the elapine snakes. As a great number of the species have the head covered with small scales in place of regularly-arranged shields, they may be told almost at a glance. Still there is considerable variation in form from the slender tree vipers to the hideous-looking adders of Africa. A certain proportion of the species have a comparatively slender body and a head provided with regularly-arranged shields, as noted among the innocuous and the venomous colubrines. There is no possibility of constructing a popular chart key that will enable the student to distinguish such species. Locality is a factor of great importance and the writer has endeavored to impart a clear idea of the general distribution of well-defined groups. A glance over the thoroughly representative series of illustrations showing the Viperine forms will do more for the student than a long description in print. Vipers have either keeled or smooth scales—mostly the former; the plates under the tail may be in one or two rows—the former the commoner character.

The vipers are divided into two families, thus:

	Examples
No head pits.	
Family *Viperidæ*.	European Viper.
The TRUE VIPERS.	Sand Natter.
Distribution: Confined to the Old World.	Tic Polonga.
	Rhinoceros Viper.
	Puff Adder.

A deep pit between the eye and nostril —on each side of head.	The Rattlesnakes.	New World.
	Copperhead Snake	New World.
	Water Moccasin.	New World.
Family *Crotalidæ*.	Fer-de-Lance.	New World.
The PIT VIPERS.	Bushmaster.	New World.
Distribution: New and Old World.	Tree Vipers	Old World.

In the United States and in Europe the poisonous snakes represent viperine types,[1] those in the former country representatives of the *Crotalidæ;* the European poisonous snakes represent the family *Viperidæ.* Rattlesnakes abound in many parts of the United States, while frequenting the swamps of the southeastern portion is a semi-aquatic Crotaline snake that is highly dangerous; northward, the place of the latter reptile is taken by the formidable copperhead snake. The European poisonous snakes are not nearly so large or dangerous; nevertheless they are poisonous enough to cause occasional loss of human life; among them are the common viper and the sand natter.

Popularly described, the venom of the Viperine snakes plays most of its havoc in the blood. The bitten arm or leg swells greatly and becomes much discolored; within the injured members the blood actually oozes from the vessels, producing a remarkable state of internal hemorrhage, this bringing great danger of attendant septicæmia from germ infection and necessitating heroic drainage. The bites of elapine snakes produce little of these local effects. The poison appears to attack the nerve centers, particularly that system controlling the muscles of the chest, and the victim meets death from an inability to breathe. It is in such cases that strychnine is a valuable alternative.

The TRUE VIPERS, family *Viperidæ.* Among the members of the *Viperidæ* are some of the most villainous-looking of all snakes; for the most part the head is flattened and heart-shaped, the body short and thick, but there are strange exceptions to the general form, as will be found in all families of snakes. In tropical and South Africa is a genus

[1] Except two small Elapine snakes in the United States.

of vipers forming the most deceptive series of snakes the writer has ever examined. They are moderately slender with gradually-tapering tail, have a very ordinary head bearing large, symmetrical shields, while the eye has a round pupil; to add to the deception, there is a loreal plate (between the eye and the nostril), as seen with the typical harmless snakes.

The CAPE VIPER, *Causus rhombeatus,* may be taken as a good example of this colubrine-like series. The scales are keeled. Above, the color is grayish with dark and angular, sometimes rhomb-shaped markings, these often margined with white. If the mouth is examined, the fangs will be found proportionately very small, looking like those of an elapine snake, but they may be raised and lowered at will and fold against the roof of the mouth when the jaws are closed, in true Viperine fashion. An adult Cape Viper is barely a yard in length. The species is common throughout southern Africa.

In its habits the Cape Viper about reverses every characteristic attributed to the family. While the vipers produce living young, this is an egg-laying species.[2] It is quick in its motions, gliding away as fast as a colubrine snake, while it has failed to keep up the dignified habits of vipers generally, of preying upon warm-blooded animals; it feeds mostly upon frogs, suddenly grasping a specimen and swallowing it amid a series of struggles, as if forgetting for the moment the existence and use of the fangs.

One of the writer's specimens deposited ten eggs on the first of September. These were creamy-white, with a tough leathery shell, adhesive in a cluster and each contained a thread-like embryo coiled like the hairspring of a watch. A measurement of one of the eggs showed it to be one and one-quarter inches long, and seven-sixteenths of an inch in diameter. Another snake laid twelve eggs on the twentieth of the same month.

[2] Another genus, *Atractaspis,* composed of small, burrowing species comes under this head.

Vipera, containing ten species, large and small, is represented in Europe, Asia, northern and tropical Africa. The COMMON VIPER, *V. berus,* the only poisonous snake occurring in the British Isles, is one of the smaller species. The forward portion of the head is covered with fairly regular shields, though these look more crowded than with colubrine snakes; the eye has an elliptical pupil. As a rule, the pattern is strong and characteristic, consisting of a dark, continuous zigzag band down the back; this may be sooty black on an olive or dark brown ground color, or dark brown on a grayish hue. There is a row of ill-defined blotches on each side and a dark bar from the eye to the neck; the abdomen is usually black. A not uncommon variety is uniform, velvety black. Following are the dimensions of an adult female specimen:

Total length	20 inches.
Length of tail	2¼ inches.
Greatest diameter	¾ inch.
Width of head	¾ inch.

The distribution of the Viper over Europe is extensive; it apparently ranges farther from the equator than any other poisonous serpent—possibly excepting a species of rattlesnake. The range is from Wales, eastward throughout northern Europe, thence eastward through Siberia to the island of Saghalien. In northern Europe it is generally abundant; it ranges southward to northern Spain. It is more abundant than the common grass snake (*Natrix*) in some parts of England and Scotland.

The Viper is a pugnacious little reptile, lying flattened and glaring at an intruder, steadily hissing with each inhalation and exhalation of the breath. Its biting motions are lightning-quick—a dart and return to the original position. This action is characteristic of the Viperine snakes. To say the snake *strikes* is to use an appropriate term. As the head is launched forward the jaws are opened to an extremely wide extent, the fangs spring forward and literally stab the object aimed for. At the instant of their penetration, there is a biting movement, during which the muscles over the poison glands are contracted and a stream of venom forced from the tip of each fang. The whole operation consumes but the fraction of a second and the student will realize how different is the manœuvre from the deliberate *bite* of the elapine snakes.

While the Common Viper is a distinctly dangerous snake, its bite does not ordinarily produce death, if efficient treatment immediately follows the injury. The first thing to be done is to place a ligature tightly above the bitten part, open the punctures with a sharp knife or a razor, suck the wounds thoroughly, then wash them with a solution of permanganate of potassium—and rinse the mouth with the same. The effect of this chemical is to oxidize and destroy the action of the poison. It should be realized that these precautions should be taken without the loss of a possible instant's time—a wait for the doctor, no matter how short it may be, is apt to prove a fatal procrastination.

Under observation the Viper is a nervous and irritable snake, feeding in erratic fashion. When it does show signs of appetite, it prefers very young mice—from the nest—and freshly-hatched birds. The species produces living young, about a dozen in number; they are quite large as compared to the parent. Dampness is exceedingly distasteful to this snake. To maintain specimens in good health they must be kept very warm and very dry.

Several small species, closely allied to the Common Viper, are found in southern Europe. Among them are *Vipera aspis* and *V. latastii.*

The SAND NATTER, *V. ammodytes,* found in southeastern Europe, cannot possibly be confused with any other European snake, as its snout is furnished with a soft horn over an eighth of an inch in length on a mature specimen. An adult is about two feet long, dull gray, with a chain of dark rhombs on the back. The species is vicious and more dangerous than the common viper. It lives in dry, sandy places. The author's specimens lived for several years, feeding upon mice and small rats. Their cage was provided with fine, dry sand and in this medium they burrowed at times. The first rays of the morning sun brought them forth to flatten and bask; as the beam of sun coming through the window changed its position during the day, they gradually shifted with it, finally coiling tightly against the side of the cage—in a compact mass—to enjoy the last afternoon rays. After a year in captivity they became very tame, gliding to the cage door and gently taking a dead mouse from one's fingers—though it must be acknowledged the author always considered it best to hold the offering by the extreme tip of the tail. After a snake inspected a mouse for a few seconds, lightly probing it with the tongue-tips, it took the morsel by the snout; if the mouse was shaken, the reptile bit hard, imbedding the fangs, then dragging the animal backward some distance, lay motionless, as if awaiting its death; after several minutes' deliberation the meal was swallowed.

One of the commonest and most deadly snakes of India is a species of *Vipera*. This is the TIC POLONGA, the DABOIA, or RUSSELL'S VIPER, *V. russellii,* a beautifully-colored reptile reaching a length of five feet. The body is pale brown with three longitudinal series of black rings enclosing spots of chocolate brown and each intensified on its outer border by a tinge of white or yellow. The series of rings on the back are somewhat the larger; some of them fuse together, forming chain-like markings. The last blotch on the back runs into a longitudinal band on the tail. There is a dark band from the eye to the angle of the mouth and another from the eye downward; also a dark blotch on each temple. The abdomen is yellowish with numerous dark spots irregularly scattered.

With this viper the scales are strongly keeled; the head is covered with small keeled scales. Under the tail the plates are in a double row. The body is fairly stout with an abruptly-tapering tail; the head is very distinct. Following are the dimensions of a fair-sized adult specimen:

Total length	4 ft., 1 inch.
Length of tail	7 inches.
Girth	6 inches.
Width of head	2 inches.
Length of head	2 inches.

The range of this snake, the largest of the Asiatic vipers, embraces India, Ceylon, Burma, Siam and the Malay Peninsula. My friend, Mr. Rudolf Weber, brought several small specimens of typical coloration from Sumatra, showing the species to occur on at least one of the larger islands. When annoyed the Tic Polonga—the name meaning the spotted snake—hisses sharply and steadily with each intake and exhalation of the breath, the body rising and falling like a bellows during the performance.

Besides the Tic Polonga there is but one other member of the *Viperidæ* in British India, and this is a species ranging eastward from the sandy regions of northern Africa, Arabia and Persia. It is brownish gray with three longitudinal series of whitish, black-edged spots. The maximum length is about twenty inches. Technically it is known as *Echis carinata.* It is common in many parts of the Indian peninsula. The bite seldom proves fatal.

It is in Africa, the headquarters of the true vipers, that we find a variety of forms of the *Viperidæ,* some slender-bodied with a prehensile tail and altogether arboreal (*Atheris*), one fair-sized genus of small, colubrine-like forms (*Atractaspis*), having shields on the head and addicted to a burrowing life, and an important genus, made up of the most hideous-looking of all snakes. The latter is *Bitis,* containing eight species.

The cobras have impressed us with a feeling of awe at their activity and viciousness, but there is a certain weird grace in their rearing pose and slender form. The present genus is striking from quite an opposite standpoint. Its members are exceedingly sluggish in their gait, while they exhibit every outline that is formidable and villainous in a snake; their bodies are so short. thick and bloated as to lack all the grace of the typical serpent; the tail is abruptly tapering and stubby. Most impressive is the huge, cruel, heart-shaped head, with its staring, cat-like eyes. The fangs are enormously developed and it is almost needless to say the bite of such creatures is usually fatal. Absolutely incongruous to the fiendish configuration and menacing actions is the coloration, which is exquisitely beautiful, suggesting the richest hues and designs of Oriental tapestry.

Most widely distributed and best known, owing to its distribution into South Africa to the Cape, is the PUFF ADDER, *B. arietans*. It is found over Africa generally, with the exception of the northern coastal region, and extends into Arabia. The length is up to four and a half feet and a specimen of this size would be nine inches in girth.

The Puff Adder lives in dry, sub-arid places, hiding in the half-burnt grass during the day or actually burying itself in the sand. At night it comes forth to seek the trails of small mammals; finding a likely spot, it lies flattened and motionless, the anterior part of the body doubled into an S-shaped loop. That silent form is wide awake and watching. Woe betide the luckless rodent that passes it! A dart of the snake seals the fate of the victim, which, pierced by the terrible fangs, seldom utters as much as an agonized squeal.

The pattern of the Puff Adder is characteristic. A freshly-shed specimen generally shows sooty black chevrons, separated by cream-colored crescents. There are, of course, variations in the body hues; on some snakes the crescents are dull buff and the chevron markings dark brown or gray. The popular title comes from the common habit of the true vipers—that of hissing violently with each inhalation and expulsion of the breath, but a habit particularly vociferous with the present serpent.

Another of these hideously-ugly snakes is the GABOON VIPER, *B. gabonica*. Its range embraces the whole of tropical Africa from Liberia to Damaraland and eastward to the East Coast. It is a creature of sterile, sandy places. When surprised, it makes no attempt to get away, flattening against the sand, making short jabs at the intruder and blowing noisily. The nostrils open on the top of the snout, while the eyes might be said to gaze upward, provisions enabling the creature to imbed itself in the sand with the exception of the top of the head, yet alert for passing objects. It is a "looper" or "sidewinder," progressing by throwing loops of the body forward in a lateral fashion, when it moves off in an oblique direction to that in which the head is pointing.

Of all the venomous snakes ever studied by the author, this is absolutely the most sinister in its aspect. The eyes are silvery white, with an elliptical pupil, and the reptile's glassy stare is strangely fascinating. Steadily inspected, the snake becomes uneasy, slowly shifting the few loops of its bloated body, then begins blowing with steady rhythm. At the expiration of each breath the head is slightly flattened, resuming its normal outlines at the next intake of air; the effect becomes uncanny and might lead the novice to believe the strange reptile is actually making horrible "faces" to frighten the observer away.

The pattern is difficult to describe, but rich and attractive, like a design of expert weaving. On the back is a series of oblong, buff markings, these enclosed within irregular brown rhombs. The pattern described is again enclosed by a chain or irregular, purplish markings. In the center of the back the patches of brown, within the purplish chain-like markings, connect the oblong blotches by figures in outline like an hourglass. On the sides are triangular purplish blotches margined with brown. The head is pale brown; from the tip of the snout to the neck is a dark streak. From beneath each eye are two broad dark bands.

To impart an idea of the truly eccentric form of the Gaboon Viper, the following measurements of an adult specimen are given; note the extremely thick body for the length:

Total length	31	inches.
Length of tail	3	inches.
Girth of body	7	inches.
Width of head	2¼	inches.
Diameter of neck immediately behind head	¾	inch.
Length of head	2¼	inches.

Some specimens have a pair of blunt horns on the snout.

Even more grotesque than the preceding snake is the RHINOCEROS VIPER, *B. nasicornis,* provided with two long —and often several smaller—horns on the snout, these being formed of single compressed shields. The effect is striking. The scales are coarsely keeled; on many old specimens the keels are developed into spiny points standing directly outward. So bristling is this scalation that a specimen handled by the writer lacerated his forearm until it bled profusely from a multitude of scratches.

The body of the Rhinoceros Viper is very stout, but the head is proportionately much smaller than that of the preceding species. It is quite a different type of snake, having smaller fangs, crawling in a different fashion and living along the river banks. Further investigation of its anatomical characters may result in its being placed in another genus than the large-headed, long-fanged species of *Bitis.* Owing to its semi-aquatic habits it is sometimes called the RIVER JACK.

The Rhinoceros Viper is, to the author's mind, the most beautifully colored of all poisonous snakes. Its gorgeous hues, when freshly disclosed by the shedding of an old epidermis, remind one of the colors to be seen in a frame of tropical butterflies. Following is a faithful description of a freshly-shed specimen:

Entire upper surface presenting the effect of variegated velvet. A row of *pale blue,* nicked, oblong blotches on the back, each longitudinally traversed by an orange-yellow band and narrowly bordered with the same hue. The blue oblongs are set in jet-black rhombs and these in turn are bordered with *dark carmine.* Sides, with large, upright, ruddy-brown triangles, bordered with dull carmine, thence with black and externally with pale blue. Between all of the blotches and pronounced markings, the ground color is rich olive, thickly peppered with black. The head is bluish, with black dots and ornamented in the center with a sooty-black, arrow-shaped blotch pointing forward; the horns are yellow.

No more wonderfully beautiful combination of colors can be imagined. In crawling, when the muscles of the lower sides are in play, carrying the skin backward and forward, the effect is like that of a gigantic and particularly gaudy caterpillar. Coiled in its cage, the reptile from which the description was taken looked positively artificial. Unfortunately, these splendid colors are soon lost. By frequently entering the water, the snake acquires a thin coating of grime and the pattern becomes dingy. Note the difference between the frontispiece of this work and one of the plate illustrations. They represent one and the same snake. The plate illustration is that of the reptile some ten days before shedding the skin, when it appeared in its handsome coat like a butterfly emerging from the chrysalis.

Four feet is the average length of an adult Rhinoceros Viper. The *habitat* is tropical West Africa.

Much smaller African vipers are two species of the northern, desert regions, forming the genus *Cerastes*. The maximum length is about two and a half feet.

The HORNED VIPER OR ASP, *C. cornutus,* has been alleged by some historians to be the serpent figuring in the suicide of Cleopatra; others assert the beautiful queen's weird instrument of destruction to have been the Egyptian cobra.

It is impossible to mistake the Horned Viper. It is a typical creature of the desert, of a pale, sandy hue with obscure markings. Over each eye is a sharp, upright spine. Examples of the species are delicate as captives. They feed well enough for a few months, then die of various ailments —enteritis, diseases of the lungs or suppurative disorders of the mouth-parts. Eight specimens were at one time exhibited in the New York Zoological Park. They would not feed unless the temperature of their cage was over 75° Fahrenheit, continually clustering on the perforated copper sheathing in front of their cage, which metal was directly over the heating pipes. Like all desert vipers, they were continually seeking to throw sand over their backs, thus hiding their bodies. If the cage were to be provided with several inches of fine sand, nothing would be seen of the snakes during the day but the tops of their heads. In shoveling sand the reptile flattens the body to such an extent, the lower edge acts as a scoop, then by a remarkable series of wave-like motions traveling the length of the body, on either side, the snake sinks into the sand or works this over its back. To provide for this sand-loving life the eyes are placed near the top of the head, as with some water snakes (*Helicops*), but this character is more pronounced with the COMMON SAND VIPER, *C. vipera,* of northern Africa. It is without horns, but otherwise much like the preceding species. A flourishing colony has also lived in the Zoological Park. The specimens alternately endeavored to shovel sand or move rapidly about the cage in a bewildering series of loops—the reptile not actually crawling, but throwing out lateral loops, one after another, in a fashion that imparts an agile *walking* motion. The arrival of these vipers was attended with a great surprise to the writer, who momentarily thought he had discovered a "new species."

When the vipers arrived at the Park, specimens of the closely-allied horned species, *C. cornutus,* were mixed among a considerably greater number of the commoner snake. All of the horned specimens were placed in a cage by themselves; the examples of *C. vipera* were placed in an adjoining cage. Upon looking over the former lot the author was surprised to find specimens with the horns springing from a position behind the eye in place of directly above it, while the entire scalation of such specimens looked suspiciously like that of the Common Viper. A closer inspection showed an interesting condition. The clever Arab fakirs had pushed a couple of quills of the desert hedgehog, *Erinaceus auritus,* up from the roof of the mouth and through the top of the head. When these specimens were examined it was not surprising to find their mouths in a state of great inflammation. The false horns were withdrawn, the reptiles' mouths washed with an antiseptic solution, and they were soon none the worse for their protracted torture.

The *habitat* of *C. cornutus* embraces the northern border of the Sahara Desert from Algeria to Egypt·and Nubia; it also occurs in Arabia and southern Palestine. *C. vipera* is restricted to northern Africa from Algeria to Egypt. Illustrations of both species are given.

The PIT VIPERS; family *Crotalidæ.* Six genera and about seventy species form this family. Every member is immediately recognizable by the presence of a deep pit between the eye and the nostril on each side of the head. The object of this pit is not known. It has been alleged to constitute an organ of a *sixth sense,* but as man himself does not possess this sense, the function of the pit is beyond the power of his imagination. That the pit is of some importance is evident by the extensive cavity in the maxillary bone for its reception, the lining of the pit itself with a membranous skin, its connection with a secondary pit close to the eye and the significant presence of a large nerve leading from it to the brain. At any rate, from a popular standpoint the pit at once brands the Crotaline snake and enables us to abbreviate our subsequent descriptions.

Among the *Crotalidæ* we find one absolutely unique group—the Rattlesnakes. The remarkable caudal appendage is an unfailing character.

The six genera of the *Crotalidæ* may be easily separated, as follows:

Without a Rattle.

Top of head with symmetrical plates. *Agkistrodon.*
Distribution: Old and New World.

Top of head with small granular scales. *Lachesis.*
Distribution: New World. (1 species.)
Top of head with small scales. *Bothrops.*
Distribution: Tropical America.
Top of head with small scales. *Trimeresurus.*
Distribution: Old World.

Tail with a Rattle.
Top of head with symmetrical plates. *Sistrurus.*
Distribution: United States and Mexico.
Top of head with small scales. *Crotalus.*
Distribution: North and South America.

While a number of pit vipers are found in the Old World, the majority of them, the greatest variety of forms and the largest species, inhabit the New World.

Agkistrodon includes both New and Old World species, ten in number. Of the New World species we may take the WATER MOCCASIN *or* COTTON-MOUTH SNAKE, *A. piscivorous,* as a good example. It is a semi-aquatic serpent infesting the lagoons and sluggish water-ways of the southeastern portion of the United States. The average Moccasin is about four feet long, dull olive with wide, blackish transverse blotches barely showing on the back, but boldly defined on the sides. The body is very stout and heavy with an abruptly-tapering tail and a chunky, ugly head; the scales are roughly keeled. In lagoons and bayous, where food is especially plenty, the Moccasin grows to a length of six feet; these big specimens are a dingy brown or black with little traces of the markings.

This is one of the most deadly of the North American snakes. It is practically omnivorous, feeding upon fishes, frogs, other snakes, birds and small mammals. In captivity it outlives all other species. Some of the author's specimens have been captive over twelve years, breeding regularly. Several generations are living in the Zoological Park. Ten to fourteen form a litter; the young are vividly marked—pinkish, with red-brown, white-margined transverse bands and a sulphur-yellow tail.

Some of the writer's most interesting snake hunts have

been in the Southern bayous. In his reminiscences the Moccasin figures prominently.

"Keep the boat steady and look yonder," whispers my guide.

Following the direction of his cautiously-raised and pointing hand, a sight to enthuse the snake-hunter greets my eyes.

"A 'cotton-mouth' and an old timer," says the lookout.

Sunning its heavy folds on a gnarled and twisted tree that rises from the coffee-colored waters is a huge Moccasin. As our unwieldy craft glides toward it a sinister head turns in our direction, the jaws open widely, disclosing the white mouth-parts, while the outlines of a wicked pair of fangs show through their sheaths. Carefully manipulating the pole, we bring the "boat" to a stop and advance the snake-noose on a long rod of bamboo. There is a quivering flash of the forked tongue and the reptile, preferring security to combat, slides with the ease of flowing oil down the twisted branches and into the water with such smoothness of motion that no splash accompanies its disappearance. A few bubbles mark the dive and we turn to stare at one another in mutual disappointment.

We had been snake-hunting through the bayous for half the day and several dozen harmless captives filled the bags. Relieving the guide from the tiresome punting of the flat-bottomed craft, the writer had posted his faithful and enthusiastic companion on the bow as lookout as we spied this, our first cotton-mouth. But a little more than a week before the writer had left the North in a whirl of snow for a short stay in the wonderfully balmy air of the far Southern coast. From blustering winds and leafless trees to an atmosphere like the Northern June, the stately palmettoes and the live oaks with their garlands of hanging moss was a delicious change. Reptile life flourished in variety and plenty.

"That snake's an old timer and the boss of this swamp,"

said my guide. "There's not a copper-belly or a brown water snake in the bayou. He's cleaned 'em all out."

The author agreed with his companion. On more than one occasion he had noted the cannibalistic habits of the Moccasin. But the big fellow was gone and we sat looking from his sunning place to the wake of bubbles—to no avail. After due consultation we decided to try his capture at night, when he would be less wary. Marking well the location of the tree, the decision was to return on the evening of the following day. The "cotton-mouth" has the characteristic of selecting a particular roost; we were sure of finding the big fellow on the same tree.

It was late in the following afternoon that we started again for the bayous. Along the sandy trail our mules made slow progress, but their tardiness favored our work. It gave us time to examine our surroundings in a lookout for snakes and several scaly captives went into the bags. Once we stopped to investigate a hut with toppling mud chimney. The place had been deserted by the negroes during a yellow-fever scare. In the rafters a pile of corn fodder had been riddled by the rats which infested the structure. Prospects were encouraging and we were not disappointed. Coiled on one of the rude girders was a big yellow rat snake, regarding us with hostile mien. It was difficult to reach the creature, so we tried to poke him down with a pole. To this treatment he objected and struck angrily, to the accompaniment of a sharp hiss. This was too much excitement for the colored boy we had brought with us; he promptly fled, taking the mules. With the dusk rapidly settling, haste was necessary. The snake showed an inclination to crawl along the girder to the pile of fodder and would there get away. Making a jump for the girder, the writer managed to reach it with one hand, when the flimsy support gave way and saved him climbing for a mid-air tussle with the snake. Man, snake and timber landed together. Hearing the crash from outside, where he had retreated for some distance with the mules, our colored boy at once placed himself and the animals on what he considered safe ground, which proved to be about half a mile distant. The snake was soon bagged and we hunted the caravan with vigorous shouts. We found the boy and the mules at last. The former had become notorious for his cry of "hyar snaake," but his scouting was of slight value, as but a few seconds after his discovery he would be so breathless and at such a distance from the reptile, that its whereabouts was indefinite.

At length, in the light of the rising moon we started on. Against the radiance of the Southern night the trees stood black in silhouette. The sand gave way to a firm, mossy footing over which the mules moved at a more sprightly gait. We were approaching the low grounds and now and then passed a small lagoon, the waters of which steamed languidly. Not far away the bellowing of a 'gator broke the silence. The sound marked the termination of our journey by mule and we were soon in the flat-bottomed craft cutting across waters to the bayou of the big Moccasin.

Winding our way through a number of miniature islands covered with rank growth and here and there showing a matted space where an alligator had sprawled in the sunlight, we glided into shallow waters from which stood spectral trees very broad at the base and so suddenly narrowing a little distance from the water as to impart a weird aspect to this aquatic forest. To a considerable height the trunk of each tree shows a thin coating of yellow mud, illustrating the eccentricities of the near-by coffee-colored river as it rises and falls after the heavy rains, "backs up" into the low grounds or recedes so low at times within its muddy bed that the bayous become firm, dry forests during the summer heat.

The trees grow closer and as we pass under long streamers of the hanging moss our surroundings become black and uncertain. To attach the acetylene searchlight to our bow was the work of a few minutes and a path of brilliant white light pierced the darkness. It is strange that in the bright glare of a lamp of night, creatures exceedingly shy in the day may be approached and captured without difficulty. Frogs that would instinctively dive for shelter in the daylight lay staring stupidly at the rays of a powerful lamp and may be grabbed by hand before realizing their danger.

As we floated into the bayou we played the rays of the swivel lamp upon the various sections of derelict timber in an endeavor to locate the low, gnarled tree we were in search of. A few seconds passed, with our hearts beating rapidly, when we beheld this on our left—and vacant. Speechless with disappointment, my guide involuntarily swung the lamp to the right, then raised its beam in what seemed a futile examination of the place.

"Hey," he almost shouted. "There he is."

And sure enough, stretched in undulating fashion on the trunk of a fallen tree, lay the big "cotton-mouth." Huge he looked in the light of our lamp, his sides showing olive green, while the rough scales of the back seemed as black as a velvet. Slowly turning toward the boat, he gave us a glassy stare and a flash of forked tongue. It was easy work slipping a noose over that wicked head, when we swung him, writhing furiously, into the boat. As my assistant, "Charley" Snyder, turned the light inward and upon the struggling snake, the latter's villainy formed a scene that lingered long afterward with us all. Knotting and twisting about the pole, straining and contorting into uncanny shapes, jaws yawning and disclosing a pair of fangs that dribbled with the deadly yellow fluid as they rasped against everything in their reach, the picture spelled caution for us.

It was a job to thrill as we released the noose, avoiding the well-aimed thrusts of the triangular head and finally pinned that member to the floor of the craft with the heavy end of the snake-pole, when the creature was grasped by the neck. With Snyder holding open a large bag, the writer dropped the serpent within.

We stopped to rest and enjoy our pipes before starting

back: for there is always especial enjoyment about tobacco after good work is done. Our rest was cut short, however; we had barely settled down when the swamp grew hazy. This was a hint for quick return. The miasma of the Southern low grounds is far from wholesome.

The colored boy was waiting our return; we found him not at all inclined to enter into our enthusiasm about the captive. By protecting my mule with a cushion composed of pine branches to prevent the possibility of the snake biting through the bag during the return, the reptile rode comfortably enough while resting against the neck of the unsuspecting animal. Thus we started on a sleepy journey with no other incidents of interest.

The big Moccasin was shipped North. Occupying a spacious cage with other denizens of the low grounds, he survived to make a splendid exhibition specimen, under Snyder's skillful attention.

In central and southern Mexico and Central America is a snake closely allied to the water moccasin or "cottonmouth" of the United States. This is the MEXICAN MOCCASIN OR CANTIL, *A. bilineatus*. The general outlines and pattern are much like the northern ally. The coloration above is dull reddish-brown, wide darker blotches showing on the sides; these transverse bands are greatly accentuated by whitish or yellowish spots at their borders. The head is dark with a narrow but vivid yellow stripe beginning at the snout, passing backward over the eye and ending at the back of the head; beneath this, also beginning at the snout, is a broader stripe extending along the upper lip plates, thence backward to the angle of the mouth and to the neck. An old specimen from Jalisco, Mexico, shows the following measurements:

Total length	3 feet, 1 inch
Length of tail	6¼ inches.
Diameter of body	1¾ inches.
Width of head	1⅜ inches.
Length of head	1⅞ inches.

The habits are semi-aquatic.

Most beautiful in coloration of the North American pit vipers without rattles is the COPPERHEAD SNAKE, *A. mokasen.* The range is east of the Mississippi River, from southern Massachusetts to northern Florida, though in the extreme southern part of its distribution this snake crosses the valley of the great river and occurs commonly in Texas to the Rio Grande. The ground color is pale brown crossed by rich reddish-brown blotches. The uniform, coppery tinge of the head has prompted the popular name. The Eastern phase has the bands very narrow on the back and wide on the sides, resembling in outline, when looked at from above, an hourglass or a dumb-bell. Texas specimens have wider and fewer bands. A big Copperhead Snake is a yard long.

This highly-venomous serpent is partial to various conditions. In the North it lives in or in the immediate neighborhood of thick forests, where, when coiled, the peculiar pattern might be mistaken for a small heap of brightly-colored, fallen leaves. In the South it shuns the swamps proper, frequenting the plantations. It is not a particularly vicious snake, preferring to glide for ambush rather than fight. In areas where the species is particularly common, accidents are practically unheard of. The food consists of frogs, small birds and rodents. About a dozen young are produced at a birth; they have a sulphur-yellow tail.

Several species of *Agkistrodon* occur in the hill regions of India. *A. blomhoffii* inhabits eastern Siberia, China, Siam and Japan.

Trimeresurus, with close to twenty rather terrestrial and arboreal species, is represented in southeastern Asia and Malaysia.

In Mexico, Central and South America and the West Indies are large terrestrial and arboreal species that are among the most deadly of all snakes and having enormously-developed fangs. The upper surface of the head is covered with small scales. They represent two genera—*Lachesis* and *Bothrops.* We will first consider the largest species of tropical America, standing alone in its genus—a magnificent viper, attaining a length of twelve feet. Its scalation is so rough as to suggest the surface of a pineapple and its tail ends in a long, thin spine, suggesting an ancestral relationship to the rattlesnakes.

This terrible creature is known under several titles—the SIROCUCU, the MAPEPIRE and the BUSHMASTER; its technical name is *Lachesis muta.* The *habitat* embraces Central and tropical South America. A few words will convey an impression of the striking coloration—once seen never to be forgotten. The ground color is reddish yellow, approaching a pinkish hue on some specimens and crossed by blackish bands, rhomboidal in shape on the back, narrowing as they approach the abdomen; some of the blotches enclose patches of the ground color. There is a black streak from the eye to the angle of the mouth.

Though the longest of the Crotaline serpents, the Bushmaster is not a thick-bodied reptile. Its build is gracefully slender and it is highly active for a pit viper. A ten-foot specimen when coiled shows less bulk than a six-foot diamond rattlesnake of the Southeastern United States—*Crotalus adamanteus.*

To Mr. R. R. Mole of Port-of-Spain, Trinidad, the writer is much indebted for valuable information concerning this interesting snake and for the few living specimens that have ever been exhibited in the United States. In a capacious cage in the Reptile House of the New York Zoological Park, supplied with tropical vegetation, generous hiding places and an abundance of food, the story with each specimen has been the same—a stubborn, suicidal fast. So high strung and nervous is the organization of this snake, to force food down its throat in an endeavor to keep it alive is to kill it. The shock of overpowering it seems to benumb the reptile and hinders the subsequent assimilation of the forced meal. Not one specimen has been induced to feed, nor has the writer ever heard of a captive that has fed voluntarily. Thus the life in captivity is, at the longest, four to five months. There is always difficulty in shedding the skin. It appears probable, that in a wild state the reptile softens the skin by burrowing into vegetable débris, thence sloughing off the epidermis in this soft medium.

The Bushmaster seems to be the only species of Crotaline snake that lays eggs—as originally described by Mr. Mole. An extract from a letter by Mr. Mole to the writer follows:

> I believe the *Lachesis* (which I hope you received safely) contains eggs. You will remember that one I had laid a batch of some ten or twelve eggs three years ago. I have since learned that similar bunches of eggs have been occasionally found by hunters in holes inhabited by the Paca, *Cœlogenys* and the Armadillo and other burrowing animals, in which specimens of *Lachesis muta* are often found. I have seen these snakes dug out of such holes, but I have only seen the eggs laid in my cage. The snake is most frequently found on slight eminences—seldom in hollows. The hole I most clearly recollect was in the side of a hill and about five feet deep, and had evidently been made by some burrowing animal. I am told by those who have seen them that the eggs are usually found some three or four feet in. Our temperature is about 76° Fahrenheit in January, and in September about 79° Fahrenheit. It occasionally reaches 90°. I think the woods are cooler than other parts of the island, and I think there may be a little difference beneath the surface of the ground—that is to say, the temperature is lower. The earth was red alluvial clay. I am reminded by Mr. Urich, who has read this letter so far as it has gone, that in many parts of the country there is a large quantity of vegetable débris. Probably you will be able to arrange a cage in which this *Lachesis* will lay her eggs and perhaps bring them out, for I think they incubate them. They will be due some time in August. My own idea is that snakes from the tropics are generally kept in cages which are far too dry and hot for them to do well. I hope this letter may be of service to you in further advancing general knowledge of the habits of our big Pit Viper.

Unfortunately, the splendid specimen referred to in the letter died on the way North.

An example from Costa Rica measured 11 feet, 4 inches. The fangs, measured along the curve, were one and three-eighth inches long.

From a reliable source the writer is informed that a man

bitten in the thigh by an eight-foot Bushmaster died in less than ten minutes—the long fangs apparently wounding an important blood vessel.

Another of these formidable reptiles receives its most familiar title—the FER-DE-LANCE—from the Creole-French. This is *Bothrops atrox.* The definition of the name signifies—head of a lance, and is appropriate, as the snout is pointed, the temporal region swollen and the aspect of the head like a javelin point. The distribution is from southern Mexico into tropical South America; the species is also found in the Lesser Antilles on the islands of St. Lucia and Martinique, where, on the sugar plantations, it has been a constant menace to human life, but is disappearing on these islands.

The length is from five to six feet. The coloration is olivaceous gray, crossed by dark bands narrowly margined with dull yellow or greenish. Unlike the pattern of the Bushmaster, these bands are narrower on the back than on the sides; they widen considerably as they extend downward. Several species of similar pattern and configuration inhabit Central America and tropical South America. They give birth to large litters of young—as many as three dozen in a brood.

To appreciate the life of this nocturnal prowler we must draw a crude pen picture of the tropics and nowhere can we select a more appropriate spot than the beautiful island of Martinique. Prior to the cataclysm, when Mont Pelee let down its pall of death, the Lance-Head Snake was becoming menacingly common in many parts of the island. The eruption killed great numbers of the snakes, but in proportion to those areas saved from the rain of ashes by the winds, the danger from poisonous snakes has not been materially lessened.

It is night over the tropical luxuriance of Martinique—the night born only in the Caribbean. During the sultry day preceding, the sun has beaten down upon the palms and tangled vines until its merciless rays drove all the forest dwellers into shelter. But the great red orb has plunged away into the west, bringing sudden half-light and quicker darkness.

In the trunk of a mighty tree that has long since succumbed to a bolt from a passing shower, the Fer-de-Lance has been coiled and waiting for the night. The interior of the hollow trunk is damp and forms a snug resting place for the velvety folds of the snake. Around it crawl large scorpions, while clinging high above in the rotting shaft a nervous bat prepares for flight. This creature creeps toward a crevice in the tree; with the unfolding of the clammy wings a few particles of débris fell upon the snake and, awakened from its day sleep, the reptile relaxes its coils and crawls slowly from the hiding place to stop and lay staring with ever-open eyes at the surrounding blackness. The bat still rasps and flutters, but the prowlers of the night are not yet abroad and seem to be held in waiting for something. Only the insects yet show activity. The flash of the luminous beetles glow here and there, while a centipede, leaving a phosphorescent trail, crawls near the snake, showing the tree-trunk to be well patronized.

Slowly the undergrowth begins to stand in silhouette against the eastern sky and the tropic moon appears to call forth the creatures who love and await her light. The leaves of the stately palms soon glow blue and against the purple sky the bat takes wing. Crawling slowly from the tree the snake flattens in the moonlight. Its body rises and falls regularly as it inhales the air of the night. Now it yawns away the last vestige of sleep. As the mouth opens the cruel fangs swing forward. These instruments are thus momentarily unlimbered: for they must work to a nicety, as the night will show. There is a quivering flash of the black, forked tongue and, following a clearing through the grove, the snake starts off in gliding undulations. Sometimes the ground dips slightly, but over these rough surfaces goes the serpent with the ease of running water. Strangely the creature's green and yellow tints blend with the vegetation over which it glides. If it were motionless some thoughtless creature might approach its doom with little warning. The triangular head is alert with cat-like eyes and playing tongue: for the Fer-de-Lance is hungry, as hunting has been poor for some time. Night after night the miasma has hung thick and heavy in the brush and rose to float away only as the hated daylight was approaching. Moreover, strange rumblings have shook the ground, so frightening the wood rats and agoutis they could not be found in places accessible to the snake. But these troubles are apparently over. The night is brilliant and though the lagoon steams slowly, the mists float away among the tree tops.

Suddenly the snake's eyes dilate and it glares fixedly ahead.

Then comes a shadowy something down the trail, half running, half jumping, with numerous stops.

Drawing the scaly body into a series of loops the reptile waits.

Again its body colors blend with the surroundings while the glitter of its eyes might well be mistaken by the unwary for drops of dew scintillating in the moonlight.

Nibbling here and there upon a tender sprout, the quarry approaches. It is a young agouti, an animal having kinship with the rat, but in looks and actions resembling a deer in miniature. This little creature has just left its wary parent. She has tried to keep her two careless youngsters with her on high ground, but the little fellows, only a short time weaned, persist in rollicking from her side and into the thickets where danger lurks. With limpid eyes half closed and nostrils dilated, as there is a feeling that all in the glade is not to her liking, she watches one of the precious family searching for food in the hollow. With a tremulous, crooning sound she entreats its return, but curiosity has prompted the young animal to explore. Just ahead a bed of bright toadstools must be examined, and a little way off some tender sprouts look inviting.

The little creature is so lost in the enjoyment of the ramble that the mother's calls are unnoticed until a strange scent causes it to stop and sniff in imitation of the parent. Curiosity overcomes an immature instinct; yet it advances, though more cautiously—and toward the snake.

There is no sound to alarm, no sight of living creature but itself.

It is nosing among the green sprouts when something strange causes the large dark eyes to open widely. A flickering black object quivers in the moonlight—the serpent's tongue. With tendons taut and ready to bound away, the young animal peers curiously at the strange phenomenon. Again the mother's crooning call, yet temptation prompts an instant's investigation and a step forward and then—the sinister outlines of the snake are seen, but too late. A turn for a dash for safety is followed by a dart of the cruel head. There is a flash of white mouth-parts and the fangs are sunk in the agouti's trembling body and as quickly withdrawn.

The low cadence of the insect chorus is broken by a series of piercing squeals as the fated animal staggers to retrace its way. Already the venom is doing its work, though enough consciousness is left in the throbbing brain to distinguish the plaintive call of the terrified mother.

One last effort to reach her side, when the limbs give way and the animal sinks to the ground to writhe in its death struggles.

With head and neck outstretched, the Fer-de-Lance waits quietly for the end and, when it comes, glides slowly around the victim, touching it lightly with the tongue tips. And then the feast, the swallowing of an animal entire that is many times the diameter of the feaster's neck.

At length grasping the agouti by the nose, the reptile pushes one side of the upper and lower jaw forward, inserts the hooked swallowing teeth in the flesh of the victim and pulls the jaw bones back into place. The operation is repeated with the other side of the head. This process of dislocation working in alternation while the agouti is pulled into the mouth and down the throat which stretches to receive it. During this operation the poisonous fangs assist. The prey is steadily engulfed, though the distended skin of the reptile marks its progress down the latter's body. The snake yawns lazily and the distended jaws assume their normal position. An appetite of a fortnight has been satisfied. With progress slower than before the reptile drags its way over the mossy trail, stopping occasionally to drink the moisture from a concave leaf on the return to the lair.

Suddenly the snake throws its body into a coil and glares savagely up the valley while the tail beats a rapid tattoo—the posture of defense.

That strange trembling of the ground again which betokens harm, and from where?

But what glow is this that comes during the hours allotted to creatures of the night, changing the palm leaves previously bathed in blue to ruddy, coppery tinge? A great red column gushes skyward from Pelee. A mighty sound as of thunder rends the air, while high above, a tumbling mass of vapors rush across the heavens and draw an impenetrable canopy. Then in the light of volcanic fires comes a withering blast of hot and deadly vapor down the valley. A shower of bombs crashes through the trees and lies hissing and steaming upon the damp, rich soil.

In their terror the forest dwellers flee blindly and in vain. Through the ravine comes pouring a torrent of boiling mud, while a choking dust falls heavily, entombing the jungle and its life.

When daylight dawns, a day of smoke and stifling gases, the life is gone. Where in the thickets lurked the snake and its associates is a drifting waste of gray dust and scoriæ from which rises here and there a burned and blackened tree. Pelee mounts grandly in the vapors. The giant rests, but a dull plume of smoke floats from the crater, following the wind. Thus did Nature's forces turn against her creatures—against mankind as well.

The smaller New World species of *Bothrops* are mostly arboreal, having a prehensile tail. They are commonly known as Palm Vipers and frequently come North in the fruit steamers, hidden in bunches of bananas. The most frequent stowaway is the HORNED PALM VIPER, *B. schlegelii,* with graceful, slender body, but an extremely wicked-looking, heart-shaped head; the stubby tail is of great value as a prehensile appendage.

Quite distinctive is the scalation of the head. Over each eye is the usual supraocular plate, but this is separated from the eye by several smaller shields, generally two or three, that are erect and horn-like. The colors are prettily arranged, usually green, thickly powdered with black and showing at regular intervals blotches or spots of red or pink, bordered with olive. Curious yellow, albanistic specimens are quite common. The length of an adult is about two feet; a specimen this size has the tail two inches long, the diameter of the body about three-quarters of an inch and the width of the head one and an eighth inches—the latter showing a greater width than the diameter of the thickest part of the body. Central America generally, southward to Colombia and Ecuador, forms the *habitat.*

From the actions of captive examples the habits seem to be quite arboreal; for such an existence the reptile appears admirably suited in the possession of the prehensile tail which is dexterously employed in the animal's rather slow progress from branch to branch or in supporting it as it rests. The specimens under observation seemed quite gentle; they seldom offered to bite when disturbed. An evidence of this snake's good nature was illustrated in a startling fashion by a specimen donated to the Zoological Park. A friend of the author, engaged in the fruit business, discovered a brightly-marked snake gliding about the storeroom, evidently having arrived from the tropics in a bunch of bananas. Picking up the serpent on a stick, he was surprised to find it displayed the utmost good nature. Thus encouraged, he took the reptile home with the intention of keeping it as a pet. That evening the snake was given the liberty of the drawing-room table, while the gentleman's little daughter actually handled the creature as its pretty colors were generally admired. It would not eat, however, and a week later was brought to the writer's office by the little girl, who carried it in a thin pasteboard box. The astonishment of the author may be imagined when he discovered a specimen of this deadly lance-head issuing from the box in leisurely fashion upon the child's hand.

The species feeds largely upon young birds, catching them by a dart of the head from an ambush of tangled vegetation, when the prey is held in a tenacious grip, the fangs imbedded, until the poison has done its work.

Southeastern Asia, and Malaysia, forms the *habitat* of numerous species of *Trimeresurus,* mostly arboreal, some of them bright green. Some have the same prehensile tail as the New World smaller species of *Bothrops.*

The RATTLESNAKES. The two genera of New World serpents coming under this head need no general description, owing to a strong and unvarying characteristic—the rattle. The real use of this strange appendage is unknown to Science, despite a fusillade of theoretical assertions. That the serpent has the rattle for the sole purpose of warning away its enemies is a wholly fallacious and ridiculous idea. Years of careful study of the various species of rattlesnakes have tended to convince the author it would be but bold guesswork to assert just what Nature has intended the snake to do with the rattle. *Incidentally,* the appendage is a warning to intruders—but many species of harmless and poisonous snakes without a rattle vibrate their tail when angered. It is possible the rattle is intended as a call during the breeding season: for snakes, particularly the Crotaline species, are highly sensitive to vibrations. Again it is possible the rattle may be employed to attract the prey. We will not theorize, but explain what we really know about this interesting organ.

The rattle consists merely of hollow segments of dry, horny skin, one loosely fitting into another. Its growth is from the base of the appendage—the end of the tail proper—hence the terminal joint, ring or segment of the rattle is the oldest one. It is a mistake to imagine the age of a snake may be told by counting each segment of the rattle as a year. Each time the snake sheds its skin a new ring or segment of the rattle is uncovered at the end of the tail; here it is important to explain that rattlesnakes shed from two to three skins a year—that is, during the warm months. At birth the snake has merely a "button" to represent the future rattle. The first ring uncovered is larger than the button, and each subsequent ring yet larger, until the reptile has attained its full growth, when all of the segments produced are of uniform size. If a snake has a perfect rattle—a button at the tip and successively larger segments—and three joints of the rattle are counted as a year, a fair idea of the snake's age may be acquired. If all the segments are of a uniform size, the reptile has lost the segments of its youth—possibly many more of them—through wear or accident, and no idea of the serpent's age can be ascertained except that it is a perfectly mature specimen. The usual number of "rattles" is from ten to twelve.

About two dozen species of rattlesnakes are recognized. The majority of them are restricted to the United States and northern Mexico. The Southwest of the former country is their headquarters, ten species occurring in that region. Several species are restricted to Mexico and Central America. But one occurs in South America, where its range is extensive.

Following is a list of the species:

Pigmy Rattlesnake,	*Sistrurus miliarius.*	S. E. U. S.
Massasauga,	*Sistrurus catenatus.*	Central U. S.
Edward's Rattlesnake,	*Sistrurus c. edwardsii.*	S. W. U. S.
Mexican Pigmy Rattlesnake,	*Sistrurus ravus.*	Mexico.

South American Rattlesnake,	*Crotalus terrificus.*	Mex. to So. Am.
Black-Tailed Rattlesnake,	*Crotalus molossus.*	S. W. U. S.; Mex.
Texas Rattlesnake,	*Crotalus atrox.*	Texas to Calif.
Mojave Diamond Rattlesnake,	*Crotalus scutulatus.*	S. W. U. S.; Mex.
San Lucan Diamond Rattlesnake,	*Crotalus lucasensis.*	Lower Cal.
Tortuga Diamond Rattlesnake,	*Crotalus tortugensis.*	Lower Cal.
Cedros Island Rattlesnake,	*Crotalus exsul.*	Cedros Is.; L. Cal.
Red Rattlesnake,	*Crotalus ruber.*	S. W. U. S.
Diamond-Back Rattlesnake,	*Crotalus adamanteus.*	S. E. U. S.
Timber Rattlesnake,	*Crotalus horridus.*	Eastern U. S.
Prairie Rattlesnake,	*Crotalus confluentus.*	Central U. S.
White Rattlesnake,	*Crotalus c. mitchellii.*	S. W. U. S.
Pacific Rattlesnake,	*Crotalus c. oregonus.*	Western U. S.
Tiger Rattlesnake,	*Crotalus tigris.*	S. W. U. S.
Lower California Rattlesnake,	*Crotalus enyo.*	Lower Cal.
Horned Rattlesnake,	*Crotalus cerastes.*	S. W. U. S.
Green Rattlesnake,	*Crotalus lepidus.*	S. W. U. S.; Mex.
Price's Rattlesnake,	*Crotalus pricei.*	S. W. U. S.; Mex.
Mexican Rattlesnake,	*Crotalus triseriatus.*	Mexico.
Upland Rattlesnake,	*Crotalus polysticus.*	Mexico.
Stejneger's Rattlesnake,	*Crotalus stejnegeri.*	Mexico.
Willard's Rattlesnake,	*Crotalus willardi.*	Arizona; No. Mex.

An examination of the list will show the student that practically every part of the United States is inhabited by one or more species of rattlesnakes, which, in conjunction with the eastern moccasin and the copperhead, constitute a formidable array of dangerous snakes. Compared with the number of species of harmless serpents the poisonous species are much in the minority; yet it should be realized the United States is wonderfully rich in reptile life. Over a hundred species of snakes are found in this country; *of this number seventeen are poisonous.* Besides, there are ninety-seven species of lizards; but of the latter only a single species is venomous—the Gila Monster of the desert Southwest. The majority of the poisonous species are found in the southern latitudes, though the few northern species are so abundant that venomous snakes are actually more common in some sections of Pennsylvania and New York than in the South.

In the face of this general occurrence of dangerous reptiles in the United States accidents to man are rarely recorded. This may seem remarkable as compared with conditions in India, where, as has been explained, there are over twenty thousand deaths annually from the bites of snakes. But it should be remembered that in India a large part of the population goes about bare-legged, while the venomous snakes prowl into the immediate domains of man —even into the gardens and under houses. As the student has already noted, there are three groups of venomous snakes in North America—the Coral Snakes, the Moccasins and the Rattlesnakes. The characteristics of the small Elapine serpents (Coral Snakes), the Water Moccasin and the Highland Moccasin (Copperhead Snake) have already been considered, while we may dispose of the Rattlesnakes with a simple suggestion and that is to *look for the rattle,* a prominent and positively unique organ among snakes. Its presence immediately brands the owner. Though there are a number of species of Rattlesnakes, the characteristic naturally appeals to all. The amateur naturalist, prospector and the farmer are not so particular as to the exact species; what they are desirous of ascertaining is, whether a snake may be *dangerous.* The presence of a rattle shows this to be invariably the case.

In the New England States and the Middle Atlantic States, there are but two species of poisonous snakes. These are the Timber Rattlesnake and the Copperhead Snake. The Blacksnake, Water Snake, Flat-Headed "Adder," Checkered "Adder" and other serpents with formidable titles are wholly innocuous. If we include the Lake Region and the Ohio Valley we must consider another poisonous species, the Massasauga, *Sistrurus catenatus;* this is a small rattlesnake of a slaty gray marked with a chain of deep brown blotches.

South of central North Carolina, thence throughout the Gulf States, we find several more venomous species, as follows:

The Diamond-back Rattlesnake, *Crotalus adamanteus,* largest and most deadly of the North American serpents;

the Pigmy Rattlesnake, *Sistrurus miliarius,* a diminutive species; the Water Moccasin, *Agkistrodon piscivorous,* and the Coral Snake, *Micrurus fulvius.* The two latter species have been heretofore treated.

Thus we have an idea, collectively, of the various dangerous snakes of the eastern United States. Incidentally it might be said that the Timber Rattlesnake and the Copperhead Snake range southward to the northern portion of the Florida peninsula. In the extreme South the Copperhead also extends its range westward to the Rio Grande, in Texas. The distribution of the western snakes may be appreciated by an examination of the list on a preceding page.

Sistrurus contains three small rattlesnakes recognized by the large, regularly-arranged shields on the top of the head. The PIGMY RATTLESNAKE, *S. miliarius,* also called the Ground Rattlesnake, is common in the southeastern portion of the United States. The total length is about twenty inches and the coloration is attractive, consisting of a gray body hue with a row of jet-black saddles; between which, on the dorsal region, are interspaces of a reddish tinge. The rattle is so tiny it can be heard but a few feet. If met with prompt and efficient treatment the bite of this species is seldom followed by dangerous symptoms. A larger species of *Sistrurus,* the MASSASAUGA, *S. catenatus,* inhabits the Central States, whence a variety of it extends into the Southwest.

The typical rattlesnakes—genus *Crotalus*—have the top of the head covered with small scales, except, with a few species, a few crowded plates directly over the snout.

One of the most showy species is the SOUTH AMERICAN RATTLESNAKE, *Crotalus terrificus.* Two phases of coloration are found. On each the ground color is rich yellow or pale olive; a chain of large brown rhombs, bordered with light yellow, extends along the back. The species ranges from Mexico, through Central America, thence well over South America. The South American phase is much the handsomer, having a pair of vivid longitudinal bands on the neck; this marking is utterly lacking on the Mexican and most of the Central American examples. This species has a very small head, while the scales of South American specimens are so coarsely keeled as to resemble the scalation of the bushmaster, *Lachesis muta.* The length of an adult is up to seven feet.

As an interesting phase of the South American rattlesnake it is appropriate to mention a strange specimen described by the author in 1904. It was taken inland from Managua, Nicaragua, in a dry, sandy region. The scalation was coarse and of a uniform blue-gray like pumice dust. It was slightly over a yard long, though it appeared to be full grown, as the segments of the rattle were of uniform size. This specimen was presented to the Museum of Comparative Zoology, at Cambridge. It proved to be an example of albinism that occurs among rattlers of the species in the arid region.

In the United States the rattlesnakes exhibit a great variety of pattern but we have several species with the rhomb-like markings of the South American serpent. Largest and most dangerous of the North American species, the DIAMOND-BACK RATTLESNAKE, *C. adamanteus,* confined to the southeastern portion of the United States, grows to a length of slightly over eight feet, while *it attains the greatest weight of any known poisonous serpent.* The bite of this terrible brute is usually fatal, often within less than an hour's time. The fangs are of greater length in proportion to the reptile's size than of any other North American poisonous snake. All the Viperine snakes of the tropics and sub-tropics appear to possess fangs of greater proportions than of serpents in the temperate zone. For example, we observe that the fangs of the Fer-de-Lance are proportionately much longer than of any snake found in the United States.

While in the South the writer gathered some startling facts about the big "Diamond Rattler." A young Englishman, hunting quail, had been bitten, and died in less than half an hour. One of our dogs, creeping under a deserted cabin, came yelping out to die within a few minutes. "Diamond-backs" were all about us, but it was difficult hunting them owing to their nocturnal habits. The writer's first experience with one of these snakes was interesting, if not dramatic. We were passing through the hammocks on our way to a night hunt for water snakes in the bayous.

It was dark as we entered the lonely trail and once we were startled. Silently making our way, as the feet of the mules sank noiselessly into the sand, our nerves were set a-quiver by a series of piercing squeals. Then came an advancing thrashing through the undergrowth and across the beam of the guiding lantern sped a rabbit, evidently pursued by some nocturnal creature.

"Queer," muttered the guide; "mighty queer. A rabbit don't holler unless something's got hold of him."

We stopped to listen. While the frightened animal had crossed the sandy trail and dashed into the heavy growth on the opposite side, it had not gone far, for there was silence. Suddenly from the direction whence it had disappeared came an irregular rustling of the leaves. Through the brush nothing could be seen. The guide looked at me squarely. His face had assumed a solemn expression.

"What's the matter?" was my query.

"That rabbit's kicking his last," he answered. "I know the noise they make in the leaves when they're done for. I've shot plenty."

"Kicking his last? Why, what on earth—" but an idea had dawned on the author.

"Diamond-back," was the guide's slow answer.

The mention of that word brings a thrill when in such surroundings. One of the deadly snakes was prowling near by. It was a stab from its long fangs that had killed the rabbit. Would the creature follow the trail of the prey and cross the path?

"We will get one of the big bags ready and wait for him," was the author's suggestion.

Silently handing over the desired receptacle, the guide climbed on his mule and drew his legs over the animal's back. The colored assistant trembled perceptibly but did not care to leave our company in the darkness. We waited long and patiently, starting at every sound, but the serpent failed to appear.

At length we started on our hunt. The return was uneventful until we arrived at the scene of the rabbit episode, where curiosity compelled a stop. The guide had dismounted and was examining the trail with the small lantern which proved so handy in night journeys. He appeared excited and there was just reason.

Across the fine sand of the trail was seen the path of a snake. Straight as the course of a wheel it led from where the fated "cotton-tail" had sped across the open, thence into the thicket whence the rabbit had dashed to be overcome by the poison. From the direct course of the serpent's path we at once recognized it to be that of a rattlesnake, and, from its width of fully three inches, a Diamond-back of great size. Nor was this the only discovery. A little distance on was another path of a snake, wider and more deeply imprinted in the sand.

And so we realized that after we had gone on, the slayer of the rabbit had crossed the trail, devoured its prey and with heavy body dragged the scaly length back into the thicket and away in the hammock to hide under the leaves of some dwarf palmetto.

Many times as we afterward passed that spot we searched for the monster, and without success.

The TEXAS RATTLESNAKE, or WESTERN DIAMOND RATTLESNAKE, *C. atrox,* ranges from the sub-arid regions of Texas westward to California. It is the commonest rattlesnake along the Mexican boundary. The entire coloration is paler, of more faded appearance than the big southeastern species to which it is closely related, while the tail is chalky white with bold black rings. Following are the measurements of a big specimen exhibited in the Zoological Park:

Total length	71½ inches.
Girth	9½ inches.
Weight	9¾ pounds.

The common *Crotalus* of the Plains Region, the PRAIRIE RATTLESNAKE, *C. confluentus,* may be recognized by a series of *rounded* and well-separated blotches on the back; the body color is yellowish brown, the blotches darker. The PACIFIC RATTLESNAKE, *C. c. oregonus,* has a similar pattern, though wider bars under the eye; some specimens are black. Neither of these snakes grows much longer than three and a half feet. They range southward to Utah and northward slightly over the boundary of the United States.

One of the most beautiful of the North American rattlesnakes occurs in the eastern portion of the United States from Vermont to northern Florida. This is the TIMBER or BANDED RATTLESNAKE, *C. horridus.* In the North the majority of the males are black, and some of them are so intensely black the entire upper surface is without a suggestion of transverse bands, looking precisely like velvet. The females, to the contrary, are a beautiful sulphur yellow, ornamented with irregular brown or black transverse bands. Sometimes these bands assume the form of a chain of rhomb-like markings. A freshly-shed specimen is wonderful in the richness of its tints and no matter how strong may be the prejudice, few can fail to appreciate Nature's generosity in the distribution of her colors. Although this peculiar color characteristic of the Banded Rattlesnake is very constant, it sometimes happens that in New York, New Jersey, Pennsylvania and the neighboring states, black females are occasionally found. The writer has, however, never examined a yellow male from the district given. In the South, where the surroundings are quite different, the species assumes an entirely different phase—pinkish, with sooty black bands and a rusty red stripe on the back; this variety lives along the coastal region and is called the Cane-Brake Rattlesnake. The northern phase is essentially a mountain snake, haunting the immediate vicinity of ledges.

Our last species is a curious little snake of the deserts of the southwestern United States, the HORNED RATTLESNAKE or SIDEWINDER, *C. cerastes.* Its length is seldom more than a yard. Over each eye is a blunt, upright horn. The coloration is in keeping with a desert life; pale yellowish or pinkish with obscure blotches, like the hues of the African desert vipers.

The method of getting over a yielding soil is exactly like that employed by the species of *Cerastes,* of Africa, already described. In snakes so widely separated in classification and *habitat,* this eccentric trait is an admirable example of Nature's trend toward perfect adaptation.

PART IV

THE TURTLES AND TORTOISES
ORDER *TESTUDINATA*

THE ORDER *TESTUDINATA*—TURTLES AND TORTOISES

From all other reptiles these creatures may be immediately recognized by the "shell"—this forming a bony fortress, from which are thrust the head and the limbs.

The words *tortoise, turtle,* and *terrapin* have been used indiscriminately. Some writers embrace both the terrestrial and semi-aquatic species under the term *tortoise,* thus:—land tortoises and water tortoises, while they apply the name *turtle* to the marine species only. Others designate semi-aquatic and marine species as *turtles,* and place the strictly terrestrial members under the head of *tortoises. Terrapin* is a term that has been applied at one time or another, among all of the groups. At the beginning, it is best to straighten this tangle and the writer proposes to popularly divide the species thus:

TORTOISES—the strictly terrestrial species.

TURTLES—the semi-aquatic and marine species.

TERRAPINS—those hard-shelled, fresh-water species that are edible and have a recognized market value.

Before going into structural details, it is necessary to have a bird's-eye view of the classification; over two hundred species are recognized.

CLASSIFICATION OF THE ORDER *TESTUDINATA* *

Family *Dermochelidæ;* represented by a single species—The Leathery Turtle or Trunk Turtle.

* This summary is presented mainly to indicate the scope of this division of reptiles. It is practically revised, but to keep such a list "up to date" with regard to scientific nomenclature is almost an impossible task, without constant access to world sources of literature by technical workers engaged in investigations of priority, relationships affecting grouping of species, elimination oı disproved forms, and addition of new species.

Genus *Dermochelys;* 2 species; Tropical and semi-tropical seas.
Family *Chelydridæ.* Snapping Turtles; North and Central America.
Genus *Chelydra;* 3 species; semi-aquatic; No. Am. and Central Am.
Genus *Macrochelys;* 1 species; semi-aquatic; No. Am.
Family *Dermatemydæ.* Fresh-water Turtles.
Genus *Dermatemys;* 1 species; semi-aquatic; Central America.
Genus *Staurotypus;* 2 species; semi-aquatic; Central America.
Genus *Claudius;* 1 species; semi-aquatic; Mexico.
Family *Kinosternidæ.* The Musk and Mud Turtles.
Genus *Sternotherus;* 3 species; semi-aquatic; North America.
Genus *Kinosternon;* 11 species; semi-aquatic; No. Am.; Mex. and Central Am.
Family *Platysternidæ.*
Genus *Platysternon;* 1 species; semi-aquatic; Southern Asia.
Family *Testudinidæ.* Largest family of the Chelonia; embraces the greater number of the turtles (and terrapins) and all of the terrestrial species —the tortoises. Represented in the Old and New World.
Genus *Kachuga;* 7 species; semi-aquatic; India.
Genus *Callagur*; 1 species; semi-aquatic; Malay Pn.; Borneo.
Genus *Batagur;* 1 species; semi-aquatic; Malay Pn.; India.
Genus *Hardella;* 1 species; semi-aquatic; India.
Genus *Morenia;* 2 species; semi-aquatic; India.
Genus *Orlitia;* 1 species; semi-aquatic; Malaysia.
Genus *Deirochelys;* 1 species; semi-aquatic; No. America.
Genus *Chrysemys;* 2 species; semi-aquatic; North Am.
Genus *Pseudemys;* 12 species; semi-aquatic; North and So. America.
Genus *Ocadia;* 1 species; semi-aquatic; China.
Genus *Malaclemys;* 2 species; semi-aquatic; North America.
Genus *Graptemys;* 2 species; semi-aquatic; North America.
Genus *Geoclemys;* 5 species; semi-aquatic; East Indies; Japan.
Genus *Bellia;* 2 species; semi-aquatic; Malaysia.
Genus *Clemmys;* 9 species; semi-aquatic; So. Europe to Japan; North Am.
Genus *Emys;* 2 species; semi-aquatic; No. Am.; Europe.
Genus *Terrapene;* 4 species; terrestrial; No. Am.; Mexico.
Genus *Nicoria;* 6 species; terrestrial; Cent. and So. Am.; East Indies.
Genus *Cyclemys;* 6 species; semi-aquatic; East Indies.
Genus *Geoemyda;* 3 species; semi-aquatic; Malay Archipelago.
Genus *Chaibassia;* 2 species; terrestrial; India.
Genus *Kinixys;* 3 species; terrestrial; Africa.
Genus *Pyxis;* 1 species; terrestrial; Madagascar.
Genus *Homopus;* 4 species; terrestrial; Africa.
Genus *Gopherus;* 3 species; terrestrial; North America.
Genus *Testudo;* 47 species; terrestrial; Old and New World.
Family *Cheloniidæ.* Sea Turtles.
Genus *Eretmochelys;* 2 species; tropical and semi-tropical seas.
Genus *Caretta;* 3 species; tropical and semi-tropical seas.
Family *Pelomedusidæ.* Fresh-water Turtles. Old and New World.
Genus *Pelusios;* 7 species; semi-aquatic; Africa.

Genus *Pelomedusa;* 1 species; semi-aquatic; Africa.
Genus *Podocnemis;* 7 species; semi-aquatic; South America—6; Madagascar—1.
Family *Chelydidæ.* Fresh-water Turtles. Old and New World.
Genus *Chelus;* 1 species; aquatic; South America.
Genus *Hydromedusa;* 2 species; semi-aquatic; South America.
Genus *Chelodina;* 4 species; semi-aquatic; Australia; New Guinea.
Genus *Rhinemys;* 1 species; semi-aquatic; South America.
Genus *Hydraspis;* 7 species; semi-aquatic; South America.
Genus *Platemys;* 2 species; semi-aquatic; South America.
Genus *Emydura;* 7 species; semi-aquatic; Australia; New Guinea.
Genus *Elyseya;* 1 species; semi-aquatic; Australia.
Family *Carettochelydidæ.*
Genus *Carettochelys;* 1 species; thoroughly aquatic; New Guinea.
Family *Trionychidæ.* Soft-shelled Turtles. Aquatic. Old and New World.
Genus *Trionyx;* 15 species; No. America; Africa and Asia.
Genus *Pelochelys;* 1 species; East Indies.
Genus *Chitra;* 1 species; East Indies.
Genus *Cycloderma;* 2 species; Africa.
Genus *Emyda;* 3 species; East Indies.
Genus *Cyclanorbis;* 2 species; Africa.

Family *Dermochelidæ* of the two representatives of this family, the LEATHERY TURTLE, LUTH, or TRUNK TURTLE, *Dermochelys coriacea,* is a strictly marine animal, and seems to be the survivor of an ancient group. Externally, it differs from the few other marine turtles by the tough, leathery covering of the carapace and plastron in place of horny shields; from this fleshy integument rise seven heavy and bony keels (on the carapace). The vertebræ and ribs are not rigidly attached to the carapace as with *all* other chelonians. The carapace and plastron are actually composed of a large number of irregularly-shaped plates; except where these protrude—on the upper shell—in the shape of keels, or heavy ridges, they are imbedded in the oily, fatty substance, like whale blubber, that externally presents a leathery appearance and suggests a popular name for the animal.

Like the other marine turtles, the present reptile differs from other chelonians—the fresh-water species—in having the limbs developed into huge, seal-like "flippers" or paddles. Yet the appearance of the limbs and head is quite different from corresponding parts of the structure of the well-known Green Turtle and the Loggerhead Turtle: for with the present reptile these members are not, on mature individuals, covered with shields or plates; the dark, smooth skin of the head and the enormous bare flippers are characters strikingly suggestive of a seal.

If this turtle is to be compared with the four species that make up the family *Cheloniidæ*—the Green Turtle, Hawk's-Bill Turtle, and two species of Loggerhead Turtle, gross examination might point to a general similarity of structure. It is true that the Leathery Turtle and the other sea turtles have much the same paddle-like limbs, but this similarity in development merely signifies the process of evolution along similar lines in two widely-separated groups; it is an admirable example of adaptation. Incidentally, it might be explained that the species composing the *Cheloniidæ* appear to be highly specialized forms that have originated from the *Testudinidæ,* while the Leathery Turtle represents ancestral forms that have, decades since, joined the army of fossils.

Inhabiting tropical and semi-tropical seas of both hemispheres, attaining a length of shell of four feet, or a total length from snout to the tip of tail of over six feet, this sea giant reaches a weight of a thousand pounds. On a large example, the powerful forelimbs have a stretch of ten feet and, in spite of the creature's great weight, carry it through the water in a graceful fashion that recalls the flight of a hawk. In the New World, it is sometimes lured northward in the fickle current of the Gulf Stream, when, coming in contact with colder waters, it flounders aimlessly and is either harpooned by fishermen, or battered to death and cast on the beaches of Long Island or Massachusetts during the northeast storms.

The Leathery Turtle never comes to the shore except to deposit its eggs. The food consists of mollusks and seaweeds. Its flesh is of no market value.

The technical definition of the next family relates partly

to the method of bending the neck when the head is drawn back, and in certain osteological characters.

When the head is retracted the neck bends in an S-shaped, *vertical* curve.[1] The pelvis is not fused to the shell. *Carapace* (upper shell) and *plastron* (lower shell) are coated with horny shields.

Family *Chelydridæ,* the SNAPPING TURTLES. Four species compose this family; three inhabit North America; the other is a native of Mexico and Guatemala. From the other New World turtles, these formidable brutes are strikingly distinct. Their huge head, alligator-like tail, the flabby, projecting folds of skins about the limbs and the ridiculously small, cross-shaped plastron are striking features of the structure; add to these the rough carapace and the somber coloration, nowhere relieved by a bright streak or spot, and the general aspect is so sinister that it imparts more of the feeling inspired by a thick-bodied, poisonous serpent than that of a turtle.

Though the much aborted plastron is of absolutely no protection to the fleshy parts, these strong-jawed creatures are by no means handicapped. Their vicious, beady eyes are ever alert and their motions in biting are lightning quick. The jaws of a full-grown individual of the Common Snapping Turtle could readily sever a man's finger and the big Alligator Turtle could as easily amputate a hand.

It is from their darting motion in biting, fully as quick as a serpent's stroke, that the species of this family have acquired the name of *Snapping* Turtles. They are persistently aquatic and usually haunt fair-sized bodies of muddy water. In keeping with the habits, the feet are broadly webbed; they are provided with very stout, blunt nails.

The COMMON SNAPPING TURTLE, *Chelydra serpentina,* is one of the smaller representatives of the family, yet it grows to a weight of forty pounds and is ponderous as compared with the greater number of American fresh-water

[1] If not actually, at least within a decided vertical plane.

turtles. The carapace of a large example is about fourteen inches long. On the rear margin, the upper shell is coarsely serrated; it has three blunt, broken keels, their height varying according to age. Old specimens are comparatively smooth, while the young are so rough as to look grotesque. On the under surface, the tail is covered with broad plates; this appendage is almost as long as the carapace. Above, the color is dull brown; the plastron is dingy yellow. ROSSIGNON'S SNAPPING TURTLE, *C. rossignonii,* of Mexico and Guatemala, differs from its North American ally in having a much broader plastral bridge.

The Common Snapping Turtle is abundant over an extensive area. It is found in southern Canada and throughout the United States generally east of the Rockies, thence southward, through Mexico, to Ecuador. It is a bold and aggressive animal, not hesitating to attack water fowl, which it drags beneath the surface to drown, when it tears up the prey by means of the combined efforts of strong mandibles and forefeet—often assisted by several members of its kind that are continually roaming over the river-bottom in search of plunder. Occasionally it takes the bait of a fisherman, when its prodigious struggles to free itself from the hook lead the excited sportsman to believe that he has made a finny capture beyond all power of imagination. Prompted by a continually hungry stomach this reptilian terror resorts to various devices in the capture of prey. Often it half imbeds itself in the mud, in a lane traversed by schools of fishes, and here it darts at the ill-fated victims as they approach without suspicion an object that looks exactly like a muddy rock, streaked here and there with moss; another device is to prowl along the edge of a pond or stream in search of frogs, which in turn are squatting, snout toward the bank, on the watch for insect prey.

During June or in July, the female Snapping Turtle leaves the water in search of a place to deposit her eggs. She often wanders a considerable distance, sometimes a mile or more and may deposit her eggs in most incongruous places—such as the middle of a country road or on an elevated knoll in a dry meadow. The little turtles have a long trip to the water, but the mother's idea appears to be that the eggs are much safer when remote from pond or stream. The eggs, to the number of several dozen, are perfectly spherical with a very thin, though hard and brittle shell. After the eggs have been deposited, the turtle rears herself upon the front feet, when the débris slides from her carapace, leaving the eggs covered. In wallowing fashion she emerges from the burrow and trudges clumsily back to the water. Stories are frequent about Snapping Turtles evincing a liking for terrestrial wanderings. These relate to the purpose of the female in constructing a nest for the young.

The ALLIGATOR SNAPPING TURTLE, *Macrochelys temminckii,* is distinguished from the common species by its greater size, the high and decidedly tubercular keels of the carapace, the yellowish hue of the upper shell and head, and *the absence of large plates under the tail.* Among the American fresh-water turtles, it is a veritable giant, as it attains a weight of considerably over a hundred pounds; a large specimen will have a head twenty-five inches in circumference. The *habitat* embraces those rivers that empty into the Gulf of Mexico from western Texas to western Florida; northward, the species ranges to Missouri.

With a head as large as that of a bull-terrier and jaws that can chop up an ordinary broom handle, the dangerous nature of this enormously strong and vicious brute may be imagined. Its temper is quite in keeping with its looks. In all of his attempts at photographing the species the writer has failed to secure a picture unless confronted by a pair of widely-gaping jaws. On one occasion, a leg of the tripod was bitten off clean and always were the diminutive but bright, sunken eyes watching the movements of the writer's feet with an intensity of purpose that inspired caution.

The dull, yellow shells of these big turtles exactly match the coffee-colored waters of the lower Mississippi, where they are common. Lying motionless upon the oozy bottom they are approached by unwary fishes, when a dart of the head procures the prey. Captive specimens do not feed well unless provided with means of hiding; from such the head is frequently protruded, when the tip of the conical snout barely touches the surface of the water in a search for air. If a large fish—like a shad—is thrown into the tank, it is devoured by a series of clean-cut bites that match the conformation of the turtle's jaws.

Family *Dermatemydæ*. The fresh-water turtles composing this small family are restricted to southern Mexico and Central America. Their structure shows them to be intermediate between the *Chelydridæ* and the *Kinosternidæ*. They are characterized by their very short tails. *Dermatemys* has a *wide* plastron connected with the upper shell by a broad bridge. The single species, *D. mawii*, has a shell about a foot long, when adult; it is olive above and yellowish beneath; the sides of the head are speckled. *Staurotypus* has the carapace much flattened, with three, faint keels; the plastron is narrow and cross-shaped like that of the snapping turtles, while the front lobe is hinged. Shells of adult specimens are about a foot long. *Claudius* differs from the preceding genus in having the front lobe of the plastron rigidly attached.

Family *Kinosternidæ*, the MUSK AND MUD TURTLES. This is a small family of rather diminutive turtles, confined to the New World. It is composed of two genera—*Sternotherus* and *Kinosternon*. The former is represented by three species, which, by their aborted plastron, large head and pugnacious disposition appear like miniature snapping turtles; they are usually called Musk Turtles. Eleven species, called Mud Turtles, form the genus *Kinosternon*. From the members of the former genus they may be told at a glance by their wide plastron. With both genera the structure of the plastron is peculiar; the central portion or "bridge" is broad and firmly united to the upper shell, while the front and rear portions—the lobes—are hinged and movable; these lobes afford little or no protection to the species of *Sternotherus,* but with some of the species of *Kinosternon* fold up tightly against the carapace in a fashion that has caused the name of "box" turtles to be applied to some of these reptiles. It should be understood, however, that the box turtles proper are the species of *Terrapene,* belonging to the family *Testudinidæ,* and the structure of their plastron is altogether different; the lower shell is divided by a central hinge and attached to the carapace by elastic cartilage.

The Musk and Mud Turtles are denizens of muddy rivers and lakes. All are of dull colors. The general hue of the upper shell is olive or brown, the shields narrowly and obscurely margined with black. The upper shell of all of the species is bluntly oval and exhibits no traces of the flaring or serrated margin of many turtles. To the novice the various species might look very similar and be exceedingly difficult to tell apart. Among the Mud Turtles, the structure of the plastron is the most important feature for identification.

Genus *Sternotherus,* the MUSK TURTLES. If the carapace were not so smooth and oval the species might easily be mistaken for young snapping turtles. The head is proportionately very large, with tapering, conical snout. In accordance with the aquatic habits, the feet are broadly webbed. The shell of a large specimen is not over four inches long.

The COMMON MUSK TURTLE, *Sternotherus odoratus,* is abundant in the eastern states, from southern Canada to the Gulf of Mexico; in the northern portion of the range it occurs as far westward as Illinois; southward it ranges into Texas. A mature specimen has a carapace three or four inches long; the plastron is much shorter than the upper shell. A specimen with a shell four inches long would have a head an inch broad. The young have a pyramidal shell that is very sharply keeled on the rear of the back;

as the turtle matures the shell becomes globular and perfectly smooth.

This species may be told by the bright yellow lines on each side of the head; both of these begin at the snout; one passes over and the other beneath the eye. The SOUTHERN MUSK TURTLE, *S. minor,* looks much like the preceding reptile, but the head bands are broader and broken. It is found in the southeastern part of the United States.

The KEELED MUSK TURTLE, *S. carinatus,* by its spotted head differs from the northern species, though it evinces a stronger characteristic in the sharp keel on the upper shell, which is retained through life. The head is very large and broad. Some specimens are of a uniform brown, while many display bold, black markings on the upper shell. From Georgia to the Gulf States and westward to Arizona, this turtle is fairly common.

Musk Turtles are persistently aquatic, agile swimmers, pugnacious, ever hungry and thus a terror to small fishes. Much to the disgust of fresh-water fishermen, they have a habit of greedily swallowing a hook and when brought struggling to the surface exude such a foul, musky odor that the sportsman's only thought is to quickly cut the line and drop the snapping, disagreeable little animal back into the water. In muddy streams, from which the country lad has practically exterminated the frogs, the spotted turtles and the "terrapins," Musk Turtles may abound and yet seldom be seen. Unlike the familiar, yellow-spotted turtles *(Clemmys)* that bask upon derelict timber, or along the bank, the reptiles under consideration keep to the water and either prowl along the soft bottom or hide in the shadows of roots or projecting edges of the shore. A dart of the powerful head means the immediate finish of an unwary "pollywog," fish or insect larva.

Genus *Kinosternon,* the MUD TURTLES. From the species of *Sternotherus* the present turtles are told by the broad plastron, the front and rear lobes of which are so well hinged and adjusted that they close well up against the upper shell, affording great protection to the fleshy parts. Eleven species are recognized; six are found in the United States. It is owing to their habit of frequenting streams of very muddy water they have received their popular name. Like the musk turtles, they exude a strong, musky odor when first handled. The Mexican and Central American species have a shell six inches long.

A widely distributed example and one common in many portions of the eastern United States is the COMMON MUD TURTLE, *Kinosternon subrubrum,* having a shell four inches long when fully adult; the head is about three-quarters of an inch broad. This species ranges from southern New York to the Gulf of Mexico and westward to the Mississippi Valley. The upper shell is broader and more flattened than that of the musk turtles; with the latter this species might be confused, but the wide plastron forms an unfailing mark for distinction. On the carapace of the young are three faint keels; adults show no traces of any but an obscure central keel. Above, the color is dull olive or brown, the shields narrowly margined with black. Most specimens have the head speckled.

A southern variety *(hippocrepis)* appears to be closely allied to the preceding. Distinguishing marks are the more elongated shell and the arrangement of the colors on the head in broad, orange bands. In the lower Mississippi Valley it is a common turtle. BAUR'S MUD TURTLE, *K. baurii,* inhabits the southeastern portion of the United States and is unique in having three yellow bands on the upper shell. The YELLOW-NECKED MUD TURTLE, *K. flavescens,* looks much like *K. subrubrum* and differs from that species in the structure of the plastron. The sides of the neck are generally bright lemon-yellow and the carapace ruddy brown or dull yellowish. The range is from Arkansas and Texas to Arizona.

The ARIZONA MUD TURTLE, *Kinosternon sonoriense,* has a shell six inches long when adult. It is the largest of those species found in the United States. By the very flat bridge of the plastron, the under shell looking as if it had been crushed in, this turtle appeals strongly to the Mexican and Central American species. Both lobes of the plastron close tightly, affording complete protection to the fleshy parts.

In the red, muddy waters of the Colorado River this turtle is common enough; in currents that are swift and practically opaque with thick deposits of silt, it would seem that the animal would choke and require no eyes for its strictly aquatic existence. Arizona and New Mexico form the *habitat.* Southward, in Old Mexico, is found a closely related species known technically as *Kinosternon integrum,* with a flat, crushed-in plastron and lobes that close as perfectly as do those of the true box turtles—*Terrapene.*

So thoroughly at home in the water are the species of *Kinosternon* they may be kept in deep tanks, without any means of resting above or near the surface, yet under such conditions will flourish for years. Their swimming movements are graceful and deliberate. Much of the time is spent in crawling over the bottom. In coming to the surface for air there is no apparent hurry, but a slow, treading motion of the limbs, with webs widely extended. Captive Mud Turtles will eat chopped fish, earthworms and raw beef. In a wild state they are veritable scavengers.

A single species represents the family *Platysternidæ.* It inhabits southern China, Burma and Siam. The proportionately very large head with hooked mandibles and the long tail cause this animal to resemble the New World snapping turtles—*Chelydridæ;* it really stands intermediate between that family and the *Testudinidæ.* The carapace is much flattened; the plastron is broad and possesses a square front lobe. In a peculiar structure of the skull—"the temporal region completely roofed over"—the species is, from a technical point of view, absolutely unique among chelonians. A large example has a carapace five inches long; with head and tail outstretched the turtle will measure fourteen inches.

Family *Testudinidæ;* TURTLES, "TERRAPINS" and TORTOISES. This large family is represented in all temperate and tropical parts of the globe except Australia and Papuasia. Its great variety of species range from the persistently aquatic with their broadly webbed feet, to the marsh-loving turtles, with which the webs are imperfectly developed and finally to the tortoises—chelonians with club-shaped feet; all tortoises are strictly terrestrial, some of them inhabiting the deserts.

On all the species the shell is covered with horny shields. With the majority the head may be completely withdrawn into the shell. There are nine plastral bones.

Several North American genera stand as typical in representing the structure and habits of the semi-aquatic species. These are:

Chrysemys, Malaclemys, Graptemys, Pseudemys; the AMERICAN TERRAPINS. We will adopt the general title of Terrapins for the species of these genera, as many of the members involved are sold in large numbers in the markets, where they bring from moderate to very high prices, according to their kind. All of the terrapins grow to a fair size, having a shell from eight to fourteen inches long. Many have the upper shell attractively marked while the head and neck are vividly striped with yellow—or red. Of all the North American terrapins the best known is the Diamond-Back Terrapin, *Malaclemys centrata,* which is a favorite and costly article of food.

Genus *Chrysemys.* A great majority of the species inhabit North America; the remainder occur in Mexico and Central America. Of the several North American members of the genus, the PAINTED TERRAPIN, *C. picta,* is thoroughly familiar. There can be no doubt about the identity of this pretty creature: for the blackish or olive upper shell with its yellow-bordered shields and the striking vermilion bars and crescents on both upper and lower series of marginal shields are strong distinguishing characters; the plastron is immaculate yellow. Head and neck are brightly striped; the former with yellow, the latter with red and yellow. This is one of the smallest of the terrapins; a fully grown adult has a shell six inches long. The carapace is perfectly smooth. Eastern North America generally is inhabited by this attractive reptile. Closely related to it is the WESTERN PAINTED TERRAPIN, *C. marginata,* characterized by the narrow yellow margins of the larger shields and an elongated, blackish patch on the central portion of the plastron. The *habitat* embraces the Central States—Illinois, Ohio, Indiana and Iowa, and southward in the Mississippi Valley. BELL'S TERRAPIN *(subspecies bellii)* occurs west of the Mississippi, has vein-like markings on the carapace and less red on the marginal shields; on the plastron is a curious, scribbled, blackish pattern. Another small species, the CHICKEN TERRAPIN, *Deirochelys reticularia,* has rather an elongate carapace marked with a network of fine yellow lines; there are no red markings on the marginal shields. A large shell is eight inches long. This species has a very long, snake-like neck. It inhabits the southeastern portion of the United States.

These smaller terrapins are generally familiar. They are often called "pond turtles" and may be seen sunning themselves in rows on derelict timber, from which they tumble clumsily when frightened. Once in the water their broadly-webbed feet take instant hold and they scurry to the bottom where they hide in the aquatic vegetation. When they again approach the surface, it is with the greatest caution. Only the snout and eyes are thrust above the water. In this position they paddle about inspecting the outlook until thoroughly satisfied that all danger has gone when, one after another, they clamber on their favorite roosts for another sun-bath. Omnivorous in their feeding, they chase small fishes, tadpoles, frogs and the larvæ of aquatic insects; the tender shoots of water plants are also eaten.

The species of *Pseudemys* are larger and we note a tendency of the shell to be higher, besides deeply furrowed with numerous parallel grooves. The greater number of the larger terrapins inhabit the southeastern portion of the United States. In the markets, where they are kept in cold vats to keep them from running down in flesh, they are to be seen in large numbers; here a mixture of species may often be observed, yet commercially they are considered under a general title—Slider Terrapins. This is supposed to distinguish them from the more valuable Diamond-Back Terrapin. A "Slider" weighing three or four pounds will bring from seventy-five cents to one dollar in the eastern markets during the proper season—the fall and winter months.

Of these large species, TROOST'S TERRAPIN, *P. troostii,* may be commonly seen. Owing to its somber coloration it is unique among the members of its genus. The carapace is flattened, smooth and of a dull olive, irregularly blotched with black. On most individuals the head and neck are uniform blackish, which absence of bright stripes is an important point to be considered in identification. An adult shell is from eight to ten inches long and three inches high; a nine-inch example will weigh three and three quarter pounds. Troost's Terrapin is found in Illinois, Missouri, Tennessee and Mississippi.

Like all of the terrapins, the preceding species grows very long claws; on frequent male individuals these are three-quarters of an inch long and terminate in such sharp points that a vigorously kicking animal requires some care in handling. Moreover, these reptiles are not to be trusted, though they seldom actually dart at one's finger like the snapping turtles. When alarmed they completely withdraw the head and limbs, but a spirit of curiosity soon prompts the head to peep a short distance from the protective armor; then it is that the razor-like mandibles spring open at a slight movement on the part of an observer and close in lightning fashion upon any object that may touch them. The writer has seen a nervous turtle cleanly amputate a chunk of its own forelimb as it felt that member come in contact with the jaws; if the mandibles miss the intended object they come together with a snap that intimates unpleasant possibilities for the unwary.

The COOTER, *P. concinna,* of the southeastern United States is a large, handsome terrapin, with olive, yellow-barred carapace; each of the marginal shields contains a yellow, vertical line; pale, crescentic markings cross from one of these shields into another. The head is striped with orange and red. A near relation is the FLORIDA TERRAPIN, *P. floridana,* at once distinct by the very high, dome-like shell and the diminutive head. Apparently restricted to southern Georgia and Florida, this fine terrapin attains a length of shell of fourteen inches and a weight of fourteen pounds.

The YELLOW-BELLIED TERRAPIN, *P. scripta,* and the MOBILE TERRAPIN, *P. elegans,* are showy creatures, commonly seen in the markets. The former shows a decided wrinkled (rugose) formation on the upper shell; the latter is characterized in having a broad, scarlet band on each side of the head. Each reaches a length of shell of ten inches. The Yellow-Bellied Terrapin seems to be restricted to the coast region of the eastern United States, from Virginia to Georgia, while its near ally ranges over a wide area—Ohio to Kansas, southward to the Gulf States and westward in the southern portion of the range, to the lower Rio Grande.

The several Central American terrapins are attractively marked. *P. ornata* has a pale olive carapace, barred with pale green and yellow; the head is vividly striped. One terrapin ranges into South America as far south as Argentina.

Very young terrapins are beautifully marked and colored. On most of them the pattern of the adult is intensified to such a degree that they look like strange little flowers or variegated leaves. For the aquarium they are attractive additions, though unpleasant companions for the fishes, as between feeding times they bite off fins or tails, or do not hesitate to commit murder among the more diminutive finny inmates of the tank. These quarrelsome youngsters are fond of earthworms and chopped raw beef.

Adult terrapins (representing the larger species) are practically omnivorous. They will eat snails, young craw-fish, minnows or sections of larger fishes, tadpoles and frogs, while they frequently browse on the leaves of aquatic vegetation. When captive, they will greedily devour lettuce leaves if such be thrown upon the surface of the tank.

All of the terrapins are semi-aquatic. The extensively webbed hind feet form powerful swimming organs. Some of the species frequent swift, clear rivers with rocky beds; others, the slower and muddy streams; a few prefer the still waters of extensive, marshy areas. In the winter they dig into the mud under shallow water and undergo a period of stupor as long as the water remains icy. Occasionally, during pronounced thaws when the ice temporarily disappears, a venturesome reptile emerges from the mud and, with motions so slow and benumbed as to suggest a run-down automaton, crawls to the water's edge and employs the long dormant lungs. But these February thaws, with their fleeting, fickle hints of spring, are generally fatal to the deluded creature. Too stupefied to again imbed itself in the mud, it dumbly wanders along the margin, its movements becoming slower as night comes on with a falling temperature; then the wind sets in from the north, bringing heavy ice in which the animal is imbedded. In the spring a few shells are to be found floating along the river bank. They tell a mute story of impatient turtles that the sun has enticed from their hibernating quarters.

Genus *Malaclemys*. From *Pseudemys* the two species composing this genus are technically separated by the structure—with the present genus—of the inner margin of the jaws. Behind the sharp edges of the mandibles the jaws are provided with very broad and flat crushing surfaces; scientifically these processes are known as the *alveolar* surfaces of the jaws. This indicates a food involving mollusks; and such is actually the case. All of the species feed more or less upon snails. The species are also characterized by a strong keel on the carapace. This is often so high and tubercular as to produce a strongly serrated outline to the curve of the back; otherwise, the shell may be quite smooth, except with specimens of the "Diamond-Back" Terrapin. Like the members of *Pseudemys,* these turtles grow to a fair size—eight to twelve inches long, in shell. Like the former terrapins, they are sold regularly and in large numbers in the markets. One of them is a strong favorite—a favorite of epicures. The "Diamond-Back" brings four times the price of its near relations and is unique in inhabiting the *salt* marshes of the eastern coastal region.

Female examples of *Malaclemys* are considerably larger than the other sex and have proportionately much broader heads.

One of the requisites in making up a champagne dinner and consequently a valuable and well-known market delicacy, the DIAMOND-BACK TERRAPIN, *Malaclemys centrata,* ranks first in importance among the members of its genus. Large specimens have a shell nine inches long. Each of the larger shields of the carapace contains a number of coarse, concentric grooves, their angular outlines being responsible for the popular name. The upper shell is dull brown or olive; the plastron is orange-yellow, often blotched with gray or showing concentric rings of this color. From the other species of *Malaclemys* the Diamond-Back Terrapin differs materially in the head markings; there are no traces of stripes; the head is pale gray profusely sprinkled with black dots, while the mandibles are flesh color.

Contrary to the habits of other terrapins, the "Diamond-Back" is found only in the vicinity of salt or brackish water; it inhabits the salt marshes of the Atlantic Coast from Massachusetts to Florida and the southern borders of the Gulf States to Texas. Occasional examples are found well up the larger rivers though always within tide line. This terrapin seems to be most abundant along the coasts of North and South Carolina.

The market demand for the Diamond-Back Terrapin once threatened extinction. Prices had steadily risen. As a consequence a number of terrapin "farms" have been established. Twenty years ago "Diamond-Backs" were expensive enough, the price for eight-inch terrapins being about sixty dollars per dozen. A dozen terrapins of this size are now worth about seventy-five dollars—sometimes more; terrapins of this size weigh barely three pounds each. If a specimen has a shell five inches long, or under, it is of little market value and may be bought for about $1.50; however, for every half inch above the five-inch limit, the price is laid on with an energy that staggers any but the connoisseur.

If kept in a tank of fresh water, the Diamond-Back Terrapin does not thrive, as its fleshy parts are soon attacked by a fungus, which soon kills the reptile. The infection may be killed by placing the terrapin in a bath of strong salt water and keeping it there for forty-eight hours. Yet it seems to be more susceptible to the growth, when placed back in the fresh water, than before; a condition probably owing to the weakened and softened skin. Captive individuals will thrive if enough salt is stirred into the water of the tank to give it a slightly brackish taste; the food should be chopped clams and oysters, shrimps, small crabs and fish; most captives are fond of the small "periwinkle" snails that abound on the mud flats. The food is always eaten under water.

From the diamond-back terrapins the species of *Graptemys* appear quite different, owing to their comparatively smooth shells.

Following is a tabulated list of the species and subspecies:

A. *Keel on the carapace moderately developed.*

Upper shell olive, with a net-work of fine yellow lines.

GEOGRAPHIC TERRAPIN, *G. geographica.*

Habitat: Mississippi Valley and western portions of the Atlantic States.

B. *Keel rising in the form of tubercles, causing the outline of the back to appear strongly serrated.*

Olive, with large black blotches. A few narrow yellow lines on head; a yellow crescent behind each eye.

CRESCENT TERRAPIN, *G. pseudogeographica.*

Habitat: Valley of the Mississippi.

Shell colored like preceding. Narrow yellow lines on head; a yellow spot behind each eye.

KOHN'S TERRAPIN, *G. p. kohnii.*

Habitat: Lower Mississippi Valley.

Habitat: Alabama.

Olive; each of the shields encloses a yellow ring that is bordered internally and externally with dark brown.

OCELLATED TERRAPIN, *G. p. oculifera.*

Habitat: Lower Mississippi Valley.

The above species are sold commonly in the markets.

Geoclemys is a small genus made up of rather diminutive, semi-aquatic turtles inhabiting the East Indies, China and Japan. The shell is high and narrow; most of the species have three sharp keels on the back.

REEVE'S TURTLE, *Geoclemys reevesii,* of China and Japan, will thrive for years in captivity. Few of these turtles have a shell over four inches long; above, the shell is dull uniform brown; the color beneath is dark yellow. Many specimens have silvery white eyes, which appear very sharp and cunning. Reeve's Turtle will eat worms, raw meat, fish and tender leaves. It is an agile swimmer and when frightened will dive beneath the shadow of a log or rock. The approach to the surface is slow and cautious; the snout is barely poked out of the water while the animal supports itself by a slow, treading motion of the hind feet; at such a moment a slight commotion will cause the turtle to hysterically reverse its position, frantically paddle to the bottom and remain there for a longer period than before. While captives become tame enough to scramble from the water and take food from the hand, they are naturally timid; if handled they exude such a foul and disagreeable odor from special glands near the base of the tail that one does not feel inclined to again become familiar.

Clemmys is another genus embracing semi-aquatic species,

that inhabit southern Europe, Asia, China, Japan and North America.

The IBERIAN TURTLE, *Clemmys leprosa,* occurs in southern Spain, Portugal, Morocco, Algeria and well into northwestern Africa. Old turtles have a smooth, flattened shell. Their colors are somber—olive above, greenish-yellow beneath. The carapace is about eight inches long.

Gadow explains that the specific name—*leprosa*—has been inspired by a disease that attacks many specimens, giving them a leprous appearance. They abound in streams and pools that partially evaporate during the hot season, then become very stagnant. Wallowing in the unwholesome waters the shell becomes attacked with a fresh-water alga. The infection makes its way through cracks and sutures of the shields, resulting in gangrenous spots and patches.

As a captive, the species is hardy. A half dozen examples have lived for over five years in the reptile house of the New York Zoological Park. Fish, raw beef, earthworms and lettuce leaves form the greater part of the food, whch is always consumed under water.

Clemmys caspica, found from the southern borders of the Caspian Sea southward through Persia, is a near relative of the preceding turtle. One of the distinguishing features consists of yellow streaks on the shields of the upper shell.

Following the rules of technical classification, we find the genus *Clemmys* to be next in order. Only four species are known. All of these are North American.

In our progress toward the terrestrial chelonians, we find among the members of the present genus certain traits that call for a halt, that we may note the first indications of habits that relate to those of the true tortoises. *Two of the species of Chelopus are able to swallow their food while out of the water.* Right in line with this characteristic we find that the same species wander away from the pool or stream in search of tender shoots and berries. In conformity with such habits we also observe a considerable reduction of the webbed formation of the feet.

There are four New World species of *Clemmys.* The shields are smooth, or contain coarse, concentric grooves.

Largest of these is the Wood Turtle, or Wood Terrapin, *C. insculpta,* inhabiting eastern North America. In each shield of the carapace a series of concentric grooves rise in pyramidal fashion; at the rear margin the shell flares upward and is strongly serrated. Above the color is dull brown, with obscure yellow markings; the plastron is yellow, with a large, dark blotch in most of the shields. Most characteristic is the coloration of the limbs and neck, which are brick red. An eight-inch shell signifies the maximum growth.

Here we find a turtle that seems to be in the midst of the process of adopting terrestrial habits. It often wanders into swampy woods, feeding on berries, tender vegetation and insect larvæ; thus it may leave the water for the greater part of the summer. Yet it is an admirable swimmer. Many individuals persistently haunt the borders of streams and ponds like the typical, semi-aquatic turtles and terrapins.

The Wood Terrapin is edible and was once collected in such quantities it was threatened with speedy extinction. Through the efforts of Madison Grant, President of the New York Zoological Society, a bill was passed in the state of New York, prohibiting the collecting, for market purposes, of this species and the box turtle *(Terrapene carolina).*

Considerably smaller, Muhlenberg's Turtle, *C. muhlenbergii,* is distinct in being blackish, with a vivid orange patch on each side of the head. Few specimens have a shell longer than three and a half inches. Marked with faint concentric grooves, the general effect of the upper shell is black. Closely examined, it may appear marked with obscure, reddish, radiating blotches.

Restricted in its *habitat* to southern New York, New Jersey and eastern Pennsylvania, this singular little turtle is comparatively rare; nor is it generally distributed over the small area it inhabits. Most of the writer's specimens have been caught on Staten Island, N. Y. They were found along marshy borders of small, clear streams. In captivity the species displays an ability to feed while out of the water, eating different kinds of fruit; it is also carnivorous.

Owing to its black shell and head, the COMMON SPOTTED TURTLE, *C. guttata,* bears a superficial resemblance to Muhlenberg's Turtle. It will be seen, however, to lack the large and brilliant orange spot on each side of the head, while the back is generously sprinkled with round, yellow spots. The upper shell is quite smooth; when the turtle is fully mature the shell is about four inches long.

Ranging from southern Canada to South Carolina and westward to Ohio this abundant species is generally familiar. In fresh-water bogs it exhibits a seemingly social spirit. Certain miniature islands of bunch grass are matted down by clusters of turtles that go there regularly to bask and an old log may be so thickly covered that several turtles have been forced to roost on the shells of those having secured favorite spots. Thus the little colony takes a bath in the life-giving sun, with limbs sprawled out in comical fashion and ever-attentive eyes on the lookout for danger. Ludicrous results follow the approach of the human observer, as there is a panicky scramble for the water, a series of splashes, then a desolate log without sign of life.

Unlike the two preceding species the Spotted Turtle does not seem to be able to eat while out of the water, so its habits are strictly in accord with the typical fresh-water turtles and terrapins. Similar in its habits is the Californian species, *C. marmorata;* the carapace is blackish, decorated with numerous yellow specks or radiating lines; there is a decided similarity in the markings of some specimens to the European Pond Turtle, *Emys orbicularis.*

As we consider the genus *Emys* we have advanced another step nearer the terrestrial chelonians: for the present species feed while out of the water and are quite at home on land—but they never leave damp places and their feet are sufficiently webbed to make them agile swimmers. Two species are known. Strange to explain, they are remarkably alike in structure and coloration, yet one inhabits the New World while the *habitat* of the other is across the seas—in Europe and Africa.

Here we must note a peculiar structure of the under shell—the plastron, which is attached to the upper shell by elastic cartilage and divided near the center by a cartilaginous hinge; thus the lobes are movable. The structure shows a near relationship with the true box turtles, of *Terrapene*—the succeeding genus. However, the ability to close the lobes against the carapace is not nearly so well developed as with *Terrapene*. In fact, it principally involves the anterior lobe. Hence the origin of a popular name often applied to the American species—the Semi-Box Turtles.

BLANDING'S TURTLE or the SEMI-BOX TURTLE, *Emys blandingii,* inhabits southern Canada and the northeastern portion of the United States. By its form alone it differs from other turtles of the United States: for the shell is elongated, high and globular. Most of these turtles are black above, thickly speckled with yellow. Narrow and not wider than the long, snake-like neck, the head is black above and vivid lemon yellow beneath.

In Ohio and Illinois, Blanding's Turtle is a very common reptile. The shell of an adult is about eight inches long. After observing a large series of specimens the writer is led to believe that Blanding's Turtle is erratic in habits. Some specimens refuse to leave the immediate vicinity of a pond or stream, where they crawl out on logs and rocks to sun and tumble into the water when frightened; such examples feed on fishes, tadpoles and frogs. Others wander into damp woods, where they lead a practically terrestrial life, feeding on tender vegetation, berries and insects. Captive examples will take their food from a tray like true tortoises, eating raw beef, lettuce and celery. Incidentally, they are as quick in the water as the flat-shelled terrapins and perfectly at ease in swallowing their food beneath the surface.

The EUROPEAN POND TURTLE, *Emys orbicularis,* occurs abundantly in central and southern Europe, Asia Minor and extreme northern Africa. Of lesser proportions, it also has a proportionately flatter shell than the American ally. Above, the color is brownish, or black thickly speckled with yellow—sometimes marked with radiating lines of the pale hue. On very old turtles, the yellow markings fade until the shell is uniform brown or blackish. The average length of a fully-grown shell is about five inches. In habits this species seems to be more persistently aquatic than the American turtle.

Another step up the scale of evolution! We are confronted by strictly terrestrial chelonians, but are still considering the *turtles*. The genus *Terrapene* is composed of nine American turtles that have forever left the water; they lead the same life as the true tortoises. We cannot call them tortoises as they yet have well-defined traces of webs on the hind feet. Their race will ultimately develop into tortoises; at this stage of their development we must at once note the high, globular shell, the thick and stubby front feet, and the slow gait, like that of the species of *Testudo*.

The BOX TURTLES are rightly named. Attached to the carapace by elastic cartilage, the plastron is divided by a cartilaginous hinge. We find practically the same structure as observed with *Emys,* but so perfectly developed that the animal is encased in a veritable, tightly-closed box in time of danger. In most cases the plastral lobes close so tightly against the lower margin of the carapace that it is impossible to insert a broom-straw at any part of the union. Moreover, the strength of the muscles that draw up the divisions of the plastron is astonishing. Ingenuous, indeed, has been Nature in protecting these creatures.

Five of the Box Turtles inhabit the central and eastern

portions of North America; four occur in Mexico. The maximum length of shell is about seven inches.

The COMMON BOX TURTLE, *Terrapene carolina,* has a moderately oval shell with a distinct though flattened keel. There are four claws on the hind foot. While the markings are extremely variable, they are always thick and blotchy, often forming broad yellow E's on the side of the shell. Most of the males have bright red eyes and a concave area on the central portion of the lower shell. This species inhabits the northeastern United States, east of the Mississippi River and as far south as South Carolina. An average-sized specimen has a shell 5¾ inches long, 4¼ inches wid and 3 inches high.

From the cultivated areas the Box Turtle is rapidly disappearing. It inhabits dry woods, hiding under low, thick bushes at night or during rainy weather. When abroad it hunts for berries, tender shoots, earthworms and insects. During the blackberry season the mandibles and front feet of most specimens are much stained with the juices. Wild turtles are very timid. When picked up they close the lobes of the plastron tightly. Thus securely encased the reptile remains as long as disturbed and if carried about by the collector will show little signs of life for hours, except a slight release of the front plastral lobe to facilitate breathing.

Kept as pets, Box Turtles become so tame they will take food from the hand and it is hard to induce them to close the box-like shell; in many instances they get so fat it would be impossible for them to do so. In this condition a turtle may become frightened and in closing one-half of the plastron forces the fleshy parts from the other, and *vice versa,* with ludicrous results in the case with a timid specimen. The writer's turtles would take a variety of food. All were particularly fond of earthworms. Raw meat, lettuce, celery, and the leaves of clover, as well as the blossoms, were also eaten—besides various kinds of fruit. Frogs and salamanders were not safe in the vivarium, as they were invariably attacked and partially eaten. One turtle was seen to eat a slug, which slimy creature caused the reptile considerable trouble, causing it to rub its smeared mandibles on the ground and against its paws for a full half hour after.

If a Box Turtle is thrown into the water it floats like a miniature buoy, but is decidedly awkward and hysterical in gaining the shore. The stubby limbs work spasmodically and progress is usually erratic.

As the fall approaches, the Box Turtle selects soft ground and commences to burrow. The progress is not hurried; the reptile may dig but six or eight inches in a week. It literally grovels into the ground, which closes over the back when the animal is but three or four inches down. After the first light frost—barely tingeing the surface—the ground becomes chilled and the reptile partly benumbed; the noonday sun warms it back to life and with a warning; then it burrows with more energy, sinking to a depth of fourteen to sixteen inches, when the winter sleep begins.

The eggs of the Box Turtle are oval, with an exceedingly thin though brittle shell. Curiously enough, the young are seldom seen; they are quite flat, with a broad and decided keel. The eggs hatch in about ninety days.

The THREE-TOED BOX TURTLE, *T. triunguis,* has a keel on the carapace, but the shell is shaped like that of the former kind. Little or no traces of yellow markings are visible on the upper shell which is dull brown or olive. From Missouri to Georgia and southward to the Gulf States the species is fairly common.

The Southern Box TURTLE, *T. major,* is restricted to Florida, southern Georgia and southeastern Texas. As examples of this kind have a shell seven inches long, the present species is the largest of the genus. It has a higher, narrower and more globular shell. Nor does the upper shell agree with the other box turtles in flaring sharply upward at the rear margin; there being only a slight intimation of this. Besides the structural differences stated, a glance at the coloration will show it to be strongly characteristic. It is regular and composed of close-set, narrow greenish lines radiating from the center of the shell. In the dry and sandy pine woods the writer has found many turtles of this kind; they may often be found hiding under the leaves of the dwarf palmetto.

One of the Box Turtles found in Mexico—*T. mexicana*—has three claws on the hind foot. This may be nothing more than a subspecies of the former.

The PAINTED BOX TURTLE, *T. ornata,* may be told by the absence of a keel on the carapace. In the shape of bright yellow bars the markings radiate from the center of the shell. The scales on the limbs are generally tinged with pink. This reptile is found from Indiana to the Rocky Mountains and southward into Mexico; it has four toes on the hind foot.

In the lists of scientific classification there exist several genera between *Terrapene* and those land chelonians called *tortoises,* the latter distinguished by their dome-like shells and stubby feet, without vestiges of webs that resemble, in miniature, the feet of an elephant—the resemblance relating principally to the hind feet. Among the several genera placed immediately before the tortoises—these mostly Oriental—we find species that are semi-aquatic, though few of them are dependent upon the water for obtaining their food, as are the typical flat-shelled turtles and terrapins.

With the tortoises we arrive at chelonians so removed in structure and habits from the turtles that there comes a temptation to place them in a family by themselves. This step would be necessary if a few of the preceding genera were unknown. As matters stand, a technical arrangement of the chelonians shows us, step by step, the relationship of the high-shelled tortoise of the deserts to the depressed, persistently aquatic turtle with its broadly webbed feet.

The TRUE TORTOISES. True tortoises are embraced within five genera. These are *Kinixys, Pyxis, Homopus, Gopherus* and *Testudo.* The latter is the most extensive genus, containing about forty-five species; *Kinixys* contains three species; *Pyxis* is represented by a single tortoise and *Homopus* by four species.

To these mostly slow-moving and—in the human eye—ungainly creatures, we must award the standard for the highest degree of intelligence among reptiles. Tortoises appear to exhibit reasoning powers equal to the warm-blooded animals. Their wanderings are often extensive, but they are not vagrant prowlers like the greater number of snakes and lizards. They have a dwelling place—a burrow, or hollowed-out spot among rocks or bushes; to this they return after their explorations with a regularity rivaling the "instinct" of the fox and other den-dwelling mammals. Some tortoises inhabit desert areas under a sun almost unendurable to the human; these desert species live in long burrows from which they prowl by night or during the dawn to clusters of cacti and other sparse vegetation of such regions, where they browse. All tortoises inhabit areas that are at least comparatively dry. Many are so grotesquely marked as to suggest weird coffers that might hold the jewels of some princess of the past. New World species are few. Africa is the home of the greater number.

Genus *Kinixys,* the HINGE-BACKED TORTOISES. Tropical Africa is inhabited by three of the most grotesque members among tortoises; their shells suggest an attempt of Nature to construct something unique with a somewhat overdone result. The rear portion of the upper shell is hinged and can be drawn down tightly against the plastron, which, in front, projects forward like a battering ram. About the margin the upper shell flares upward. Altogether the effect is irregular. A romantic observer might be led to believe that these tortoises are ashamed of their make-up, as they snap the limbs and head inward at the least intimation of a shadow or vibration, when the hinged part of the upper shell is pulled downward; the forearms are so bony and fit so tightly together, the protection they afford is complete, unless the enemy be a long-clawed cat or an iron-jawed hyæna.

The species of the genus *Pyxis, P. arachnoides,* inhabiting Madagascar, has the front lobe of the plastron hinged.

Genus *Gopherus.* All portions of the shell are rigid. The three representatives are the only North American tortoises.

They may be concisely defined, thus:

I. *Carapace considerably longer than wide.*
 Several much-enlarged bony plates on inner surface of forearm. GOPHER TORTOISE, *G. polyphemus.*
 Habitat: South Carolina and Florida to western Texas.
 No enlarged bony plates on forearm.
 AGASSIZ'S TORTOISE, *G. agassizii.*
 Habitat: Deserts of the southwest United States.

II. *Carapace nearly as wide as long.*
 BERLANDIER'S TORTOISE, *G. berlandieri.*
 Habitat: So. Texas; Mexico.

Adult examples of all these species are of a dull, uniform brown above. Young and half-grown individuals have a dull yellowish blotch in the center of each shield.

Most generally known is the dingy GOPHER TORTOISE, *Gopherus polyphemus,* of the southeastern United States. Rather flattened on the top, the shell of old tortoises is perfectly smooth; on the young the shields are marked with concentric grooves. Over the entire forelimb is an armor of bony and protruding plates that assume the formation of conical shields on the inner surface—or, more properly, the inner *margin,* as the forelimbs are much flattened for the purpose of digging. A fully grown shell is twelve inches long—straight measurement, with calipers. Possessing a shell this size a tortoise weighs from eight to ten pounds.

In dry, sandy, almost barren areas of the Southern States, burrows of the Gopher Tortoise may be found on all sides. The writer observed many in open sandy country, plentifully sprinkled with a growth of scrub oaks. Over these wastes, during the middle of the day, the heat of the sun was so intense that the writer's horse showed marked signs of distress. No tortoises were seen at such times, though tracks in the sand were numerous. Such could be traced a considerable distance from a burrow, then back again—sometimes into another burrow. The burrows were at intervals of about twenty-five feet apart. They could be detected from a considerable distance by the mound of sand thrown out by the animal. As a rule the shafts were sharply oblique for a yard or slightly more, when they assumed a more gentle slope. Each was peculiar in being dug in the same outline as a traverse section of the animal's shell. Burrows of young tortoises were precisely like those of the old ones in regard to the outline and the little mounds of scooped-out sand were in many instances not more than three inches high.

From dawn until eight or nine in the morning, the tortoises were found prowling. When the old ones were approached they sank to the sand with a sharp hiss, drew in the head and limbs, and remained motionless. Young tortoises were not so stoical about capture, making for a burrow with some show of agility. When picked up they kicked and scratched in a thoroughly vigorous fashion.

If not kept perfectly dry—besides very warm—captive tortoises survive only a few weeks. Given proper quarters they live indefinitely, probably reaching an age of considerably over a hundred years. Mainly herbivorous, they will eat lettuce, celery, grass and clover as well as different kinds of fruit; berries are a favorite food.

Throughout tropical South America may be found a tortoise with a much elongated shell, black above with a bright yellow spot in the center of each shield. We might call this species the SOUTH AMERICAN TORTOISE; technically, it is known as *Testudo denticulata.* Large shells are eighteen inches long. In addition to the bright blotches on the shell, is a bright coral hue tingeing the scales of the fore-limbs.

The ABYSSINIAN TORTOISE, *T. sulcata,* ranks as one of the largest of the African tortoises. In several ways it is characteristic, for the shell is rather flattened and of a uniform horn color. An adult has a shell twenty inches long.

Head and limbs are yellowish; the latter are encased in big, bony spurs.

The STAR TORTOISE, *T. elegans,* is a really beautiful creature, though of moderate size. The carapace is very high and dome-like, each shield containing concentric grooves rising like steps; above, the shell is jet-black, with striking pale yellow markings, arranged thus:—The summit of each shield is yellow and from it radiate vivid yellow lines. Particularly striking are the plastral markings, as the under shell is black with two clean-cut yellow stars. This is an Indian tortoise. The GEOMETRIC TORTOISE, *T. geometrica,* is an African species, high-backed, with similar markings. Closely allied is the fine LEOPARD TORTOISE, *T. pardalis,* of tropical Africa, reaching a weight of seventy-five pounds. The shell is very convex.

The EUROPEAN TORTOISE, *T. græca,* having a shell about seven inches long, is common in southern Europe. Its pale olive shell with black-bordered shields is rather pretty. Nearly allied is the IBERIAN TORTOISE, *T. iberia,* of southern Europe and northern Africa.

GIANT TORTOISES. Among the species of *Testudo* are some of the most remarkable of living reptiles. Such are the gigantic tortoises inhabiting small, isolated groups of islands in the tropical Pacific and the Indian Ocean. Though the great sea turtles outclass the present creatures in weight, the latter are, in comparison to other tortoises, of astonishing proportions. Survivors of an age when reptiles grew to an enormous size, successive generations of these tortoises have lived through periods when an atmosphere reeking with humidity promoted fantastic and luxuriant vegetation upon which browsed the great herbivorous lizards; then with the passing of innumerable centuries, during which volcanic disturbances shattered whole continents and cast up new ones, race after race of scaled and plated monsters degenerated and perished. As illustrations of what reptile life has been we have only to examine in the museums fossil remains so gigantic that they stagger our comprehension as to how actual flesh and muscle could coat and move such ponderous bones. Through a strange and apparently incidental provision of Nature, the giant tortoises, the crocodilians and one lizard-like creature—the Tuatera—have survived unchanged through bewildering ages of time; other reptiles of the present show every phase of the obliterating sway of degeneracy.

Compare the Giant Tortoise that has trod unchanged out of the past, with a modern tortoise of average size. What a difference in proportions is seen! It is fortunate for mankind that no such comparisons are possible among the lizards. Imagine an iguana magnified to such proportions! We would have a creature that could rush upon a man, tear and devour him within a moment. Diminutive indeed are the present reptiles as compared with their colossal ancestors. To one who has observed numerous, ordinary tortoises, then for the first time sees a giant tortoise, the sight is awe-inspiring and causes one to feel as if looking upon—though it be a substantial one—a ghost of the past.

The Galapagos Islands, thirteen in number, form a tiny archipelago of volcanic origin about five hundred miles west of the South American coast, and scorching under a tropical sun. Six species of Giant Tortoises are found here. Nowhere else in the New World do they occur. The Aldabra Islands in the Indian Ocean form the *habitat* of four others; and four species inhabit the Mauritius-Rodriguez group of islands. All of the species have been ruthlessly slaughtered and the drain upon the remainder by scientific expeditions has so reduced the entire group that these interesting creatures are threatened with extinction in a wild state. Several species entirely disappeared during the nineteenth century. In Europe, Asia and Africa numerous fossil remains show these creatures to have formerly inhabited the continents. In the larger zoological gardens of Europe and America are numerous living examples; the greater number are from the Galapagos Islands.

During recent years several expeditions have visited the Galapagos Islands for the purpose of collecting tortoises. The first specimens to arrive in this country were brought by the U. S. S. *Albatross,* which visited the islands in 1888; eighteen examples were shipped to Washington, D. C. In 1897, the Hon. Walter Rothschild arranged an expedition to the Galapagos Islands. It resulted in a total cost of $15,000. Fifty-nine tortoises were captured. Mr. Rothschild distributed the tortoises among the zoological gardens of Europe. He dispatched another expedition in 1900 and twenty tortoises were collected, but the trip across the United States proved disastrous; all but six of these specimens died. A fine lot of tortoises arrived in San Francisco early in 1901, brought there by Capt. William Johnson. Mr. F. B. Webster purchased the entire lot, shipping them east to his place at Hyde Park, Massachusetts. Five examples were purchased by the New York Zoological Society; six were sold to Mr. Rothschild and two to Count Peracca, in Italy; the others were bought by various zoological institutions. The members of this expedition claimed to have brought the last survivors of the tortoise colony. Expeditions of Dr. Charles H. Townsend in 1928 to Albemarle Island, of Cornelius Vanderbilt in 1928 to Duncan Island and Vincent Astor in 1929 to Indefatigable Island demonstrate that specimens of tortoises of the distinct species characteristic of each of these islands remain in the interior areas.

Testudo vicina, of Albemarle, in the Galapagos group, appears to be the largest of the New World species. An example in the New York Zoological Park weighs 310 pounds; its length of shell, on the curve, is 4 feet 3 inches, and the height of the shell, 20 inches. Records of close to 500 pounds have been noted. These tortoises grow much faster than has been alleged and may attain maturity and great size in less than twenty years. They may live a hundred years or more, but nothing approaching this period is required for their growth to largest size.

Testudo ephippium, of Duncan Island, is remarkable in having a dome-like shell, the front margin arching sharply, high above the head. In spite of the reptile's ponderous appearance, the shell is very thin, so pliable that it may be pressed inward in the center of the shields by the tip of a man's finger.

Testudo gigantea inhabits the Aldabra Islands—in the Indian Ocean. The head is very small and on a long, almost snake-like neck. This tortoise has a decidedly convex shell. An example in the New York Zoological Park weighs 240 pounds.

Many times has the writer been surprised to note the sagacity of these cold-blooded creatures. They soon learn to recognize their keeper and come lumbering to him as he enters their enclosure—the interest prompted mostly by appetite. Rearing their long neck upwards, they will take bananas from the man's hand. Rather averse to undue familiarity, they resent an attempt to touch their head by suddenly drawing back that member and emitting a hoarse exhalation of air; yet they are never hostile, though their knife-like jaws could easily crush a man's hand.

During the time of love-making the male behaves in a curious fashion. He stalks about the female in a circle, frequently stopping in a position facing the side of her shell. Here he raises as high as his stubby limbs will permit and batters his shell against her, repeating the operation a dozen times or more. This is supposed to be courtship but the resounding thumps are like the blows of a heavy mallet or a sledge and look far more ludicrous than romantic. At such times the males utter deep, trumpeting calls.

It is quite probable that the colony of these strange creatures in the New York Zoological Park will survive to be exhibited to future generations and that their stony gaze upon man's affairs may coldly observe conditions comprehended by us, of the present, only in our most speculative dreams. In time to come the morning sun-bath of these tortoises may be momentarily darkened, now and then, by the flight of passing air ships bringing visitors to the great institution, there to look, to wonder, and then to realize that the creatures before them—living remnants of the army of giant fossils—speak mutely of an epoch when their ancestors were the masters of the globe, fully as dominant as man has finally become. Could there be a more stirring illustration of the ages through which our planet has passed?

Leaving the *Testudinidæ* and its varied forms that are adapted to such strikingly different modes of life, we arrive at a highly specialized family of turtles that have taken to the sea and developed seal-like flippers. In the possession of these they resemble the Leathery Turtle, *Dermochelys,* but the parallelism relates only to a certain development of the organs of locomotion that is imperative in a marine life.

Family *Cheloniidæ,* SEA TURTLES. Three genera, with a total of seven species, make up the family. Three of the species have an extensive distribution, being found in all tropical and semi-tropical seas of the globe. They are the giants of the aquatic chelonians and exceeded in size only by the single species of *Sphargis.* The shell is covered with smooth horny shields. Developed into flat, seal-like "flippers" or paddles, the limbs form powerful swimming organs. None of the sea turtles leaves the sea except to deposit the eggs on sandy beaches; then the heavy creature waddles awkwardly and impresses one as an animal altogether out of its element. One of the sea turtles—the Green Turtle—is of world-wide renown as an article of food; another—the Hawk's-Bill Turtle—furnishes the valuable "tortoise" shell.

Genus *Caretta.* The three species are popularly known as the *Loggerhead Turtles.* From the other—the succeeding—genus of the family, the present one may be separated by a fairly constant character—this in the shape of *two* claws on each front flipper; with *Chelonia* there are seldom traces of more than one nail on the front paddle.

The LOGGERHEAD TURTLE, *Caretta caretta,* looks somewhat like the Green Turtle (*Chelonia*). From the latter species it may be told by the proportionately larger head and the presence of the two nails on each front flipper. The carapace is thick and heavy. Head and flippers are covered with coarse, leathery shields. With most of these turtles the upper shell is dull, uniform brown; some are obscurely blotched with yellow. A very large example will weigh five hundred pounds and have a shell four feet long. Three hundred-pound turtles, with a shell about three feet long, are not rare. Such are often harpooned off the northern coasts of the United States—Massachusetts and Long Island—having followed the warm current of the Gulf Stream.

Many Loggerhead Turtles are sent to the markets, though the flesh is considered much inferior to that of the Green Turtle. The meat is dark red and not unlike beef both in looks and taste.

In May and June, numbers of Loggerheads lay their eggs along the Florida coast. An enormous number of eggs is deposited, varying from fifty to a thousand, according to the size and the age of the female. The turtles generally leave the water at night, laboring over the sand to a point above tide line. Here a hollow is scooped with the front flippers, then the animal grovels in the sand, shoving it out of the burrow behind her with the rear paddles. The eggs are soon laid and well covered, when the female starts again for the sea. Her progress up the beach and the return to the water are usually so erratic that it is impossible to discover, by the tracks, the exact spot where the eggs have been deposited. Persons who make it a business to hunt for the eggs carry a sharp stick which they run into the sand at intervals along the reptile's track, thus sounding for the eggs. If unmolested, the eggs hatch in about two months' time. The little turtles seek shallow inlets until they have acquired sufficient strength to lead a strictly marine life. A small portion of the brood reaches maturity. Enemies are many in the shape of large fish and sea birds.

To discover one of these sea monsters on the beach is to experience a certain feeling of awe. The great, floundering brute, in the fulfillment of parental duties, is practically at man's mercy, yet clumsily alert. It sullenly exhales the breath with a deep, roaring sound, while the bleary, seal-like eyes stare in a seemingly vacant fashion. If a big conch shell is shoved within reach of the jaws, it is seized and crushed in a single grasp. Turned on its back, the giant is helpless. If not hindered, it makes for the sea, causing a great commotion in reaching the water, as it flounders for sufficient depth where it may find purchase for the paddle-like limbs.

Differing by the presence of ridges on the inner, crushing surface of the jaws is KEMP'S LOGGERHEAD TURTLE, *C. kempii,* recorded from the Gulf of Mexico to Hatteras. *C. olivacea* inhabits the tropical Pacific.

The GREEN TURTLE, *Chelonia mydas,* has acquired its popular name from the green hue of the fat. The shields of the carapace are smooth; on old examples they are polished; they are olive or brown, richly marbled with yellow. Though attractive and striking in its coloration, the shell is of no commercial value. Head and flippers are coarsely plated and all of the shields are vividly margined with white or yellow.

A large Green Turtle has a shell three and a half feet long. An animal of this size weighs about four hundred pounds.

This is the turtle so often seen in our markets rolled over on its back, in which position it is helpless. Although the treatment has been generally condemned as cruel, it is a necessity in keeping the turtles alive unless they can be placed in capacious tanks of sea water—an expensive process for the markets. The plastron is not so rigidly constructed as with the fresh-water turtles. If examined, it will be found quite pliable, offering little of the bony support of most chelonians. This is not a defect in the structure, as the sea turtles never find it necessary to rest their weight upon the plastron except in the brief trips shoreward to lay their eggs. Thus, if these animals are placed in a "normal" position when out of the water their great weight presses the plastron upwards against the lungs and other internal organs, causing speedy death. Those seen in the markets range in weight from forty to one hundred and fifty pounds.

The writer selected a fifty-pound specimen from a New York market and placed the turtle in a large tank to which was added enough salt to give the water a brackish taste. For several years this turtle thrived, when it met its death in a manner quite accidental. In swimming, the motions were slow, graceful and suggested the leisurely flight of a large bird—a hawk or an eagle. A single sweep of the flippers would carry the turtle about a yard; approaching the concrete side of the tank with a momentum that threatened to dash it against the hard surface, a single, easy movement of the flippers would stop the creature when a few inches away; then another sweep of the limbs changed its direction in an exploration of the pool.

Supposition has it that the food of the Green Turtle is of a strictly vegetable nature. Such was not the case with the writer's specimens. All showed a preference for fish over other food; they would also eat mussels, oysters and clams—after the mollusks had been removed from their shells; an occasional turtle would nibble at seaweeds, but immediately left such food when a dead fish was thrown into the tank. Without doubt, while in a wild state, the Green Turtle necessarily feeds largely on marine vegetation. It might be termed omnivorous and its jaws are powerful enough to crush the larger crustaceans upon which it undoubtedly feeds to some extent.

Of the *Cheloniidæ* the Green Turtle seems to be the most persistent wanderer from the warmer seas. It follows the

Gulf Stream northward along the Atlantic Coast, showing a like disposition along European shores. During the summer months frequent specimens are seen in New York Harbor, where they appear to be perfectly at home. With the approach of fall, when the waters become chilled, they become benumbed, then fall a prey to fishermen.

The HAWK'S-BILL TURTLE, *Eretmochelys imbricata,* and an allied species are unique among the sea turtles in having the shields of the carapace coarsely overlapping, like shingles—imbricate. The head is quite narrow and the upper mandible projects downward in hooked fashion, like a bill. Smallest of the sea turtles, these species have the greatest commercial value. A carapace of a very large example is two and a half feet long, while the average length is considerably below this. Smooth and translucent, the shields of the carapace are beautifully marked in marbled fashion with black and yellow, or rich brown and yellow; beneath the color is uniform yellow; the shields of the head and limbs are brown or black tinged brightly about their borders with a pale yellowish hue.

Inhabiting the tropical and semi-tropical seas of both the Old and the New World, the Hawk's-Bill Turtles are continually hunted over the greater part of their extensive range. The valuable "tortoise" shell, obtained only from these reptiles, is composed of the thin, clear, horny shields covering the bony portion of the carapace. The shields are removed from the shell by heating it, when they commence to peel and are assisted in the process by the operator. As the operation often involves a living reptile the martyred creature is turned loose afterwards, for the belief is that it grows a new coat of shields. While the theory is partially correct, actual conditions do not affirm the primary idea; for the turtle sometimes reproduces a thin veneer of shields that are of absolutely no commercial value.

At various times the writer has kept young Hawk's-Bill Turtles in small tanks that have been made brackish by adding ordinary salt to the water. His specimens were from six to eight inches long; they were voraciously fond of cut-up fish, taking the food from one's fingers. Some of them lived for over a year. In a capacious tank of sea-water, young or adult turtles will thrive indefinitely.

Another grouping of the *Chelonians* is characterized by the method of bending the neck when the head is drawn into the shell. The neck bends in lateral curves (sideways). With most of the species the characteristic is externally evident—the *side* of the head, when that organ is drawn into the protective covering of the shell, being exposed and visible. Members of this group have the pelvis fused to the shell.

Family *Pelomedusidæ*. The neck is completely retractile within the protection of the shell, which is covered with horny shields. Most of the species look like big mud turtles (*Kinosternidæ*) owing to their somber, oval shells, the tinged plastron (with some), together with the large head—terminating in a sharp, conical snout. They inhabit muddy rivers of South America, Africa and Madagascar.

Pelusios contains ten species inhabiting tropical and southern portions of Africa—and Madagascar. The plastron is wide, with a *hinged* front lobe. All of the species are dull brown or black and altogether aquatic.

Strikingly similar in habits as well as external appearance to the American species of *Sternotherus* is the AFRICAN MUD TURTLE, *Pelusios derbianus*. The young have a strong keel on the upper shell which becomes faintly defined at maturity; a fully-grown shell is a foot long. Proportionately large, with a short, conical snout, the head is a powerful biting organ. Upper and lower shells are uniform black or dingy brown; the head is paler, with numerous black streaks or dots.

For the past four years, one of these turtles has lived in the reptile house of the New York Zoological Park. During that time the writer has never observed it out of the water. It lurks under the shadow of a log. When pieces of fish or meat are dropped into the water they are snapped up with a rapidity that makes the morsels disappear as if by magic. Paddling to the surface at frequent intervals the turtle pokes the tip of the snout out of the water; a slight movement or a vibration sends it scurrying back to the dark lair.

Pelomedusa contains a single species generally distributed throughout Africa, south of the desert region; it also occurs in Madagascar. Like the species of the preceding genus, it is somber in coloration. The plastron is not hinged.

Third and last of the genera composing the *Pelomedusidæ* is *Podocnemis;* six species inhabit South America; one is found in Madagascar. They are giants among the fresh-water turtles; one of the South American species grows a shell nearly a yard long. Throughout tropical South America, east of the Andes, these big turtles are common, though their numbers have been considerably reduced in many areas by the systematic hunt for their eggs. The eggs yield a valuable oil. Necessarily associated with the great river systems, the *habitat* embraces the Orinoco, the Amazon and their tributaries. Instead of inhabiting the actual waterways the turtles dwell principally in great pools in the forests, that are filled by the rivers as they "back up" during the great freshets.[2]

The species of *Podocnemis* are of a dull brown or olive, with a very broad, flattened shell. Among all the head is rather flattened, the eyes are set close together, besides being directed slightly upwards. There is no hinge on the plastron.

An allied family is composed of truly remarkable chelonians; they are popularly called SIDE-NECK or SNAKE-NECKED TURTLES, and make up the family *Chelydidæ*. The combined head and neck of some of the present turtles more than equal the total length of the shell. This serpentine neck is altogether too long to be entirely tucked

[2] For a detailed and entertaining account about these turtles, see Bates: "The Naturalist On The River Amazon."

back into the shell, so part of it is folded sideways, along the inner margin of the shell, when the animal is frightened; thus the origin of the popular title—"Side-Neck" Turtles. About thirty species, divided into eight genera, belong to this family. Five genera are restricted to South America; the others are represented in Australia and New Guinea.

The *Matamata, Chelus fimbriata,* a South American turtle, is not alone remarkable in having a long, laterally folding neck. It is one of Nature's nondescripts, standing in a genus by itself. Each shield of its flattened shell rises in pointed fashion, giving the back an abnormally rough aspect—but most remarkable is the structure of the head and neck. The former terminates in a long, tubular snout, though at its base it is broad, flattened and heavy, with projecting, bony ridges; the eyes are small and placed so far forward the effect is quite ludicrous. Intensifying the altogether eccentric conformation are a series of flat and projecting fleshy filaments, mostly scalloped, besides studded with small tubercles; some of the filaments are voluntarily movable; the thinner ones sway with a slight agitation of the water. A full-grown Matamata with a shell eighteen inches long appeals to the human mind more like a vision of a disordered dream than a living reptile. The species inhabits the rivers of tropical Brazil and the Guianas. Strictly aquatic and alleged to employ the movable filaments to attract the prey, it probably feeds largely upon fishes.

Almost as curious are the species of *Hydromedusa,* two in number, inhabiting tropical South America. The SOUTH AMERICAN SNAKE-NECKED TURTLE, *H. maximiliani,* has a shell seven inches long and a snake-like neck and head slightly longer than the shell. The head is flattened, with eyes placed well forward. If the creature emerges from the water to sun on a log the effect is not that of a turtle, but of a very round stone with an ugly-looking, blackish snake reared from beneath it. In the writer's collection were four snake-necked turtles that lived for a number of years. For the first few weeks in captivity they were very shy, merely poking their snouts out of the water for air and scurrying to a dark corner of the tank at the least disturbance. Shyness was at last overcome by appetite. They began feeding greedily upon earthworms, pieces of fish and raw beef. If minnows were placed in the tank the turtles chased the fish with considerable agility, never stopping until the last fish was gone. After a couple of months they would take food from the writer's fingers, coming from their tank, through the door of their cage and following him about the laboratory if the morsel was held a short distance from their snouts. During such operations, the small silvery eyes looked very sharp and cunning; the sense of vision was actually acute: for the instant the food was within reach, the long neck—generally carried in a lateral, S-shaped loop—straightened like a flash, there was a snap and the food was seized. Then the reptile wandered about helplessly, as it could not swallow the food unless in the water. Placed in the tank the turtle swallowed the food at once, then scrambled out after more.

Very similar to the South American Snake-Necked Turtles are the species of *Chelodina,* four in number, inhabiting Australia and New Guinea. Of these the AUSTRALIAN SNAKE-NECKED TURTLE, *C. longicollis,* is a typical example. Above, the shell is dark brown or blackish. The plastron is dark yellow; all of the shields are margined with black. Like the New World species, the animal appears, when resting, like a flat stone sheltering all but the head and neck of a vicious-looking snake. The eyes are intensely silvery white and staring; they might lead the student to suppose that the animal had a hostile disposition. Such is not the case: for the snake-neck turtle is among the most inoffensive of chelonians. Those examples living in the reptile house of the New York Zoological Park seldom leave the tank unless to drag the shell to the edge of a partially submerged log. Here they stretch their long necks on a lookout for food, in the shape of fish and raw beef. Under such conditions they have lived for nearly five years.

Among the side-necked turtles is the family *Carettochelydidæ,* made up of a single genus and species—*Carettochelys insculpta,* provided with flat, paddle-shaped limbs like those of the sea turtles. The shell is covered with a soft integument in place of the horny shields. Little is known of this queer turtle, which seems to be entirely aquatic. Its shell is about eighteen inches long. The species is recorded from the Fly River, in New Guinea.

The family *Trionychidæ* or SOFT-SHELLED TURTLES. These interesting fresh-water chelonians are unmistakable. Exceedingly flat, with an almost round or bluntly oval shell, the animal looks as if coated with leather; there are no horny shields, either above or beneath. From the Soft-Shelled Turtles, the bony make-up of the average turtle's shell is utterly lacking—the shell is soft and pliable, except on the central portion of the back, where the skeleton lies close to the surface; the head is long, narrow and terminates in a projecting, tubular snout. In keeping with decidedly aquatic habits, the feet are broadly webbed. This is the eleventh and last of the families of *Testudinata.* From a technical point of view it is important to explain that only the three inner toes are provided with claws, and the neck, which is completely retractile, is tucked back in a vertical plane. Six genera are recognized, which represent a total of about twenty-four species.

Trionyx is represented by over a dozen species, four of which are the only New World soft-shelled turtles; the latter are found only in North America. The remaining genera are small; their members occur in Asia, the larger islands of the Malay Archipelago and in Africa. Without exception the species of all the genera frequent rivers with a soft, muddy bottom.

As the soft, flappy shell causes these chelonians to appear so different from other turtles, they might be thought comparatively helpless in time of danger. By no means are they handicapped or defenseless. The rounded head with its tubular snout and fleshy lips looks harmless enough. Hidden by the lips, however, are a pair of mandibles remarkably keen and strong; on many specimens the mandibles form the outer border of powerful crushing processes—the alveolar surfaces of the jaws; examples thus provided feed largely on mollusks. Taken at a disadvantage, out of the water, the soft-shelled turtles are savage fighters. The head darts at an offending object like that of a snake. Large turtles are dangerous: for they can amputate a man's finger—possibly his hand.

The SPINY SOFT-SHELLED TURTLE, *Trionyx spinifera,* one of the American species, derives its specific name from a peculiar development of the front margin of the carapace; this consists, on adult individuals, of a fringe of pointed, projecting tubercles. An adult has a shell a foot long. Young and half-grown specimens are beautifully marked with numerous black rings scattered over a pale olive carapace; with both young and adult the plastron is marble white. This species occurs in the Mississippi River and is common in the central and northern tributaries of the great water-way. In the St. Lawrence River, it is found as far east as New York.

A near ally is the BROWN SOFT-SHELLED TURTLE, *T. mutica,* differing in the absence of tubercular spines on the front margin of the carapace as well as by the more obscure markings of the young.

Both of these species are distinct from the other American soft-shelled turtles by the head markings, in the shape of two pale bands that extend forward and fork at the base of the proboscis. On the others, *T. ferox* and *T. emoryi,* the head markings fuse immediately in front of the eyes. The Brown Soft-Shelled Turtle inhabits much the same rivers as does *T. spinifera;* it is a less abundant reptile.

The SOUTHERN SOFT-SHELLED TURTLE, *T. ferox,* stands as the largest of the New World species, growing a "shell" eighteen inches long; an animal of this size will weigh forty pounds. On many large examples there are suggestions of spiny tubercles fringing the forward border of the carapace, which condition might cause the species to be confused with *T. spinifera.* In such cases, the head markings, already described, form a strong point for distinction—besides, the *habitat* is different. The present turtle inhabits the southeastern United States from Georgia to western Louisiana. In Florida it grows to the largest size and seems most abundant. Adults are of a pale, uniform brown; young specimens are usually so brilliantly reticulated they recall the markings of variegated leaves. A near relative is EMORY'S SOFT-SHELLED TURTLE, *T. emoryi,* inhabiting the Rio Grande and its tributaries.

Greatly esteemed as an article of diet, large numbers of the American soft-shelled turtles—particularly the southern species—are received at the markets throughout the eastern United States. In the South the colored people display an amusing and convenient way of cooking the turtles. When several are procured, the heads are chopped off and a small cut made in the soft plastron, for cleaning; at no part of the process are the outlines of the turtle materially changed. The entire animal is then rolled in meal and placed in a frying pan. It looks exactly like a big pancake —hence an appropriate, while possibly illiterate, name in some portions of the South—the "flap-jack" terrapin. It should be explained that the negroes obtain the turtles by fishing for them with the regulation hook and line. In the North, soft-shell turtles are a real annoyance to one fishing in fresh water. The reptile takes the bait with a jerk that throws the fisherman into a state of considerable excitement, only to find, after cautiously working his catch to the surface, the anticipated prize is a very angry turtle with much vigor in clawing and snapping at the sportsman's fingers. And the activity of a specimen is surprising. The head darts with a speed equal to the serpent's thrust. These movements in biting have been responsible for another common name—the snapping turtles; that name, however, rightly belongs to the big-headed members of the *Chelydridæ.* While a soft-shelled turtle is essentially a water animal, seldom coming on shore to deposit its brittle, perfectly round eggs, it is capable of rapid locomotion on land, though its actions are amusing. For an instant, when taken from the water, it may retract the head and limbs, when the leathery shell settles down about it; then the sharp snout is poked abruptly out and, without warning, the animal scrambles off, on a veritable run, thumping and bruising the soft plastron as the feet frequently lose their hold during the hysterical race from danger. To pick the turtle up without receiving either a bite or a scratch is not an easy matter, as the reptile will throw its serpentine neck backward so that the head snaps at a point near the center of the shell; at the same time the feet, with their sharp claws, kick and frantically tear at the hand of the tormentor. Placed in the water the animal disappears with a lively exhibition of paddling, the broadly palmated feet working alternately and sending it flying to the bottom. If deep water is not accessible, it grovels in the mud with such energy that a protective cloud hides it from view. When this clears away no trace of the turtle is to be seen. Patience will reward the observer. Presently a snake-like head emerges from the ooze, when a slight movement will cause this to snap back again; shortly, if the creature is not well imbedded, another mud cloud may arise and through it a disk-like object darts for better shelter.

Soft-Shelled Turtles are almost entirely carnivorous, feeding largely on fishes and frogs. Agile swimmers, they seize their prey by a dart of the head. They are dangerous enemies of all the smaller aquatic creatures. Different individuals of one species may exhibit a pronounced variation in feeding habits and such have a decided influence upon the development of the mouth parts. Some specimens have worn-down mandibles, but behind these, on both the upper and lower jaws, are very broad. flat crushing surfaces;

turtles thus provided feed largely upon mollusks—snails and mussels.

Under observation, the Soft-Shelled Turtles are hardy and live for years. They should be placed in a tank of deep water. Here they are so thoroughly at ease in the water, even though no means have been provided for emerging from it, they will live indefinitely. A thriving colony may soon be thrown into a state of bad health and ultimately lost, if rockwork or concrete is sloped out of the tank to enable the animals to crawl from the water. In crawling over the rough surface the turtles scratch and bruise the tender plastron until it is worn down to the bone. Ulcers develop, bringing speedy ill-health, then death. The observer should always remember that the soft-shelled turtles are creatures of soft, muddy places. While a bank of mud is altogether inappropriate in an aquarium, a section of a smooth, water-soaked log will answer the purpose of a resting place. In selecting a roost for his own specimens the writer has hunted for a derelict bough, four to five inches in diameter, minus the bark and quite slimy with a growth of microscopic *algæ*. This should be so fastened that about one-third of its diameter protrudes from the water. Treated thus, the writer has never examined any of his specimens that had a sore plastron. The bottom of the tank should be covered with two to three inches of fine sand, for the turtles delight in burrowing.

Among the Old World species of *Trionyx,* a character is to be at once noted in relation to the carapace—a character not apparent on the American species, except with extremely old individuals, or specimens that have become emaciated. This is the practical exposure, over the greater portion of the back (the central portion) of the sheet of bones to which are fused the ribs and vertebræ; around this is a soft, leathery margin which sinks downward as the animal emerges from the water. On the bony, dorsal sheet the sutures of the bones are sharply delineated; the entire surface is coarsely punctulated—like old bone that has disintegrated to some extent. The characteristic is not so evident on young individuals.

The GANGES SOFT-SHELLED TURTLE, *T. gangeticus,* is one of the largest of the Asiatic species. Dull olive and finely spotted with black, the shell of an adult may be two feet long. *T. hurum,* another Indian species, has a dull olive shell when adult, while the young have a startling coloration, being greenish with several pairs of round, eye-like spots on the back—each with a black center, then a yellow border and outside of this successive rings of olive and black.

One species, *T..triunguis*—the only African member of the genus—has an enormous range, extending from the Nile to the Senegal River and southward to the Congo. It is the largest of the soft-shelled turtles, growing a shell over a yard long and attaining a weight of over two hundred pounds. In all parts of the *habitat* this turtle is hunted and eaten by the natives.

Emyda embraces three soft-shelled turtles confined to India. In the rear the plastron is provided with a pair of cartilaginous flaps closing against the shell as the limbs are withdrawn; when the head and forelimbs are pulled inwards the forward portion of the carapace is pulled downward in flap-like fashion; thus, all of the fleshy parts are concealed when the animal is frightened. It will be appreciated, however, that the animal is in much the same plight as the foolish ostrich, alleged to bury its head in the sand; for the soft-shelled turtle could be easily torn to pieces by the combined action of teeth and claws of a hungry animal. A similar development of the plastron relates to the genera *Cyclanorbis* and *Cycloderma,* both of tropical Africa.

INDEX *

* Italic numbers relate to a *description* of a species, when other references are indexed.

D

E

PLATES

HEADS OF AMERICAN ALLIGATOR AND AMERICAN CROCODILE

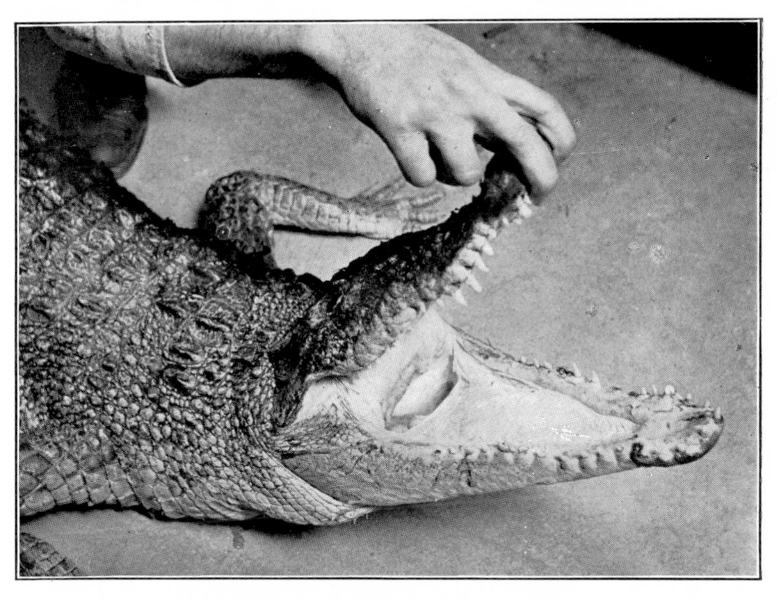

HEAD OF INDIAN CROCODILE *Crocodylus porosus*
Showing throat-valve at base of tongue.

NILE CROCODILE *Crocodylus niloticus*
Distribution: Africa generally and Madagascar.
Grows to a length of sixteen feet.

WEST AFRICAN CROCODILE *Crocodylus cataphractus*
Distribution: West Africa.
Does not attain so large a size as the Nile Crocodile.

SALT-WATER CROCODILE *Crocodylus porosus*
Distribution: India to North Australia. Occurs at sea.
Grows to a length of twenty feet.

BROAD-NOSED CROCODILE *Osteolæmus tetraspis*
Distribution: West Africa.
Reaches a length of six feet.

BROAD–NOSED CAIMAN *Caiman latirostris*
Distribution: Tropical South America.
Attains a length of about seven feet.

SPECTACLED CAIMAN *Caiman sclerops*
Distribution: Tropical America.
The length of an adult is about eight feet.

WHITE-SPOTTED GECKO *Tarentola annularis*
Distribution: Abyssinia, Egypt and Arabia.
Total length, six inches. Shown above and beneath.

BANDED GECKO *Coleonyx variegatus*
Distribution: Southwestern United States.
Length, four inches.

SPINY-TAILED LIZARD *Uromastyx acanthinurus*
Distribution: Deserts of northern Africa.
Attains a length of eighteen inches.

SPINY-TAILED LIZARD *Uromastyx ægyptius*
Distribution: Deserts of northern Africa.
Attains a length of twenty inches.

FLYING "DRAGON" *Draco volans*
Distribution: Malaysia.
Length of adult, eight to ten inches.

NORTH AMERICAN "CHAMELEON"
Anolis carolinensis
Distribution: Southeastern United States and Cuba.

WEST INDIAN "CHAMELEON" *Anolis sagræ*
Distribution: Bahamas, Jamaica and Central America.

ROUGH-SCALED LIZARD *Leiocephalus carinatus*
West Indies. Total length, 12 inches.

TREE RUNNER *Uraniscodon plica*
Found in northern South America.
Attains a length of 16 inches.

CONE-HEADED LIZARD *Læmanctus serratus*
Distribution: Southern Mexico.

The body is small, but excessive length of tail may produce a total length of a yard.

HEAD OF BANDED BASILISK *Basiliscus vittatus*
Distribution: Mexico to Ecuador.

BANDED BASILISK *Basiliscus vittatus*
Distribution: Mexico to Ecuador.
The total length is about two feet.

RHINOCEROS IGUANA *Metopoceros cornutus*
Distribution: Hayti and Porto Rico.
Total length, four feet.

HEAD OF RHINOCEROS IGUANA
Metopoceros cornutus

HEAD OF BAHAMAN IGUANA
Cyclura bæalopha

COMMON IGUANA *Iguana iguana*
Distribution: Tropical America.
Grows to a length of six feet.

HEAD OF COMMON IGUANA
Iguana iguana

HEAD OF MEXICAN IGUANA
Iguana iguana rhinolopha

TURKS ISLAND IGUANA *Cyclura carinata*
Distribution: Turks Island, West Indies.
The total length is three feet.

SPINY-TAILED IGUANA *Ctenosaura acanthura*
Found in Mexico and Central America.
Adult males are 4 feet long.

CHUCKAWALLA *Sauromalus ater*
Distribution: Southwestern United States.
Total length of adult, 18 inches.

COLLARED LIZARD *Crotaphytus collaris*
Distribution: Western United States.
Total length, 12 inches.

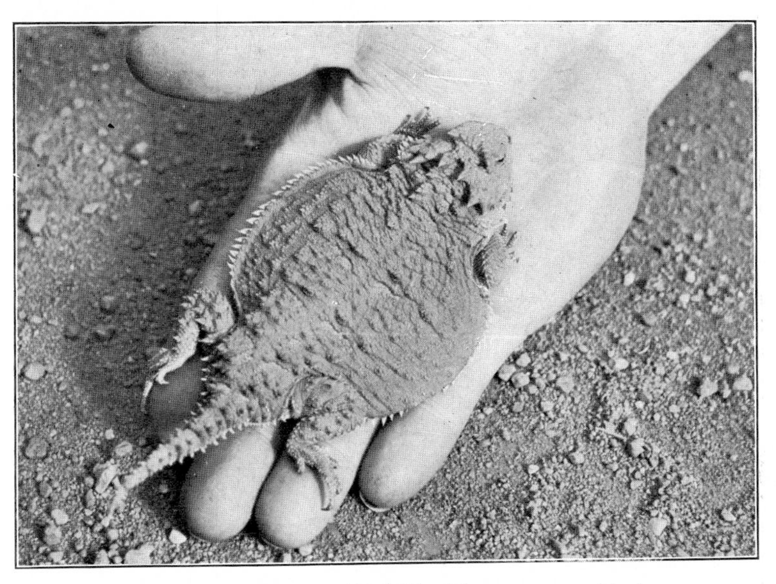

MEXICAN HORNED "TOAD" *Phrynosoma orbiculare* (Fam. *Iguanidæ.*)

Lives in the desert regions of Sonora, Mexico. Its color is a dull brick red. The horns are but slightly developed, as compared with some species of the genus.

SPINY LIZARD *Zonurus giganteus* (Fam. *Zonuridæ.*)
Distribution: South Africa in dry, rocky places.
Grows to a length of fifteen inches.

SHELTOPUSIC *Ophisaurus apodus*
Distribution: Europe and Asia.

GLASS "SNAKE" *Ophisaurus ventralis*
Distribution: North America.

SLOW "WORM" *Anguis fragilis*
Distribution: Europe and Asia.

GILA MONSTER *Heloderma suspectum*

This and the species figured beneath are the only known poisonous lizards. The Gila Monster is found in desert regions of Arizona and New Mexico. Its maximum length is about twenty inches.

MEXICAN BEADED LIZARD *Heloderma horridum*

Distribution: Arid regions from central Mexico to northern Central America.

AFRICAN MONITOR *Varanus niloticus*
Distribution: Africa generally, except in northwest portion.
Grows to a length of seven to eight feet.

INDIAN MONITOR; Kabara-Goya *Varanus salvator*
Distribution: East Indies to Cape York.
Grows to a length of eight to nine feet.

TEGU *Tupinambis tequixin*
Distribution: Tropical South America and the West Indies.
A large specimen is three and one-half feet long.

BLACK TEGU *Tupinambis nigropunctatus*
Distribution: Guianas, Brazil and eastern Peru.
The length of a large specimen is about three feet.

WHIP-TAILED LIZARD *Cnemidophorus bocourti*
Distribution: Mexico.
Total length, fourteen inches.

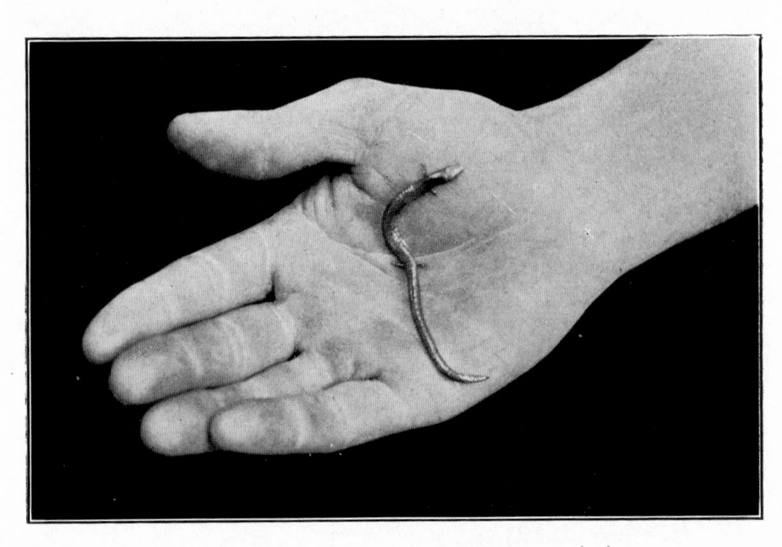

GROUND LIZARD *Scolecosaurus cuvieri*
Distribution: Tropical South America.

TWO-FOOTED WORM LIZARD *Bipes caniculatus*
Distribution: Mexico.
Total length, ten inches.

EUROPEAN WORM LIZARD *Blanus cinereus*
Distribution: Borders of the Mediterranean.
The length of an adult is nine to ten inches.

1

2

3

4

5

EUROPEAN LIZARDS

1. Sand Lizard. *Lacerta agilis.* Southern England, Europe. 2. Red Lizard. *Lacerta agilis rubra.* Europe. 3. Viviparous Lizard. *Lacerta vivipara.* England, Europe, and Siberia. 4. Wall Lizard. *Lacerta muralis.* Southern Europe and northern Africa. 5. Blue Lizard. *Lacerta muralis cærulea.* Faraglion's Rocks (Capri).

GREEN LIZARD *Lacerta viridis*
Distribution: Southern Europe.
Attains a length of twenty inches.

SAND LIZARD *Acanthodactylus boskianus*
Distribution: Northern Africa and Arabia.
Length, ten inches.

DESERT SKINK *Scincus officinalis*
Distribution: Northern Africa.
Maximum length, eight to ten inches.

SAND SKINK *Chalcides sepsoides*
Distribution: Northern Africa and Arabia.
The length of an adult is about six and one-half inches.

1

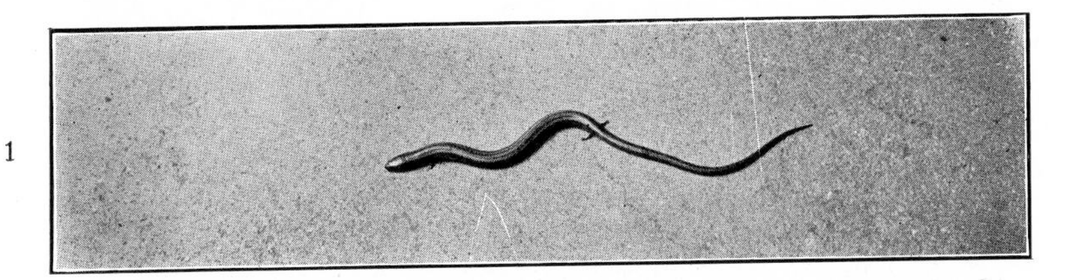

2

3

4

1. Three-Toed Skink. *Chalcides tridactylus.* Italy and northwestern Africa. 2. Ocellated Skink. *Chalcides ocellatus.* Southern Europe. 3. Giant Skink. *Tiligua scincoides.* Australia. 4. Cunningham's Skink. *Egernia cunninghami.* Australia.

CHAMELEON *Chamæleon chamæleon*
Distribution: Northern Africa, Syria, Asia Minor and southern Spain.
Noted for its wonderful color changes.

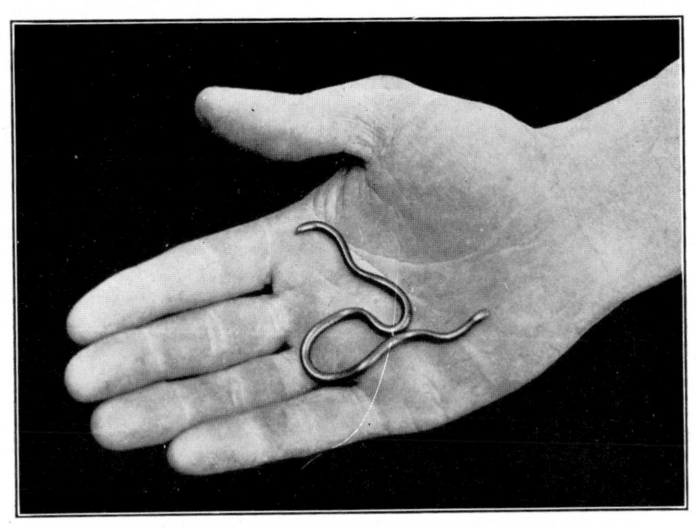

YELLOW-HEADED WORM SNAKE *Leptotyphlops albifrons*
Distribution: Tropical America.

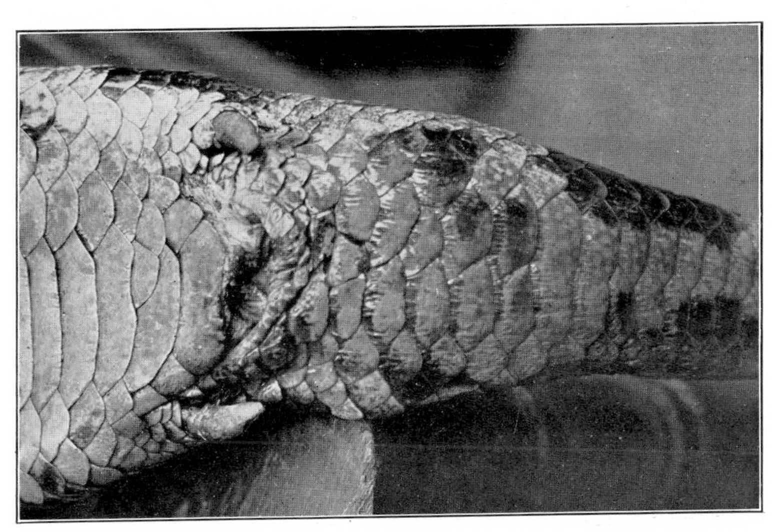

SPURS OF INDIAN PYTHON *Python molurus*
The spurs constitute the only external portions of well-formed hind legs possessed by members of the *Boidæ*.

REGAL PYTHON *Python reticulatus*
Distribution: Malaysia.
Attains a length of thirty feet.

INDIAN PYTHON *Python molurus*
Distribution: India and Burma.
Attains a length of twenty feet.

AFRICAN ROCK PYTHON *Python sebæ*
Distribution: Central and southern Africa.
Attains a length of twelve to sixteen feet.

ROYAL PYTHON *Python regius*
Distribution: West Africa.
Attains a length of five to seven feet.

DIAMOND PYTHON *Python spilotes*
Distribution: Australia and New Guinea.
Attains a length of eight feet.

CARPET PYTHON *Python spilotes variegatus*
Distribution: Australia.
Attains a length of eight to twelve feet.

ANACONDA: WATER BOA *Eunectes murinus*
Distribution: Tropical America.
Largest of the New World constricting snakes.

YELLOW ANACONDA *Eunectes notæus*
Inhabits the Guianas.
Grows to a length of fourteen feet.

SOUTH AMERICAN BOA *Constrictor constrictor*
The maximum length is about twelve feet.

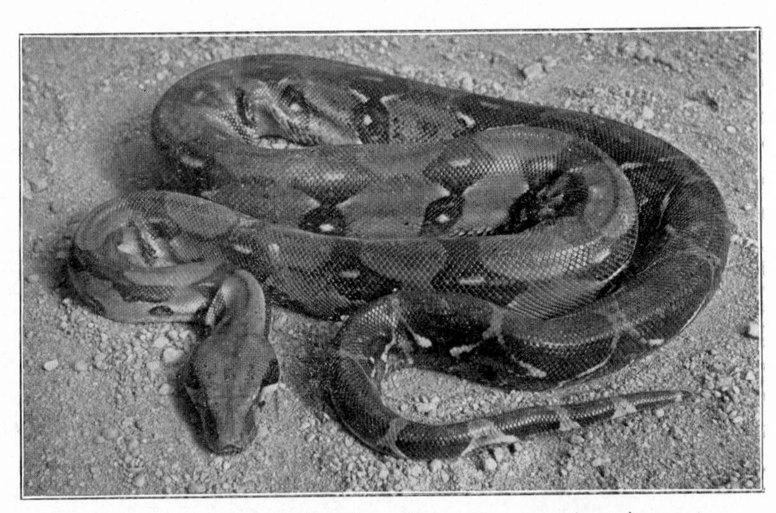

CENTRAL AMERICAN BOA *Constrictor constrictor imperator*
Distribution: Southern Mexico to northern South America.
Reaches a length of ten feet.

CUBAN BOA *Epicrates angulifer*
Distribution: Cuba and Porto Rico.
The maximum length is about ten feet.

BAHAMA BOA *Epicrates striatus*
Distribution: Santo Domingo, New Providence Is., and the Bahamas.
Attains a length of eight feet.

HEAD OF TREE BOA *Boa endyris. Life size.*

This slender boa is exceedingly vicious and is provided with very long teeth. It inhabits tropical South America. The length is about seven feet.

MADAGASCAR TREE BOA *Sanzinia madagascariensis*
Distribution: Island of Madagascar.
Grows to a length of seven feet.

ROUGH-SCALED SAND BOA *Gongylophis conicus*
Distribution: India.
The length of an adult is about a yard.

BROWN SAND BOA *Eryx johnii*
Distribution: India.
The total length is seldom over a yard.

EGYPTIAN SAND BOA *Eryx jaculus*
Distribution: Northern Africa, southwestern and central Asia.
Two feet is the maximum length.

RUBBER BOA *Charina bottæ*
Distribution: United States—Pacific Region from Oregon to California.
A full-grown specimen is eighteen inches long.

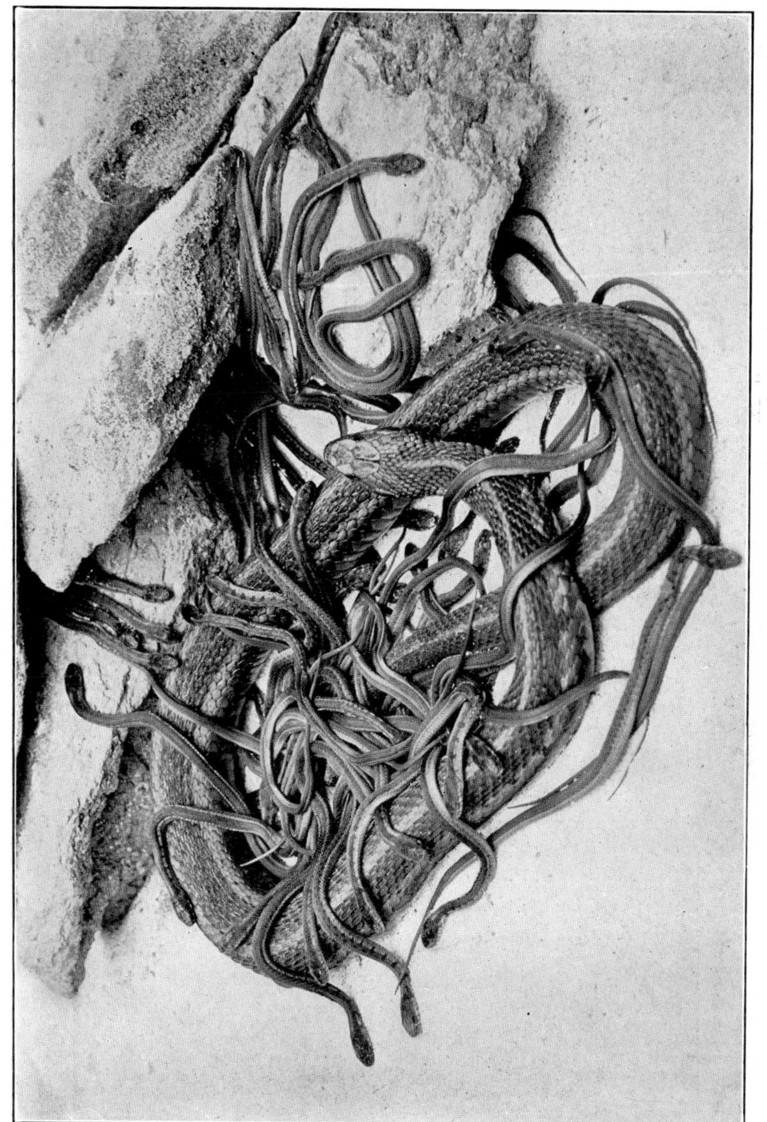

COMMON GARTER SNAKE *Thamnophis sirtalis*

The illustration shows a mother and her litter. All species of the genus *Thamnophis* produce living young. They are the most abundant serpents in the United States. The present species occurs in all parts of North America where snakes are to be found. The length of a large specimen is three and a half feet.

COMMON WATER SNAKE *Natrix sipedon*
Distribution: Eastern United States.
Maximum length, four feet.

COMMON GRASS SNAKE; RINGELNATTER *Natrix natrix*
Distribution: Europe.
Length, three to four feet.

TESSELLATED WATER SNAKE *Natrix tessellata*
Distribution: Southern Europe.
Length of adult about three feet.

BLACK SWAMP SNAKE *Seminatrix pygæa*
Distribution: United States—Florida.
The length is about two feet.

SHORT-TAILED SNAKE *Stylophis extenuatus*
A very rare species, found in Orange and Marion Counties, Florida (U. S.).
Extreme length, two feet.

DIAMOND-BACKED SNAKE *Coluber diadema*
Distribution: Northern Africa.
Length about five feet.

INDIAN RAT SNAKE *Ptyas korros*
Distribution: India, Malay Peninsula, Sumatra and Java.
Attains a length of nine feet.

BLACK SNAKE *Coluber constrictor*
Distribution: Eastern United States.
A large specimen is seven feet long.

BLUE RACER *Coluber constrictor flaviventris*
Distribution: Central and western parts of the United States.
Grows to a length of six feet.

GREEN SPOTTED SNAKE *Drymobius margaritiferus*
Distribution: Mexico to Venezuela.
Total length, four to five feet.

INDIGO SNAKE *Drymarchon corais couperi*
Distribution: United States—southeast portion.
Grows to a length of nine feet.

PILOT BLACK SNAKE *Elaphe obsoleta*
Distribution: United States—Massachusetts to Florida.
A large adult is seven feet long.

FOUR-LINED SNAKE *Elaphe quatuorlineata*
Distribution: Southern Europe.
Maximum length, about six feet.

KING SNAKE *Lampropeltis getulus*

A cannibalistic species of eastern North America. It frequently kills poisonous serpents and, though generally bitten while constricting its venomous prey to death, is quite immune to the poison.

WEST INDIAN RACER *Alsophis rufiventris*

Distribution: Southerly West Indies.
Adults are three and one-half to five feet long.

SOUTH AMERICAN WATER SNAKE *Helicops angulatus*
Distribution: Tropical South America.
Length of adult, two and one-half feet.

SWAMP SNAKE *Liophis cobella*
Distribution: Northeastern South America.
Dimensions of adult, about twenty-eight inches.

HOG-NOSED SNAKE AND HER EGGS *Heterodon contortrix*

A species inhabiting the eastern United States. Three species of this genus are known. All inhabit North America.

TEXAS HOG-NOSED SNAKE *Heterodon nasicus*

As with all the Hog-nosed Snakes, this serpent flattens the head and neck when annoyed, hissing loudly. It is quite innocuous.

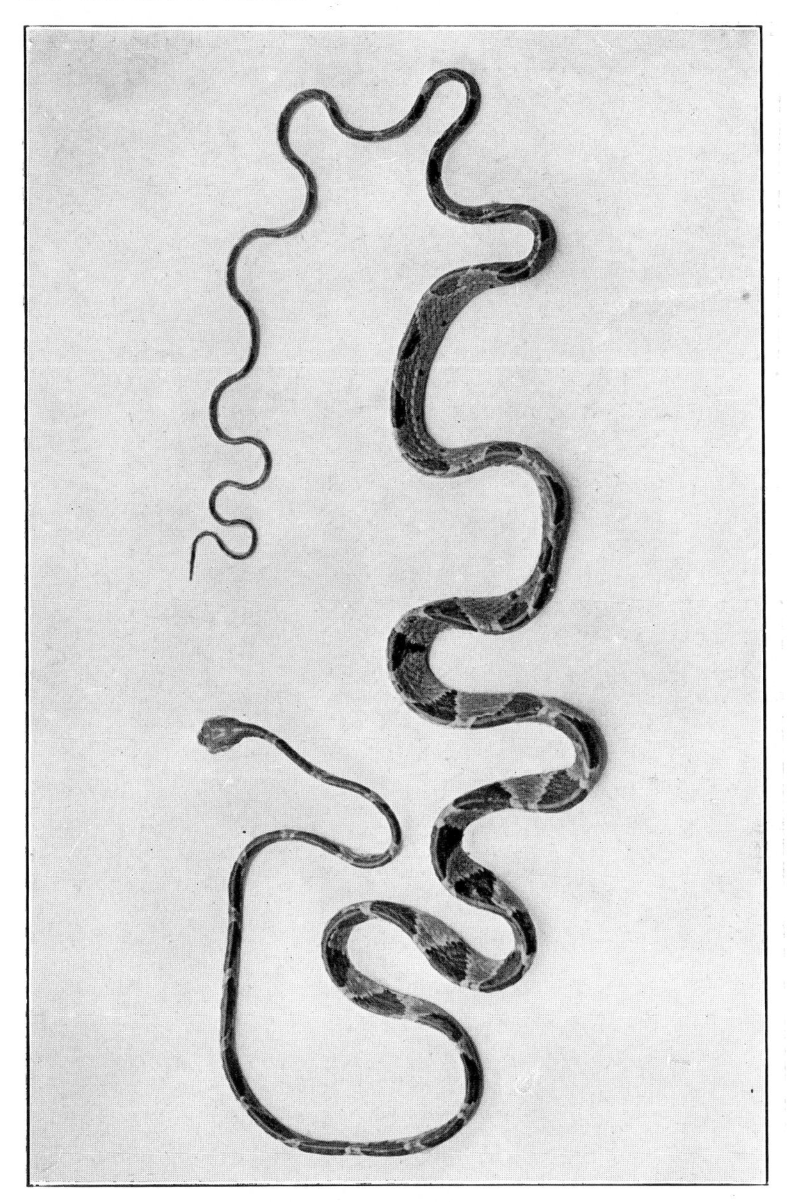

BLUNT-HEADED SNAKE *Petalognathus catesbyi*
Distribution: Tropical South America.
Length of adult, three and one-third feet.

LONG-NOSED TREE SNAKE *Dryophis mycterizans*
(Devouring a lizard.)
Distribution: India, Burma and Siam.
Grows to a length of four and one-half feet.

LONG-HEADED TREE SNAKE *Oxybelis acuminatus*
Distribution: Mexico to tropical South America.
Excessively slender; reaches a length of five feet.

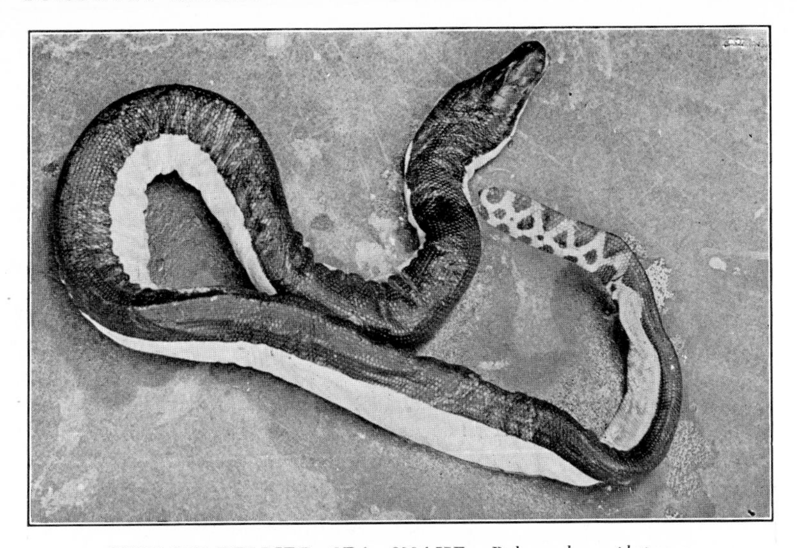

YELLOW-BELLIED SEA SNAKE *Pelamydrus platurus*

Distribution: Semi-tropical and tropical Pacific. Appears to be the only one of many species of marine serpents to occur in the waters of the New World—off the coasts of southern Mexico, Central and tropical South America. Attains a length of a yard.

RINGED SEA SNAKE *Platurus shistorhynchus*

Distribution: Western Tropical Pacific. Attains a length of five feet.

HEAD OF *PLATURUS*

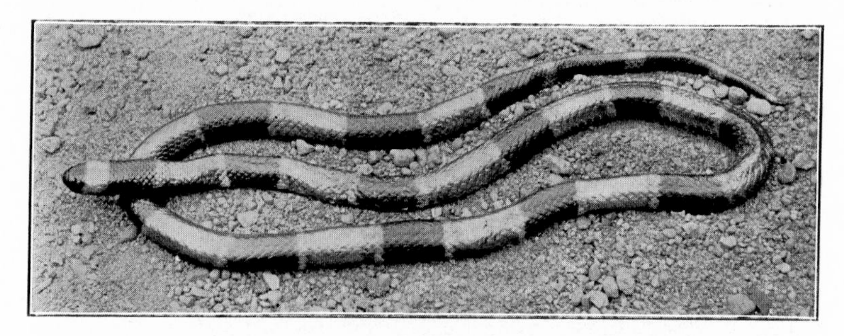

FLORIDA CORAL SNAKE *Micrurus fulvius*
Distribution: Southern United States.

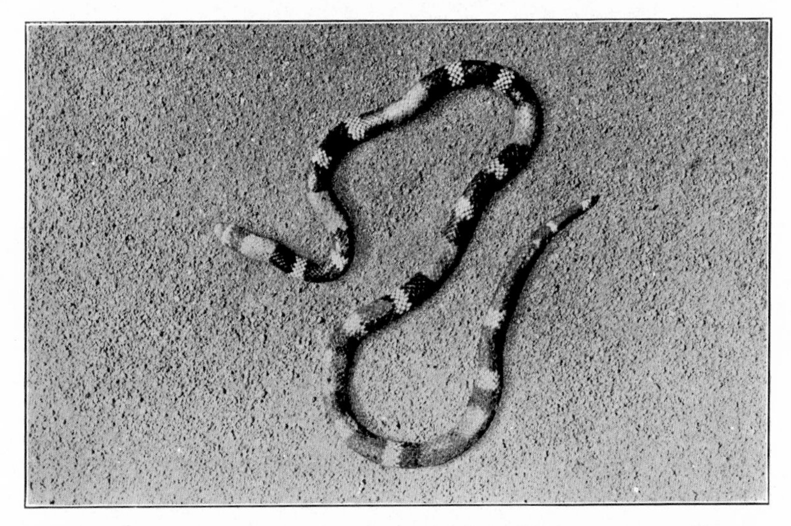

SOUTH AMERICAN CORAL SNAKE *Micrurus marcgravii*
Distribution: Tropical South America.

HEAD OF SOUTH AMERICAN *MICRURUS*
(Side and top views)

TIGER SNAKE *Notechis scutatus*
Distribution: Australia.
Attains a length of six feet.

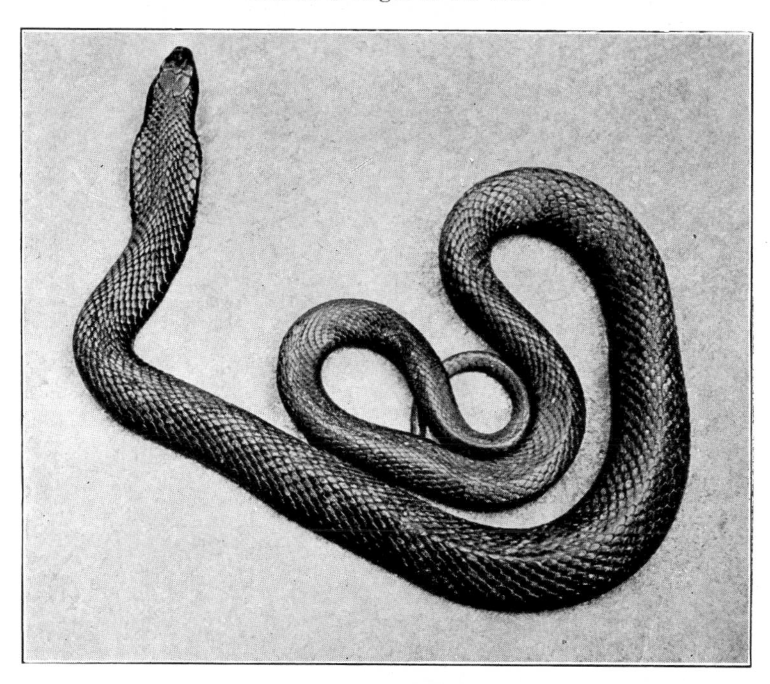

BLACK SNAKE *Pseudechis porphyriacus*
Distribution: Australia.
Attains a length of five feet.
Has a row of red scales on the lower portion of each side of the body.

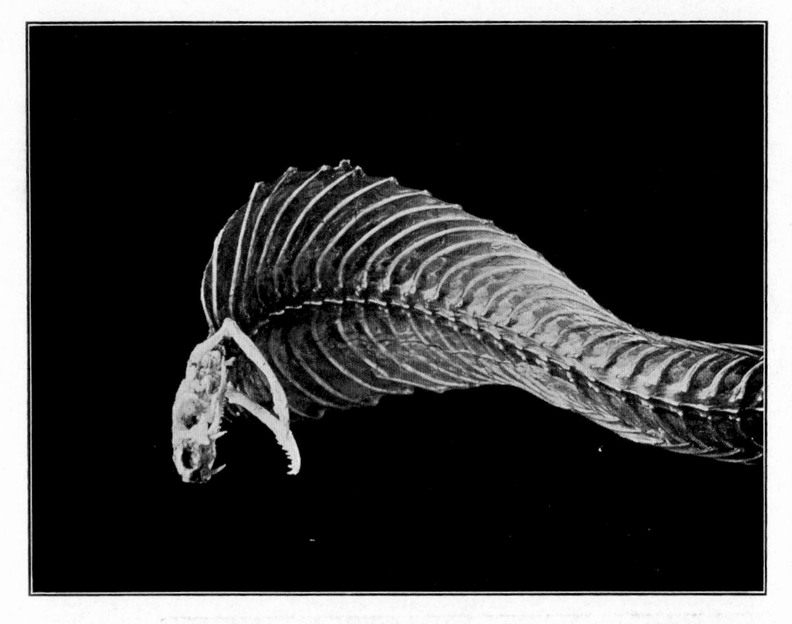

HOW THE COBRA SPREADS ITS "HOOD"

The illustration shows the elongated ribs, which, when the snake is in a passive mood, lie close to the backbone. Note the extremely small fangs of the Elapine snake as compared with the skulls of Viperine snakes on another plate.

TWO PHASES OF THE COBRA-DE-CAPELLO

Naja naja

The specimen with the spectacle marking was captured in the southern portion of the Indian Peninsula; the specimen to the right is from Sumatra.

1

2

1 a

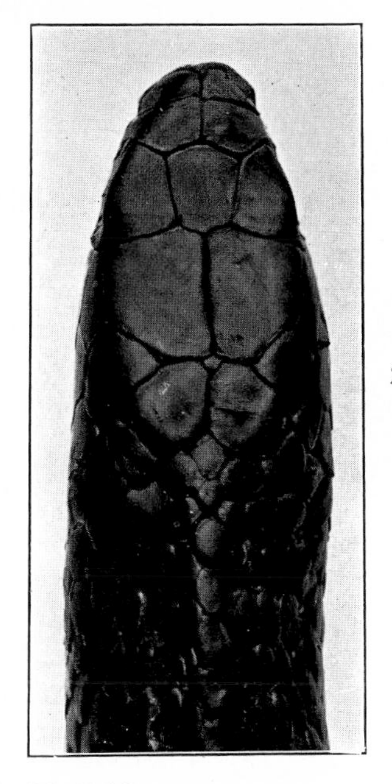

2 a

HEADS OF COBRAS

1–1 a. Egyptian Cobra, *Naja haje*
2–2 a. King Cobra, *Naja hannah*

The King Cobra reaches the greatest length of any poisonous serpent—fourteen feet, though it is a slender reptile. It is found in the Malay Peninsula and the larger islands of the Malay Archipelago.

EGYPTIAN COBRA OR ASP *Naja haje*

The upper figure shows an example in fighting position with its "hood" spread in characteristic fashion. The lower illustration portrays a cobra in passive mood.

The species seldom exceeds a length of five feet.

SOUTH AFRICAN COBRA; RINGHALS
Sepedon hæmachates
Attains a length of five feet.

HOOD OF THE RINGHALS—Seen from above.

A HINDOO SNAKE–CHARMER'S OUTFIT

The snakes rearing from the basket are cobras. The thick-bodied reptile is a specimen of the Tic Polonga or Russell's Viper. See pages describing different phases of Snake Charming.

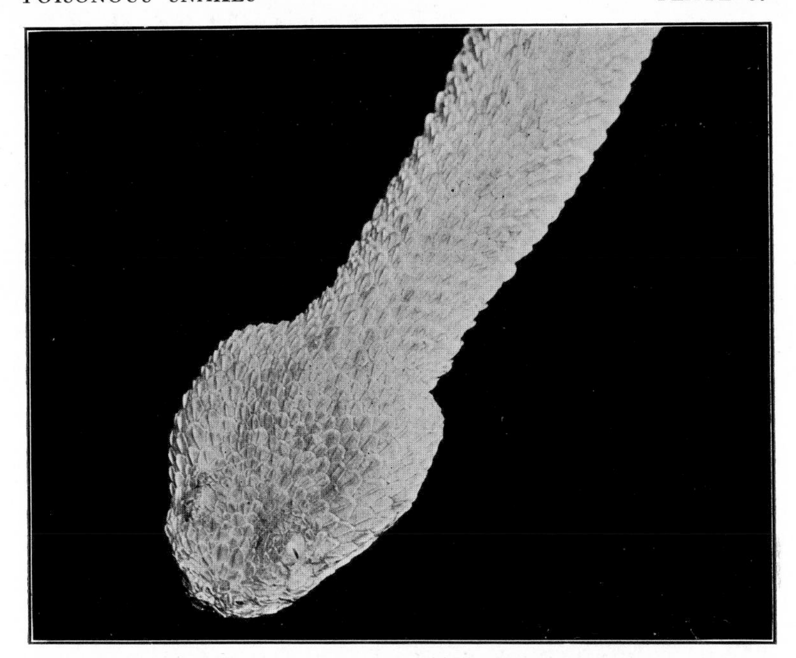

HEAD OF TRUE VIPER *Cerastes vipera*
Distribution: Egypt.

HEAD OF PIT VIPER A Rattlesnake
Distribution: New World.

CAPE VIPER *Causus rhombeatus*
Distribution: Southern Africa.
The length of an adult specimen seldom exceeds a yard.

HEAD OF THE CAPE VIPER SEEN FROM TOP
Note the resemblance to a harmless, Colubrine snake.

COMMON VIPER *Vipera berus*

Abundant in northern Europe, thence southward to Spain and eastward through Siberia to the Island of Saghalien. The only poisonous snake found in the British Isles. An adult is about two feet long.

TIC POLONGA; RUSSELL'S VIPER *Vipera russellii*

Distribution: India, Ceylon, Burma, Siam, the Malay Peninsula and Archipelago. Reaches a length of five feet.

GABOON VIPER *Bitis gabonica*
Distribution: Tropical Africa.
Length, thirty-one inches; girth of body, seven inches.

RHINOCEROS VIPER *Bitis nasicornis*
Distribution: Tropical West Africa.
Maximum length about four feet.

PUFF ADDER *Bitis arietans*
Distribution: Greater portion of Africa, Arabia.
Attains a length of four feet.

HORNED VIPER *Cerastes cornutus*
Distribution: Egypt.
Showing this reptile's resemblance to the desert sands.

HORNED VIPER *Cerastes cornutus*

Distribution: Northern border of the Sahara from Algeria to Egypt and Nubia; also found in Arabia and southern Palestine.

Total length about a yard.

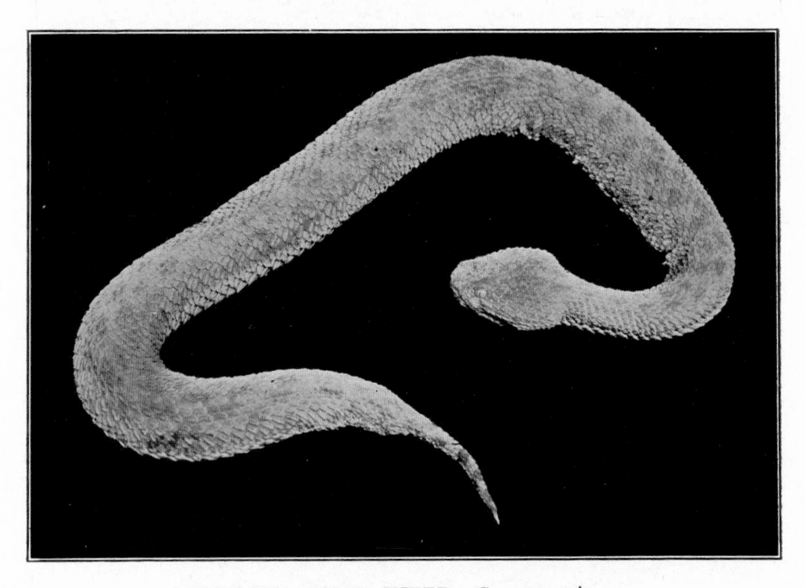

COMMON SAND VIPER *Cerastes vipera*

Distribution: Northern Africa, from Algeria to Egypt.

Total length about two and one-half feet.

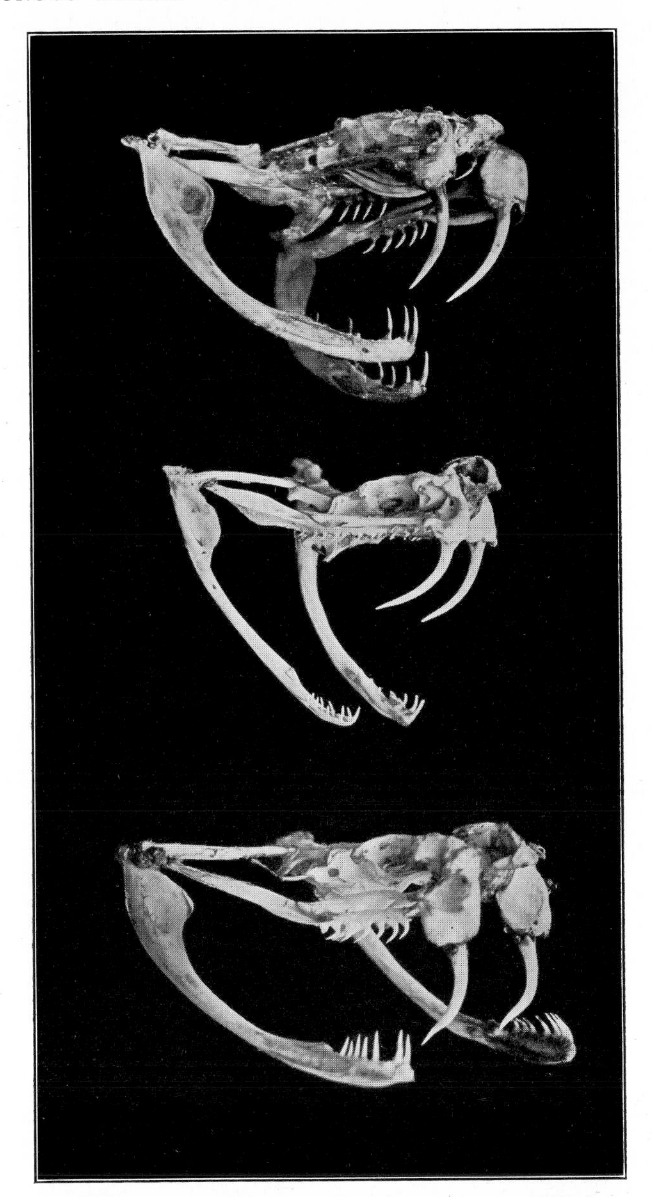

SKULLS OF THREE SPECIES OF PIT VIPERS

Bushmaster *Lachesis muta.* South America.
Fer-de-lance *Bothrops atrox.* South America.
Diamond-back Rattlesnake *Crotalus adamanteus.* United States.

The upper skull has been mounted with all its *reserve* fangs—these normally carried by every poisonous snake. The fangs are being constantly renewed; if the main pair is accidentally broken an auxiliary pair at once grows into place.

1

1 a

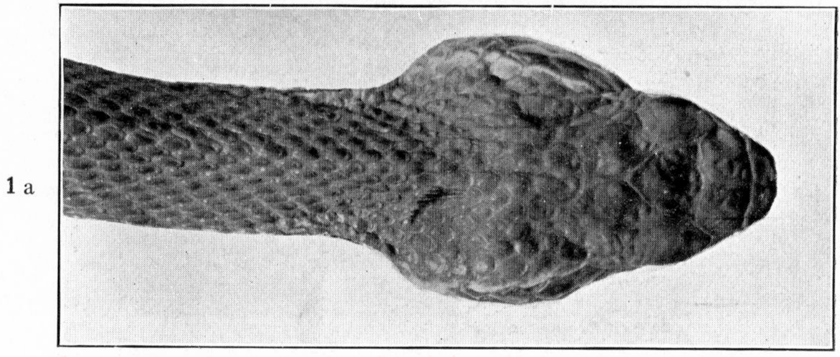

2 2 a

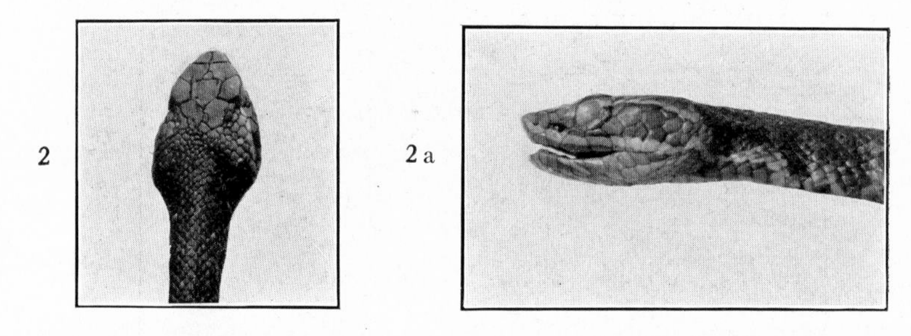

3 3 a

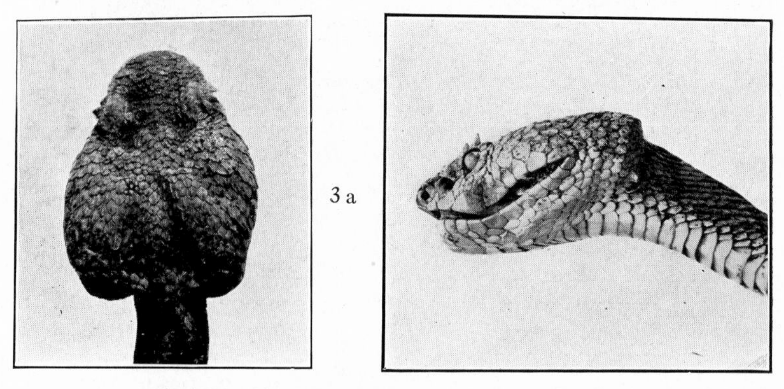

HEADS OF NEW WORLD PIT VIPERS

(Note presence of pit between the eye and nostril.)

1–1 a. Water Moccasin. *Agkistrodon piscivorus.* Southeastern United States.

2–2 a. Mexican Moccasin. *Agkistrodon bilineatus.* Mexico.

3–3 a. Palm Viper. *Bothrops schlegelii.* Central America.

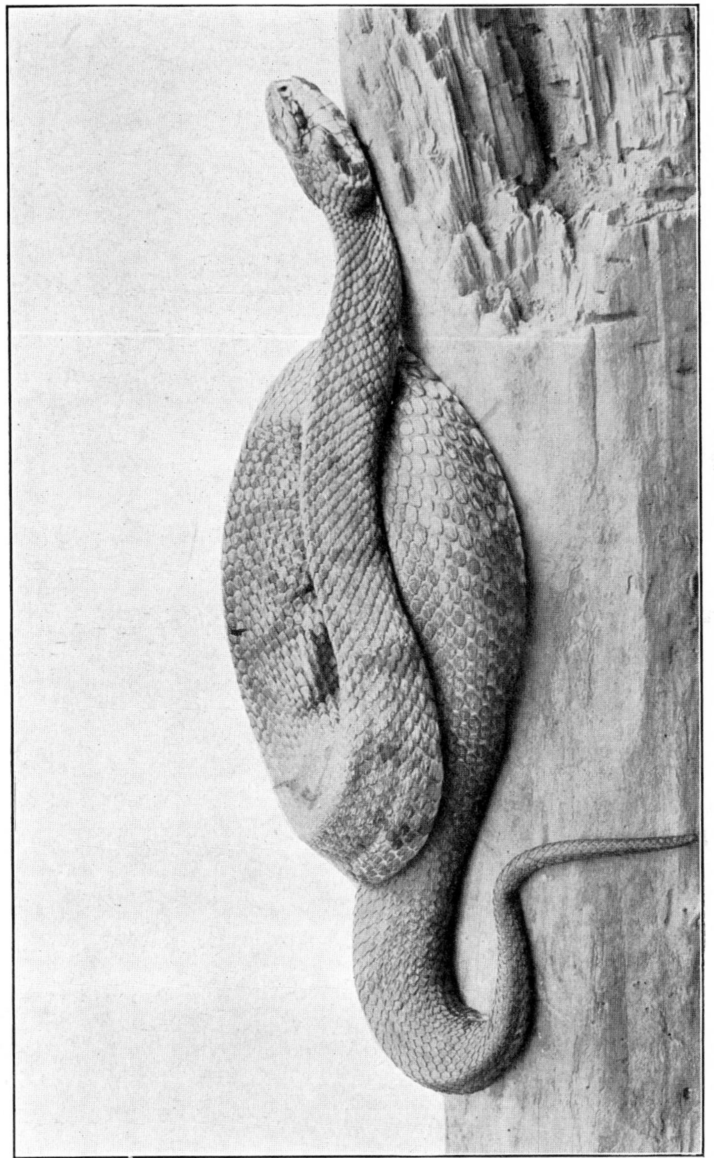

WATER MOCCASIN *Agkistrodon piscivorus*
Distribution: The southeast United States.
The maximum length is six feet.

MEXICAN MOCCASIN *Agkistrodon bilineatus*
The maximum length is about four feet.

COPPERHEAD SNAKE *Agkistrodon mokasen*
Texas phase.
Distribution: United States—eastern and central States.
A big specimen is a yard long.

1

2

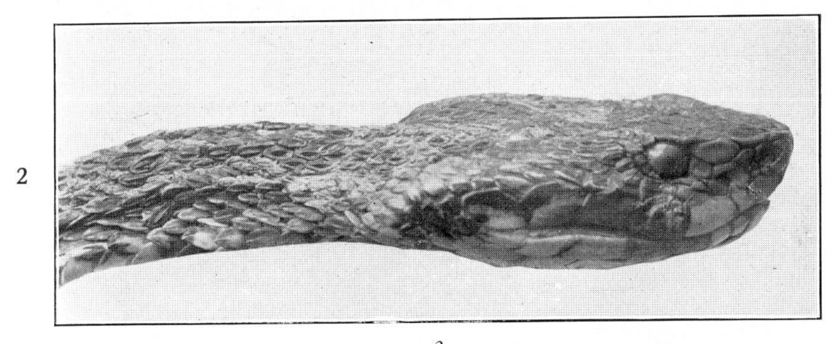

3

1 a

2 a

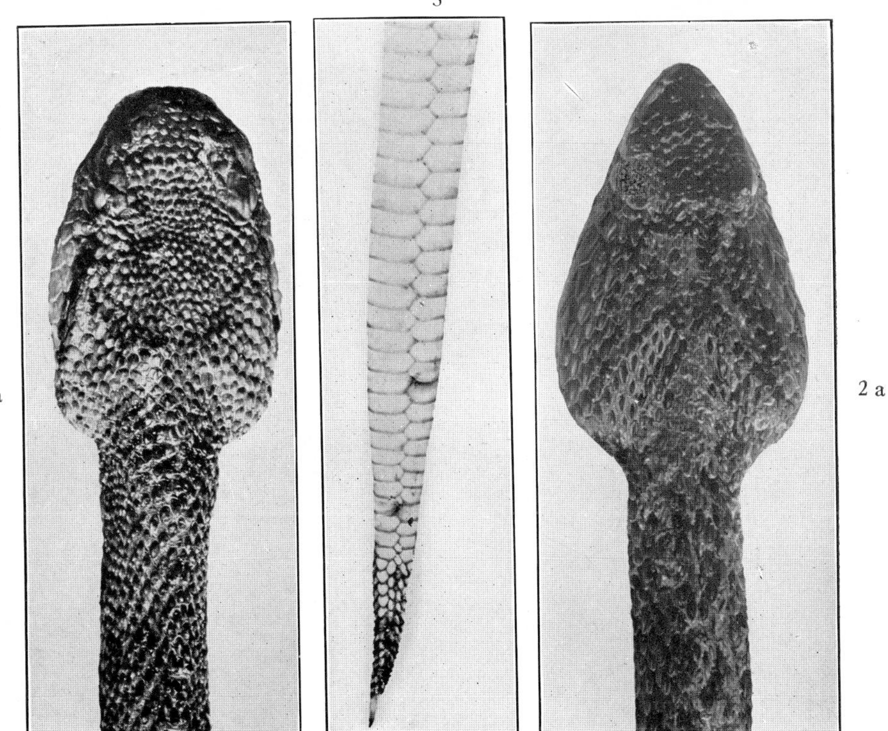

1–1 a. HEAD OF BUSHMASTER *Lachesis muta.* Distribution: South America.
2–2 a. HEAD OF FER-DE-LANCE *Bothrops atrox.* Distribution: South America.
3. TAIL OF BUSHMASTER—Seen from beneath.

BUSHMASTER *Lachesis muta*

Distribution: Central America and tropical South America. Largest of the New World poisonous serpents; attaining a length of twelve feet. The transverse blotches cover a pinkish-brown ground color.

FER-DE-LANCE; LANCE-HEAD VIPER *Bothrops atrox*

Distribution: Southern Mexico into tropical South America; found on the islands of St. Lucia and Martinique in the West Indies.

Grows to a length of eight feet.

A specimen of *LACHESIS MUTA* and her eggs.

This valuable photograph, showing a unique habit among the *Crotaline* snakes, was sent to the author by Mr. R. R. Mole, of Port-of-Spain, Trinidad. The reptile was in the possession of Mr. Mole and the photograph was taken by C. S. Rogers, Forest Officer.

HORNED PALM VIPER *Bothrops schlegelii*
Distribution: Central America. Length, three feet.

SOUTH AMERICAN RATTLESNAKE
Crotalus terrificus
Distribution: Mexico, Central America and South America generally.
Reaches a length of six feet.

GRAY RATTLESNAKE *Crotalus terrificus* (albino)
From Nicaragua.
This specimen is slightly over a yard long.

DIAMOND–BACK RATTLESNAKE *Crotalus adamanteus*

This is the largest and most deadly of the North American poisonous serpents. Its fangs are enormously developed and resemble the formidable dentition of the great vipers of South America.

TIMBER RATTLESNAKE *Crotalus horridus*

Distribution: Eastern North America.

This is the common rattlesnake of the eastern United States. Black and yellow phases are equally abundant.

HORNED RATTLESNAKE *Crotalus cerastes.*

Inhabits the deserts of the southwestern portion of the United States. Note the similarity in the pallid coloration and horns over the eyes to the sand vipers of the Sahara Desert.

1

2

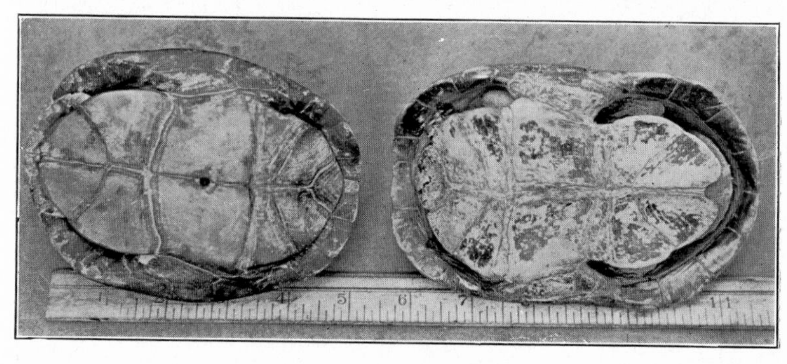

3 4

NEW WORLD MUD TURTLE

1. Musk or Mud Turtle. *Sternotherus odoratus.* Eastern North America. 2. Common Mud Turtle. *Kinosternon subrubrum.* Eastern North America. 3. *Kinosternon integrum.* Mexico. 4. *Kinosternon sonoriense.* Southwestern U. S.

EUROPEAN POND TURTLE *Emys orbicularis.*
Distribution: Europe, Asia, and northern Africa.
Length of shell, three to five inches.

ALGERIAN TURTLE *Clemmys leprosa.*
Distribution: Southwestern Europe and northern Africa.
Length of shell, four to six inches.

1

2

3

4

AMERICAN TURTLES

1. Painted Turtle (or Terrapin). *Chrysemys picta.* Eastern North America.
2. Yellow-bellied Terrapin. *Pseudemys scripta.* Eastern North America.
3. Cumberland Turtle (Terrapin). *Pseudemys elegans.* Eastern North America.
4. Geographic Turtle (Terrapin). *Graptemys geographica.* Eastern North America.

1

2

3

4

AMERICAN TURTLES

1. Spotted Turtle. *Clemmys guttata.* Eastern North America.
2. Muhlenberg's Turtle. *Clemmys muhlenbergii.* Eastern North America.
3. Wood Turtle. *Clemmys insculpta.* Eastern North America.
4. Box Turtle. *Terrapene carolina.* Eastern North America.

REEVE'S TURTLE *Geoclemys reevesii*
Distribution: China and Japan.
Length of upper shell, four to five inches.

HINGED-BACKED TORTOISE *Kinixys erosa*
Distribution: Tropical Africa.
Length of upper shell, 10 inches.

IBERIAN TORTOISE *Testudo iberia*
Distribution: Morocco and Asia Minor.
Length of shell, six to eight inches.

SOUTH AMERICAN TORTOISE *Testudo denticulata*
Large shells are eighteen inches long.

LEOPARD TORTOISE *Testudo pardalis*
Distribution: Tropical Africa.
Attains a weight of seventy-five pounds.

DESERT TORTOISE *Gopherus berlandieri*
Distribution: Deserts of northeastern Mexico and Texas.
Length of shell, ten inches.

RADIATED TORTOISE *Testudo radiata*
Distribution: Madagascar.
Length of shell, twelve to fourteen inches.

STAR TORTOISE *Testudo elegans*
Distribution: India.
Length of shell, seven inches.

STAR TORTOISE *Testudo elegans*
(Seen from beneath.)

GIANT TORTOISE *Testudo vicina*
From the Galapagos Islands.
Weight, two hundred and seventy pounds.

GIANT TORTOISE *Testudo gigantea*
From the Aldabra Islands.
The small tortoise beneath the foreleg of the big specimen is of ordinary size, having a shell 8 inches long. Weight of big tortoise, two hundred and thirty-five pounds.

YOUNG LOGGERHEAD TURTLES

Caretta caretta

Inhabiting all the tropical and semi-tropical seas the Loggerhead is a giant among Chelonians, reaching a weight of 500 pounds.

HAWK'S-BILL TURTLE *Eretmochelys imbricata*

Inhabiting the tropical and semi-tropical seas. The shell, of a very large example, is two and a half feet long. It is from this species only that the valuable "tortoise" shell is obtained.

AFRICAN MUD TURTLE *Pelusios derbianus*
A fully grown shell is a foot long.

AFRICAN MUD TURTLE AND AUSTRALIAN SNAKE-NECKED TURTLE

The illustration shows how the members of the side-necked turtles bend the neck in lateral curves in drawing the head into the shell.

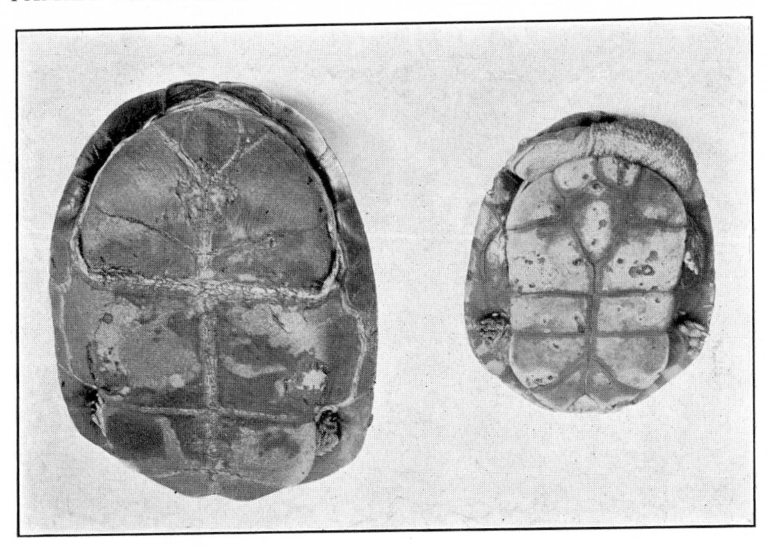

AFRICAN MUD TURTLE AND AUSTRALIAN SNAKE-NECKED TURTLE

The shells are seen from beneath. Note how these turtles bend the neck in protecting the head.

SOUTH AMERICAN SNAKE-NECKED TURTLE

Hydromedusa tectifera

The shell of an adult is about six inches long.

AUSTRALIAN SNAKE-NECKED TURTLE
Chelodina longicollis
Length of shell, six inches.

MATAMATA *Chelus fimbriata*
Distribution: Guianas and northern Brazil.
The shell of a large example is two feet long.

SPINY SOFT-SHELLED TURTLE *Trionyx spinifera*
Distribution: Ohio and Mississippi Valleys.
Length of fully grown shell, 12 inches.

SOUTHERN SOFT-SHELLED TURTLE *Trionyx ferox*
Distribution: Southeastern United States.
Length of fully grown shell, 18 inches.

PLATE 89

IN THE JUNGLE